WJEC A2 Mathematics

Study and Revision Guide

Stephen Doyle
edited by Howard Thomas

Published in 2012 by Illuminate Publishing Ltd, P.O Box 1160,
Cheltenham, Gloucestershire GL50 9RW

Orders: Please visit www.illuminatepublishing.com
or email sales@illuminatepublishing.com

British Library Cataloguing in Publication Data

A catalogue record for this book is available from the British Library

ISBN 978-1-908682-03-1

Printed by 4edge Ltd, Hockley, Essex
Printed in England by Lightning Source, Milton Keynes, UK.
10.12

The publisher's policy is to use papers that are natural, renewable and recyclable products made from wood grown in sustainable forests. The logging and manufacturing processes are expected to conform to the environmental regulations of the country of origin.

This material has been endorsed by WJEC and offers high quality support for the delivery of WJEC qualifications. While this material has been through a WJEC quality assurance process, all responsibility for the content remains with the publisher.

Editor: Geoff Tuttle
Cover and text design: Nigel Harriss
Text and layout: The Manila Typesetting Company

Acknowledgements

I am very grateful to Rick, Geoff and the team at Illuminate Publishing for their professionalism, support and guidance throughout this project. It has been a pleasure to work so closely with them.

The author and publisher wish to thank:

Dr Howard Thomas for his thorough review of the book and expert insights, observations and contributions.

Michael Angless, Amor Nanas and the team at The Manila Typesetting Company for their exacting work, patience and professionalism from start to finish.

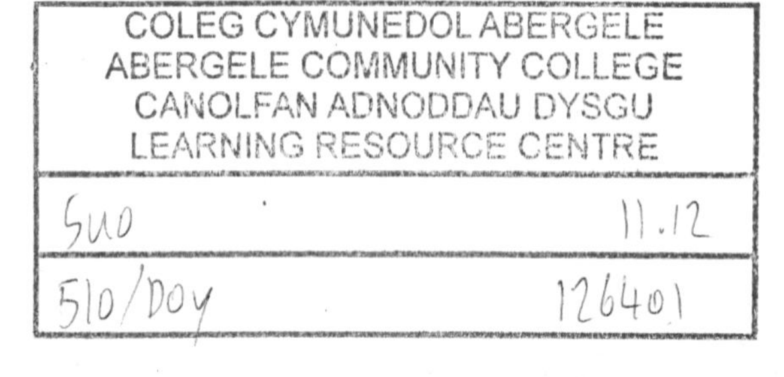

Contents

How to use this book

The contents of this study and revision guide are designed to guide you through to success in the Pure Mathematics components of the WJEC Mathematics A2 level examinations. It has been written by an experienced author and teacher and edited by a senior subject expert. This book has been written specifically for the WJEC A2 course you are taking and includes everything you need to know to perform well in your final exams.

Knowledge and Understanding

Topics start with a short list of the material covered in the topic and each topic will give the underpinning knowledge and skills you need to perform well in your exams.

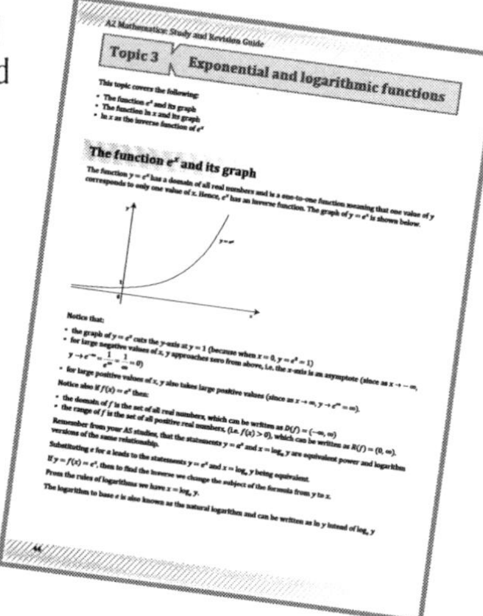

A2 Mathematics: Study and Revision Guide

Topic 3 Exponential and logarithmic functions

This topic covers the following:

- The function e^x and its graph
- The function $\ln x$ and its graph
- $\ln x$ as the inverse function of e^x

The function e^x and its graph

The function $y = e^x$ has a domain of all real numbers and is a one-to-one function meaning that one value of y corresponds to only one value of x. Hence, e^x has an inverse function. The graph of $y = e^x$ is shown below.

Notice that:

- the graph of $y = e^x$ cuts the y-axis at $y = 1$ (because when $x = 0$, $y = e^0 = 1$)
- for large negative values of x, y approaches zero from above, i.e. the x-axis is an asymptote (since as $x \to -\infty$, $y \to e^{-\infty} = \frac{1}{e^{\infty}} = \frac{1}{\infty} = 0$)
- for large positive values of x, y also takes large positive values (since as $x \to \infty$, $y \to e^{\infty} = \infty$).

Notice also if $f(x) = e^x$ then:

- the domain of f is the set of all real numbers, which can be written as $D(f) = (-\infty, \infty)$
- the range of f is the set of all positive real numbers, (i.e. $f(x) > 0$), which can be written as $R(f) = (0, \infty)$.

Remember from your AS studies, that the statements $y = a^x$ and $x = \log_a y$ are equivalent power and logarithm versions of the same relationship.

Substituting e for a leads to the statements $y = e^x$ and $x = \log_e y$ being equivalent.

If $y = f(x) = e^x$, then to find the inverse we change the subject of the formula from y to x.

From the rules of logarithms we have $x = \log_e y$.

The logarithm to base e is also known as the natural logarithm and can be written as $\ln y$ instead of $\log_e y$

44

If any formulae are included in a topic, you will be told whether you need to remember them or whether they will be given in the formula booklet.

Formulae used will be highlighted and will be included in a Topic summary at the end of each topic.

The knowledge section is kept fairly short leaving plenty of space for detailed explanation of examples. Pointers will be given to the theory, examples and questions that will help you understand the thinking behind the steps. You will also be given detailed advice when it is needed.

Another feature is Grade Boost where there are tips on achieving your best grade by usually avoiding certain pitfalls which can let students down.

Exam Practice and Technique

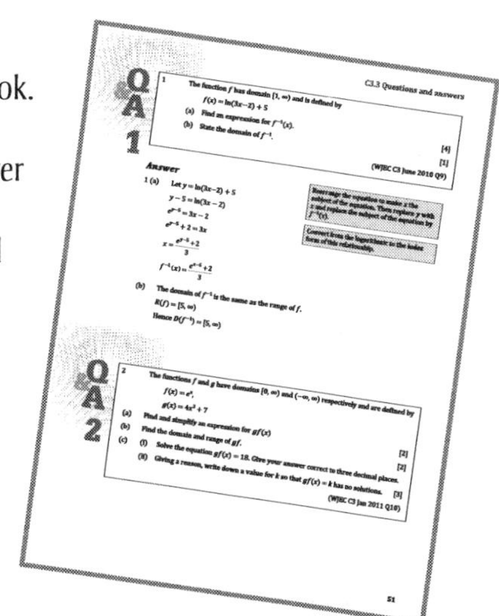

C3.3 Questions and answers

Q A 1

1 The function f has domain $[1, \infty)$ and is defined by

$f(x) = \ln(3x-2) + 5$

(a) Find an expression for $f^{-1}(x)$. [4]

(b) State the domain of f^{-1}. [1]

(WJEC C3 June 2010 Q9)

Answer

1 (a) Let $y = \ln(3x-2) + 5$

$y - 5 = \ln(3x-2)$

$e^{y-5} = 3x - 2$

$e^{y-5} + 2 = 3x$

$x = \frac{e^{y-5}+2}{3}$

$f^{-1}(x) = \frac{e^{x-5}+2}{3}$

Rearrange the equation to make x the subject of the equation. Then replace y with x and replace the subject of the equation by $f^{-1}(x)$.

Convert from the logarithmic to the index form of this relationship.

(b) The domain of f^{-1} is the same as the range of f.

$R(f) = [5, \infty)$

Hence $D(f^{-1}) = [5, \infty)$

Q A 2

2 The functions f and g have domains $[0, \infty)$ and $(-\infty, \infty)$ respectively and are defined by

$f(x) = e^x$,

$g(x) = 4x^2 + 7$

(a) Find and simplify an expression for $gf(x)$ [2]

(b) Find the domain and range of gf. [2]

(c) (i) Solve the equation $gf(x) = 18$. Give your answer correct to three decimal places.

(ii) Giving a reason, write down a value for k so that $gf(x) = k$ has no solutions. [3]

(WJEC C3 Jan 2011 Q10)

51

Being able to answer examination questions lies at the heart of this book. This means that we have included questions throughout the book that will build up your skills and knowledge until you are at a stage to answer full exam questions on your own. Examples are included, some of which are based on recent examination questions. These are annotated with Pointers and general advice about the knowledge, skills and techniques needed to answer them. There is a comprehensive Q & A section in each topic that provides actual examination questions with commentary so you can see how the question should be answered.

There is a Test yourself section where you are encouraged to answer questions on the topic and then compare your answers with the ones given at the back of the book. You should of course work through complete examination papers as part of your revision process.

We advise that you look at the WJEC website www.wjec.co.uk where you can download materials such as the specification and past papers to help you with your studies. From this website you will be able to download the formula booklet which you will use in your examinations. You will also find specimen papers and mark schemes on the site.

Good luck with your studies and revision.

Stephen Doyle

Unit C3 Pure Mathematics 3

Unit C3 covers Pure Mathematics and seeks to build on your knowledge obtained from your AS course. You may need to look back at some of the work you did in C1 and C2.

Revision checklist

Tick column 1 when you have completed all the notes.
Tick column 2 when you think you have a good grasp of the topic.
Tick column 3 during the final revision when you feel you have mastery of the topic.

		1	2	3	Notes
	1 Functions				
p8	Definition of a function				
p9	Domain and range of functions				
p11	Composition of functions				
p13	Inverse functions and their graphs				
p17	The modulus function				
p21	Combinations of the transformations on the graph of $y = f(x)$				
	2 Trigonometry				
p32	Secant, cosecant and cotangent and their graphs				
p34	The trigonometric identities $\sec^2\theta = 1 + \tan^2\theta$ and $\text{cosec}^2\theta = 1 + \cot^2\theta$				
p35	Solution of trigonometric equations making use of the identities $\sec^2\theta = 1 + \tan^2\theta$ and $\text{cosec}^2\theta = 1 + \cot^2\theta$				
p36	Inverse trigonometric functions $\sin^{-1}$, $\cos^{-1}$ and $\tan^{-1}$ and their graphs and domains				
p40	Showing by counter-example				
	3 Exponential and logarithmic functions				
p44	The function e^x and its graph				
p45	The function $\ln x$ and its graph				
p46	$\ln x$ as the inverse function of e^x				
	4 Differentiation				
p53	Differentiation of e^x, $\ln x$, $\sin x$, $\cos x$ and $\tan x$				
p55	The Chain rule				
p58	Differentiation of $\sin^{-1} x$, $\cos^{-1} x$, $\tan^{-1} x$				
p61	Differentiation using the Product and the Quotient rule				

		1	2	3	Notes
p66	Differentiation of simple functions defined implicitly				
p67	Differentiation of simple functions defined parametrically				
	5 Integration				
p77	Integration of x^n $(n \neq -1)$, e^x, $\frac{1}{x}$, $\sin x$, $\cos x$				
p78	Integration of $(ax+b)^n$ $(n \neq -1)$, e^{ax+b}, $\frac{1}{ax+b}$, $\sin(ax+b)$, $\cos(ax+b)$				
	6 Roots, iterative methods and numerical integrations				
p86	Location of roots of $f(x) = 0$ considering changes of sign of $f(x)$				
p87	Sequences generated by a simple recurrence relation of the form $x_{n+1} = f(x_n)$				
p88	Approximate solutions of equations using simple iterative methods				
p90	Numerical integration of functions using Simpson's Rule				

Topic 1 Functions

This topic covers the following:

- Definition of a function
- Domain and range of functions
- Composition of functions
- Inverse functions and their graphs
- The modulus function
- Combinations of the transformations on the graph $y = f(x)$

Definition of a function

Look at the diagram below where each element of a given set {1, 3, 5} is mapped to one element in another set, {3, 9, 15}.

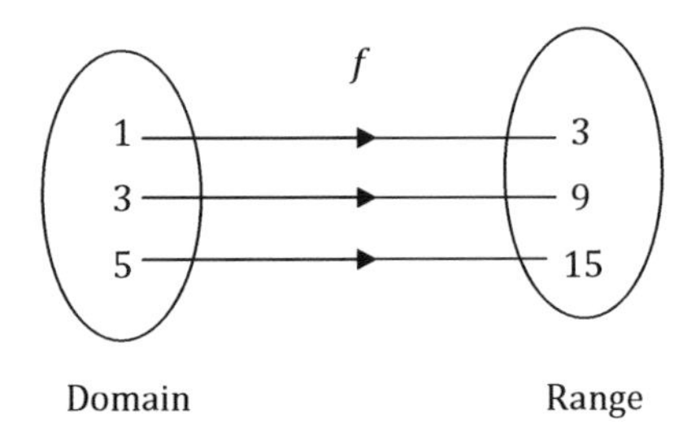

A **function** is a relation between a set of inputs and a set of outputs such that each input is related to exactly one output.

The given set (i.e. {1, 3, 5} here) is called the **domain** of the function and the set to which the domain is mapped (i.e. {3, 9, 15} here) is called the **range** of the function.

The above diagram could be represented by the following mathematical rule:

$f(x) = 3x$ with the domain $x \in \{1, 3, 5\}$ and the range $f(x) \in \{3, 9, 15\}$

A function maps each input to only one output. This is best explained by considering the following example. $y = x^2$ is a function because whatever value x takes there is only one possible y value. For example, if $x = 3$ then $y = 9$. However, if you consider the mapping $y = \pm\sqrt{x}$, and substitute $x = 4$, then there are two possible values of y (i.e. 2 or -2), so $y = \pm\sqrt{x}$ is not a function. Hence $y = x^2$ is a function, whereas $y = \pm\sqrt{x}$ is not.

Domain and range of functions

All functions have a domain and a range.

The domain is the set of input values that can be entered into the function and the range is the set of output values.

Interval notation

Domains and ranges can be expressed as intervals, using the following notation:

The use of parentheses: (a, b) means the open interval $a < x < b$ (not including the endpoints).

The use of square brackets: $[a, b]$ means the closed interval $a \leq x \leq b$ (including the endpoints).

So, $(a, b]$ means $a < x \leq b$ and $[a, b)$ means $a \leq x < b$.

The smallest value appears first and then the largest value, i.e. $(-1, 4)$, but not $(4, -1)$.

For example:

$(-1, 4)$ means all numbers between -1 and 4, not including -1 and 4.

$[-1, 4]$ means all numbers between -1 and 4, including -1 and 4.

$[-1, 4)$ means all numbers between -1 and 4, including -1 but not 4.

$(-\infty, 4]$ means all numbers less than or equal to 4.

$(-1, \infty)$ means all numbers greater than -1.

Example

The function f has domain $(-\infty, -1]$ and is defined by

$f(x) = 3x^2 - 2$

Notice the way the domain is written. The brackets show that the domain is all numbers less than or equal to -1. You will see the domain often written in this form: $D(f) = (-\infty, -1]$.

To find the range, you need to find the least and greatest values of $f(x)$, for values of x that are within the domain of f.

Round brackets are **always** used for ∞ or $-\infty$, since, by definition, we can never get there. Instead, we should consider approaching ∞ or $-\infty$.

If you sketch the curve $y = 3x^2 - 2$ and then mark the domain, you can work out the range in the following way.

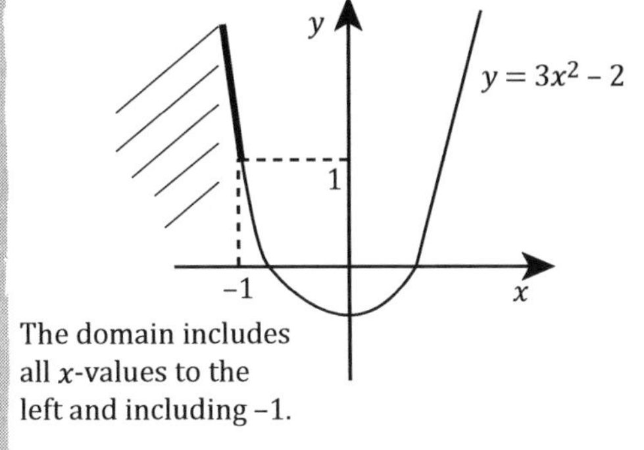

To find the y-values on the graph the x-coordinates are substituted into to the function (or the equation of the curve) like this:

$f(-1) = 3(-1)^2 - 2 = 3 - 2 = 1$

As $x \to -\infty$, $f(-\infty) \to 3(-\infty)^2 - 2 = \infty$, i.e. $f(-\infty) \to \infty$

Squaring minus infinity and then multiplying by 3 gives infinity as it is impossible to get a value larger than infinity. Also subtracting 2 from it makes no difference and it is still infinity.

You can now see that only the part of the curve emboldened is allowed owing to the restricted domain. The range of the function (i.e. the allowable $f(x)$ or y-values) is the set of numbers greater than or equal to 1, and this can be written in shorthand as $R(f) = [1, \infty)$.

The graphical representation of functions, with the inputs x and the outputs y

To understand functions you need to be able to sketch graphs. Graph sketching was covered in C1.

If you are asked to find the largest possible domain for a function then you should sketch a graph of the function to see what input values are allowable.

Take the function $f(x) = 2x^2 + 3$ as an example. You can sketch this curve by considering the transformations to the graph $y = x^2$, to produce $y = 2x^2 + 3$ (i.e. a stretch parallel to the y-axis with scale factor 2 and a translation of three units up). The following graph is obtained:

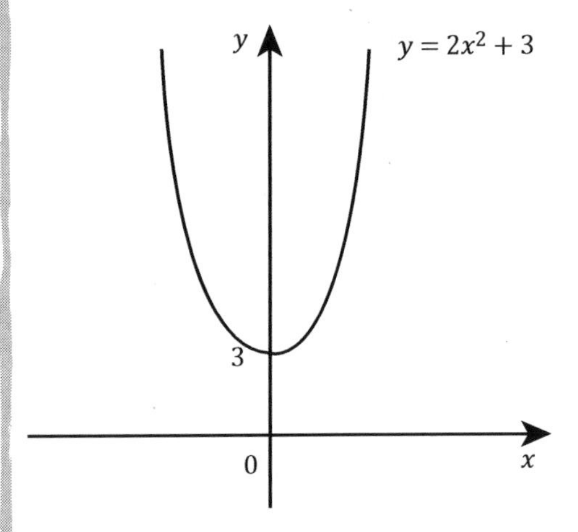

From the graph it can be seen all x-values are allowable as inputs, so the largest domain is from $-\infty$ to ∞ which can be written as $D(f) = (-\infty, \infty)$. The outputs (i.e. the y-values) are all values greater than or equal to 3 which is the range and can be written as $R(f) = [3, \infty)$.

Composition of functions

Composition of functions involves applying two or more functions in succession.

To understand this, consider the following example.

If $f(x) = x^2$ and $g(x) = x - 2$

The composite function $fg(x)$ means $f(g(x))$ and is the result of performing the function g *first and then* f.

Here, g means 'subtract 2 from it' and f means 'square it', so fg means 'subtract 2 from it' and then 'square it', i.e. $(x-2)^2$, and gf means 'square it' and then 'subtract 2 from it', i.e. $x^2 - 2$.

$fg(x)$ results from replacing x by the expression for $g(x)$ in $f(x)$
That is:

$fg(x) = f(g(x)) = f(x-2) = (x-2)^2$

The domain and range of composite functions

Provided that the composite functions exist, the domain of the composite function fg is the domain of g and the domain of gf is the domain of f.

Rule for a composite function to exist

Not all composite functions exist. For the composite function fg to exist, check that the range of g (from its graph) is a subset of or an equal set to the domain of f.

Example

① If $f(x) = x^2$ and $g(x) = x - 6$

find

(a) $fg(x)$

(b) $gf(x)$

Answer

(a) $fg(x) = (x-6)^2$

(b) $gf(x) = x^2 - 6$

Example

② The functions f and g have domains $[-3, \infty)$ and $(-\infty, \infty)$ respectively and are defined by

$f(x) = \sqrt{x+4}$,

$g(x) = 2x^2 - 3$.

(a) Write down the range of f and the range of g. [2]

(b) Find an expression for $gf(x)$. Simplify your answer. [2]

(c) Solve the equation $fg(x) = 17$. [4]

(WJEC C3 June 2010 Q10)

Answer

② (a) Now $f(x) = \sqrt{x+4}$

When $x = -3, f(-3) = \sqrt{-3+4} = 1$

To find the least value of $f(x)$, the contents of the square root must be as small as possible. By inspection you can see that this occurs when $x = -3$. Note that the least value of $\sqrt{x+4}$ occurs when $x = -4$, but this is not in the domain of f, which states that x must be greater than or equal to -3.

As $x \to \infty, f(x) \to \sqrt{\infty+4} = \infty$

As $x \to \infty, f(x) \to \infty$

Hence $R(f) = [1, \infty)$

Now $g(x) = 2x^2 - 3$

When $x = 0, g(0) = 2(0)^2 - 3 = -3$

$g(x)$ has its least value when $x = 0$. You can obtain this value by thinking about the minimum point if the function were plotted. Always check that the value of x lies within the domain (i.e. $(-\infty, \infty)$ in this case).

As $x \to \infty, g(x) \to 2(\infty)^2 - 3 = \infty$

As $x \to \infty, g(x) = \infty$

As $x \to \infty, g(x) = \infty$

$R(g) = [-3, \infty)$

Instead of using interval notation, it would also be acceptable to describe the range using words or inequality symbols, e.g. the range of g is all numbers greater than or equal to -3 or $x \geq -3$ or $g(x) \geq -3$.

(b) $gf(x) = 2\left(\sqrt{x+4}\right)^2 - 3$

$= 2(x + 4) - 3$

$= 2x + 5$

(c) $fg(x) = \sqrt{(2x^2 - 3 + 4)}$

$= \sqrt{(2x^2 + 1)}$

Now $fg(x) = 17$

$17 = \sqrt{(2x^2 + 1)}$

$289 = 2x^2 + 1$

Square both sides to remove the square root.

$288 = 2x^2$

$144 = x^2$

Remember to include $\pm$ when square rooting, and then check whether one or both values are in the domain of fg, i.e. the domain of g. In this case, both values are needed.

$x = \pm 12$

Inverse functions and their graphs

A function f produces a single output from an input. The inverse function of f reverses the process: it obtains the input of f from a given output. The inverse of the function f is written as f^{-1}. For the inverse f^{-1} to exist the function f must be one-to-one; otherwise there would be two inputs of f corresponding to a given output of f and it would be impossible to determine which input value of f (which is an output for f^{-1}) would be appropriate.

The domain of f (i.e. set of inputs) is identical to the range (i.e. set of outputs) of the inverse function f^{-1}.

To find the inverse of a function, follow these steps:

1 Let the function equal y.
2 Rearrange the resulting equation so that x is the subject of the equation.
3 Replace x with $f^{-1}(x)$ and replace y with x.

These steps are shown in the following example:

The function f has domain $[0, \infty)$ and is defined by

$f(x) = 5x^2 + 3$ and you are asked to find $f^{-1}(x)$.

Step 1 Let $y = 5x^2 + 3$

Let the function equal y.

Step 2 $x = \sqrt{\dfrac{y-3}{5}}$

Rearrange the resulting equation so that x is the subject of the equation. When square rooting there would normally be a $\pm$ placed before the root. However, here only the positive value is allowed because the domain of f is $[0, \infty)$.

Step 3 $f^{-1}(x) = \sqrt{\dfrac{x-3}{5}}$

Replace x with $f^{-1}(x)$ and replace y with x.

Example

① The function f has domain $(-\infty, -1]$ and is defined by

$$f(x) = 2x^2 - 1$$

(a) Write down the range of f.

(b) Find $f^{-1}(x)$.

Answer

① (a) $f(x) = 2x^2 - 1$

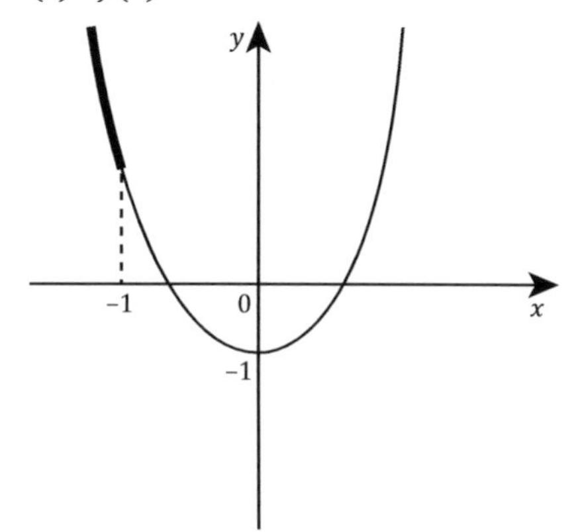

If the graph of $y = 2x^2 - 1$ is drawn, the minimum point occurs at $(0, -1)$. $x = 0$ is not allowable as it lies outside the domain for the function (i.e. $D(f) = (-\infty, -1]$). The largest allowable x value is therefore -1 and the allowable part of the curve is all points including and to the left of this value (i.e. from -1 to $-\infty$). The corresponding y-values (i.e. the range) are obtained by substituting the these two values for the domain into the equation for the curve.

$f(-1) = 2(-1)^2 - 1 = 2 - 1 = 1$

As $x \to -\infty$, $f(-\infty) \to 2(-\infty)^2 - 1 = \infty$

Hence $R(f) = [1, \infty)$

(b) Let $y = 2x^2 - 1$

$$x^2 = \frac{y+1}{2}$$

$$x = -\sqrt{\frac{y+1}{2}}$$

$$f^{-1}(x) = -\sqrt{\frac{x+1}{2}}$$

The negative square root needs to be used here because the domain of f or range of f^{-1} is $(-\infty, -1]$.

Example

② The function f has domain $(-\infty, -1]$ and is defined by

$$f(x) = 4x^2 - 3$$

(a) Write down the range of f. [1]

(b) Find an expression for $f^{-1}(x)$ and write down the range and domain of f^{-1}. [5]

(c) (i) Evaluate $f^{-1}(6)$.

(ii) By carrying out an appropriate calculation involving f, verify that your answer to part (i) is correct. [3]

(WJEC C3 Jan 2011 Q9)

Answer

② (a)

Draw or imagine the graph for $y = 4x^2 - 3$. It will have a minimum point at $(0, -3)$. However $x = 0$ does not lie in the domain.

As $x \to -\infty$, $f(x) \to 4(-\infty)^2 - 3 = \infty$

When $x = -1$, $f(-1) = 4(-1)^2 - 3 = 1$

$R(f) = [1, \infty)$

The least value $f(x)$ can take is when $x = -1$. Note that this value of x lies in the domain of the function.

(b) Let $y = 4x^2 - 3$

Rearrange for x^2 and then square root and then determine whether to use the + or – sign.

$$\frac{y+3}{4} = x^2$$

$$x = \pm\frac{1}{2}\sqrt{y+3}$$

According to the domain of f (i.e. range of f^{-1}), x could only take the negative value.

$$f^{-1}(x) = -\frac{1}{2}\sqrt{x+3}$$

$R(f^{-1}) = (-\infty, -1]$

The range of $f^{-1}(x)$ is the same as the domain of fx.

$D(f^{-1}) = [1, \infty)$

The domain of $f^{-1}(x)$ is the same as the range of $f(x)$.

(c) (i) $f^{-1}(6) = -\frac{1}{2}\sqrt{6+3} = -\frac{3}{2}$

(ii) $f\left(-\frac{3}{2}\right) = 4\left(-\frac{3}{2}\right)^2 - 3 = 4\left(\frac{9}{4}\right) - 3 = 6$

$x = 6$ is substituted into $f^{-1}(x)$

Note the function turns the value $\left(-\frac{3}{2}\right)$ into 6 and the inverse function does the reverse, changing 6 into $\left(-\frac{3}{2}\right)$. This can be used to check that the inverse is correct.

Example

③ The function f has domain $(-\infty, -1]$ and is defined by

$$f(x) = 6x^2 - 2$$

(a) Write down the range of f.

(b) Find an expression for $f^{-1}(x)$ and write down the range and domain of f^{-1}.

(c) (i) Evaluate $f^{-1}(3)$.

(ii) By carrying out an appropriate calculation involving f, verify your answer to part (i) is correct.

Answer

③ (a) As $x \to \infty$, $f(x) \to 6(-\infty)^2 - 2 = \infty$

$f(-1) = 6(-1)^2 - 2 = 4$

Consider the values of x in the domain of f that will give the greatest and least values for $f(x)$.

Hence $R(f) = [4, \infty)$

The least value in the range is 4. It is possible to have the exact value so a square bracket is used.

(b) Let $y = 6x^2 - 2$

$x^2 = \frac{y+2}{6}$

$x = -\sqrt{\frac{y+2}{6}}$

The negative square root is taken because the domain of f (and therefore the range of f^{-1}) is $(-\infty, -1]$.

$f^{-1}(x) = -\sqrt{\frac{x+2}{6}}$

Range of f^{-1} is the same as the domain of f

Hence $R(f^{-1}) = (-\infty, -1]$

Domain of f^{-1} is the same as the range of f

Hence $D(f^{-1}) = [4, \infty)$

(c) (i) $f^{-1}(x) = -\sqrt{\frac{x+2}{6}}$

$f^{-1}(3) = -\sqrt{\frac{3+2}{6}} = -\sqrt{\frac{5}{6}}$

(ii) If $x = -\sqrt{\frac{5}{6}}$ is put back into the original function the answer should be 3.

Now $f(x) = 6x^2 - 2 = 6\left(-\sqrt{\frac{5}{6}}\right)^2 - 2 = 6 \times \frac{5}{6} - 2 = 3$

Hence the answer to part (i) is correct.

The graphs of inverse functions

To obtain the graph of an inverse function, reflect the original graph in the line $y = x$. When drawing the graph the same scale must be used on both axes otherwise the graph would become distorted.

For example, the graph below shows the original function $y = 2x + 5$ and the inverse function $y = \frac{x-5}{2}$ along with the line $y = x$. Notice how the function and its inverse are reflections in the line $y = x$.

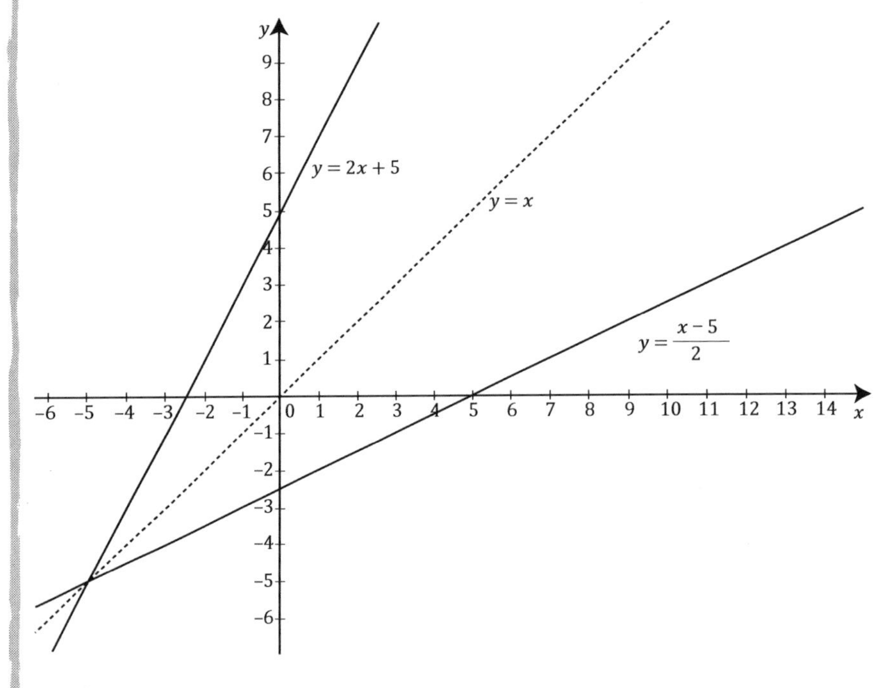

Thus to obtain the graph of $y = f^{-1}(x)$ reflect the graph of $y = f(x)$ in the line $y = x$.

The modulus function

The modulus of x is written as $|x|$ and means the numerical value of x (ignoring the sign).

So whether x is positive or negative, $|x|$ is always positive (or zero).

So $|5| = 5$ and $|-5| = 5$.

The graph of $y = |x|$ is shown here.

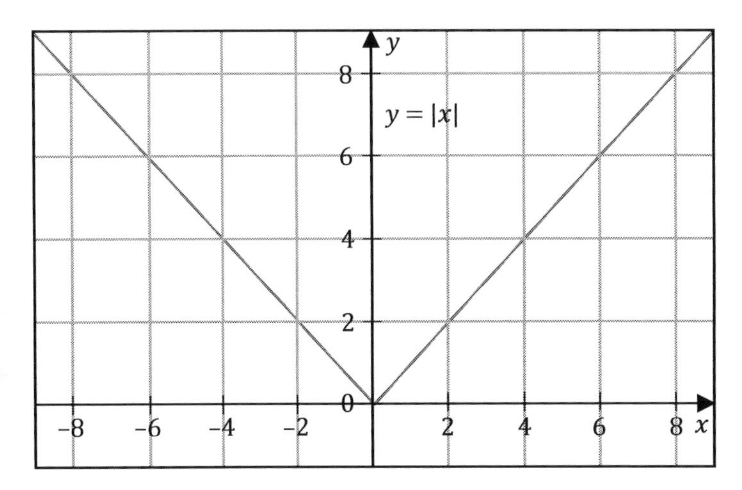

For example

$|x| = 3$ means $x = \pm 3$

$|x - 1| = 2$ means $x - 1 = \pm 2$

So $x = 2 + 1 = 3$ or $x = -2 + 1 = -1$

Hence $x = 3$ or -1

Removal of the modulus sign in both of these examples means that a $\pm$ sign must be included as shown.

Example

① Solve the following

$3|x - 5| = 9$

Answer

① $3|x - 5| = 9$

$|x - 5| = 3$

$x - 5 = \pm 3$

$x = 3 + 5 = 8$ or $x = -3 + 5 = 2$

Hence $x = 2$ or 8

Treat this just like an ordinary equation and make $|x - 5|$ the subject of the equation.

Removal of the modulus sign on the left means that a $\pm$ sign must be inserted on the right.

Example

② Solve

$3|x+1|-4=8$

Answer

② $3|x+1|=12$

$|x+1|=4$

$x+1=\pm 4$

$x+1=4$ so $x=3$

Or $x+1=-4$ so $x=-5$

Example

③ Solve the following

$$\frac{3|x|-1}{|x|+1}=2$$

Answer

③ $$\frac{3|x|-1}{|x|+1}=2$$

$3|x|-1=2|x|+2$

$|x|=3$

$x=\pm 3$

Multiply both sides by the denominator, $|x|+1$.

Example

④ Solve the following

(a) $2|x+1|-3=7$ [2]

(b) $|5x-8|\geq 3$ [3]

(WJEC C3 Jan 2010 Q7)

Answer

④ (a) $2|x+1|-3=7$

$2|x+1|=10$

$|x+1|=5$

$x+1=\pm 5$

$x+1=5$ or $x+1=-5$

Hence $x=4$ or $x=-6$

(b) $|5x-8|\geq 3$

$5x-8\geq 3$ or $5x-8\leq -3$

$5x\geq 11$ or $5x\leq 5$

$x\geq \frac{11}{5}$ or $x\leq 1$

An alternative method

$|5x - 8| \geq 3$

Squaring both sides gives

$(5x - 8)^2 \geq 9$

$25x^2 - 80x + 64 \geq 9$

$25x^2 - 80x + 55 \geq 0$

$5x^2 - 16x + 11 \geq 0$

$(5x - 11)(x - 1) \geq 0$

The critical values of x are $x = \dfrac{11}{5}$ and $x = 1$

Required range is $x \leq 1$ or $x \geq \dfrac{11}{5}$

When the contents inside the modulus sign are squared the modulus sign can be removed.

Divide through by 5 which will make the resulting equation easier to factorise.

If a graph of $y = (5x - 11)(x - 1)$ were plotted, the curve will be $\cup$-shaped, cutting the x-axis at $x = \dfrac{11}{5}$ and $x = 1$. The section of the graph needed will be above the x-axis and the required range will be less than or equal to the lower root (1), **or** greater than or

equal to the higher root $\left(\dfrac{11}{5}\right)$.

Graphs of modulus functions

The graph of $y = |f(x)|$ is the graph of $y = f(x)$ with any parts of the graph below the x-axis reflected in the x-axis.

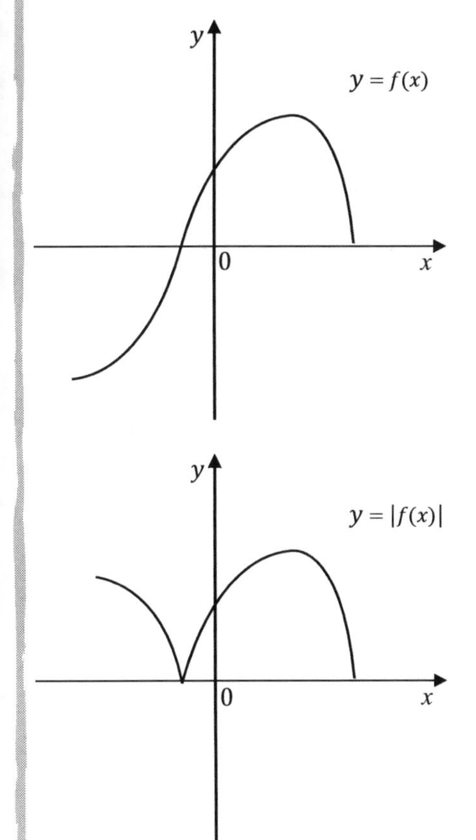

To draw the graph of $y = |x - 3|$ you can draw the graph of $y = x - 3$ by first finding the coordinates of intersection with each axis and then reflecting those parts which are below the x-axis in the x-axis.

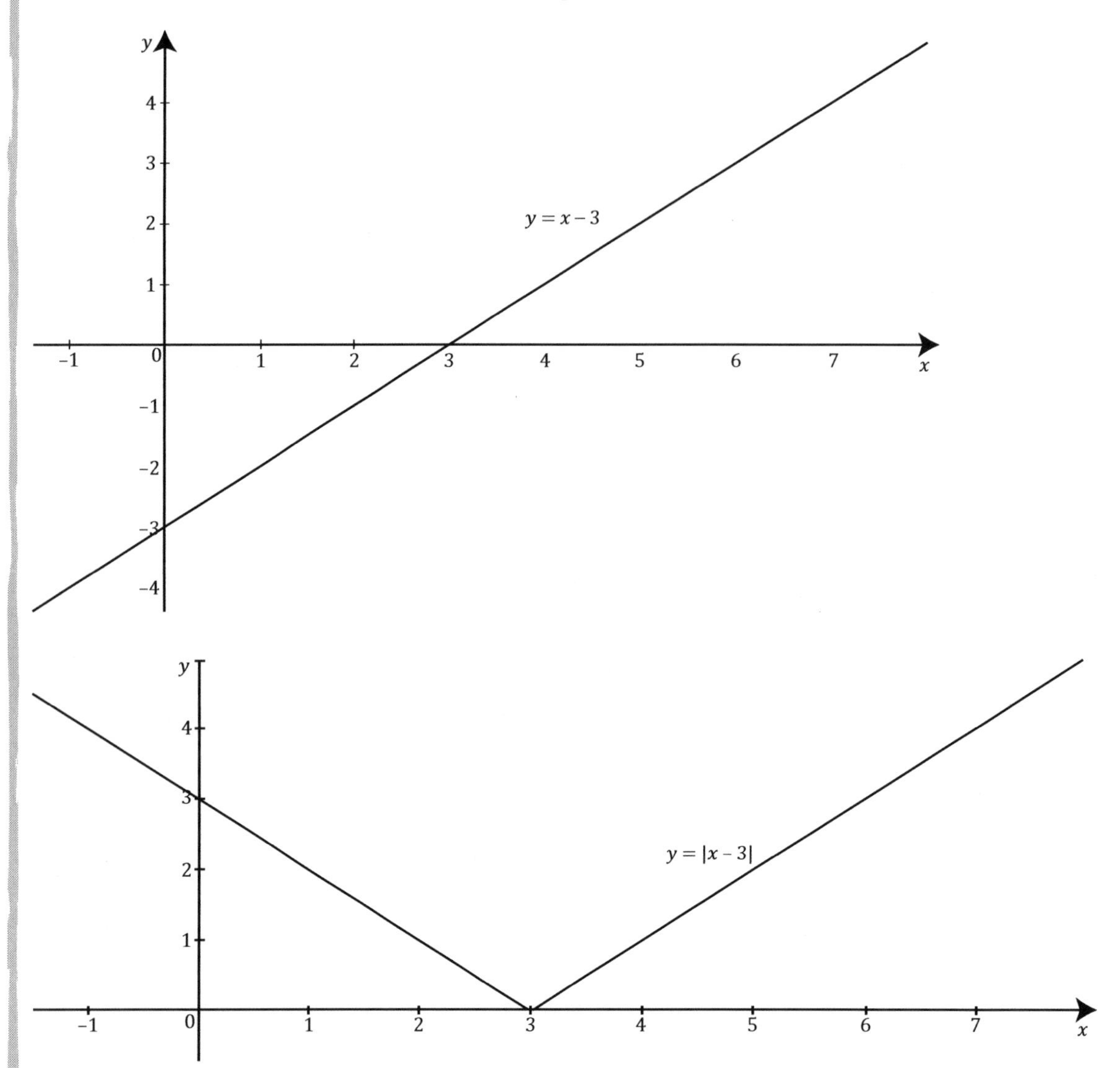

Combinations of the transformations on the graph $y = f(x)$

You came across the transformations of the graph $y = f(x)$ in AS C1. If you are unsure about transformations of curves, you should look back at your notes or C1 Topic 2 of the AS book.

For C3 you have to apply several transformations in succession.

Here is a summary of single transformations which you will need to revise.

Transformations of the graph of $y = f(x)$

A graph of $y = f(x)$ can be transformed into a new function using the rules shown in this table.

Original function	New function	Transformation
$y = f(x)$	$y = f(x) + a$	Translation of a units parallel to the y-axis. (i.e. translation of $\begin{pmatrix} 0 \\ a \end{pmatrix}$)
	$y = f(x + a)$	Translation of a units to the left parallel to the x-axis. (i.e. translation of $\begin{pmatrix} -a \\ 0 \end{pmatrix}$)
	$y = f(x - a)$	Translation of a units to the right parallel to the x-axis. (i.e. translation of $\begin{pmatrix} a \\ 0 \end{pmatrix}$)
	$y = -f(x)$	A reflection in the x-axis
	$y = af(x)$	One-way stretch with scale factor a parallel to the y-axis.
	$y = f(ax)$	One-way stretch with scale factor $\frac{1}{a}$ parallel to the x-axis.

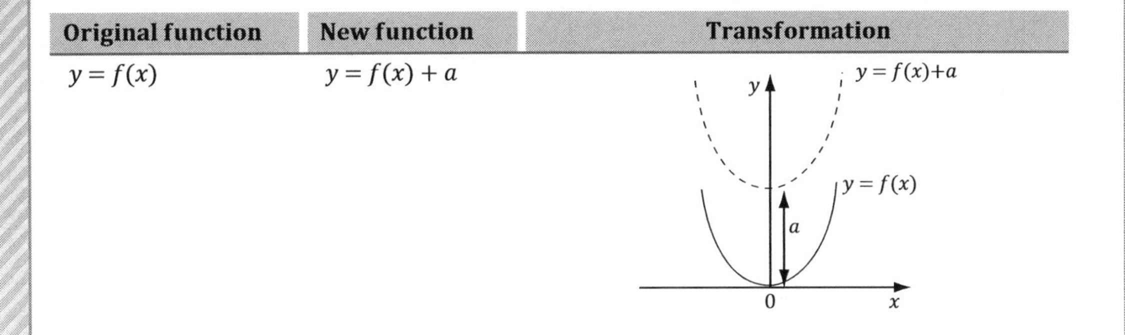

Original function	New function	Transformation
$y = f(x)$	$y = f(x) + a$	

Original function	New function	Transformation
	$y = f(x + a)$	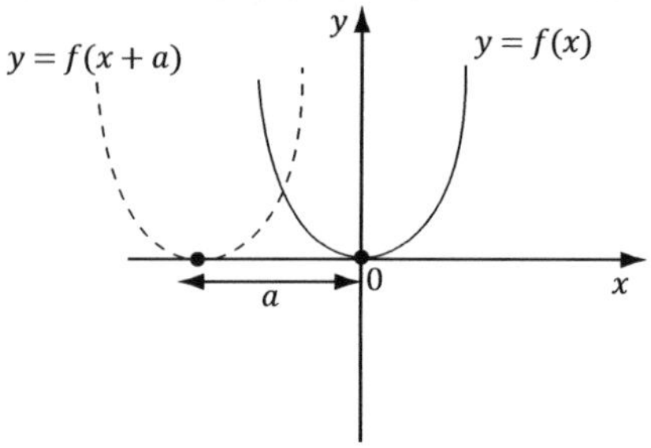 $y = f(x+a)$; $y = f(x)$; y; x; 0; a
	$y = f(x - a)$	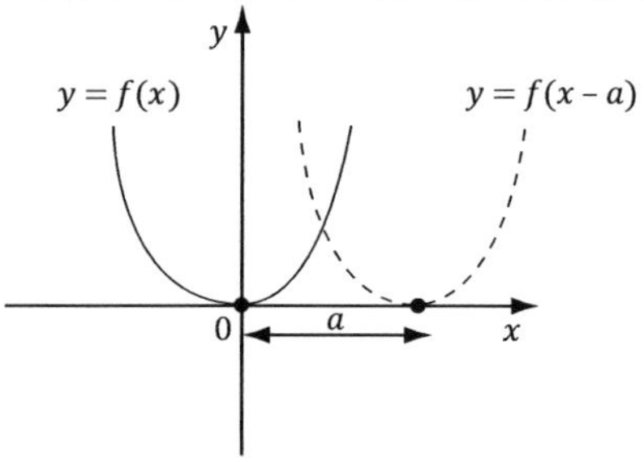 $y = f(x)$; $y = f(x-a)$; y; x; 0; a
	$y = -f(x)$	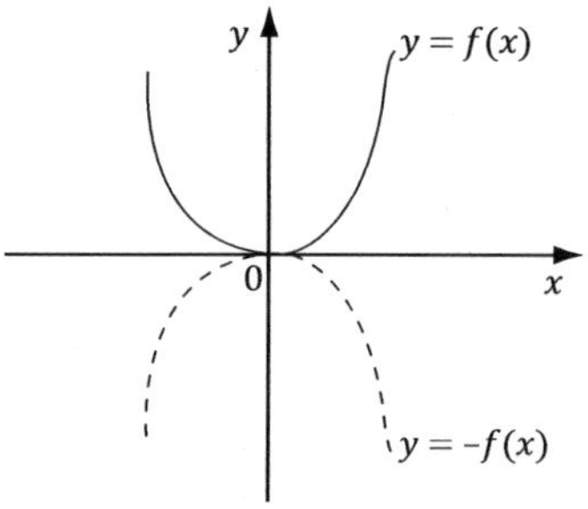 $y = f(x)$; $y = -f(x)$; y; x; 0
	$y = af(x)$ E.g. $y = 2\,f(x)$	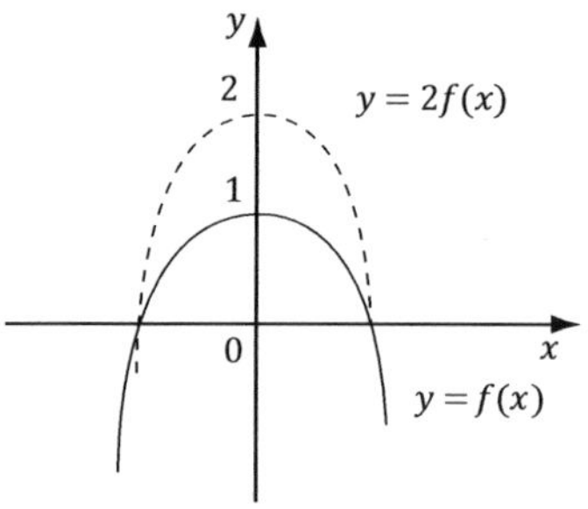 $y = 2f(x)$; $y = f(x)$; y; x; 0; 1; 2

Original function	New function	Transformation
	$y = f(ax)$ E.g. $y = f(2x)$	$y = f(x)$, $y = f(2x)$; -1, $-\frac{1}{2}$, 0, $\frac{1}{2}$, 1

Example

① The diagram shows a sketch of the graph of $y = f(x)$. The graph passes through the points $(-2, 0)$ and $(4, 0)$ and has a maximum point at $(1, 3)$.

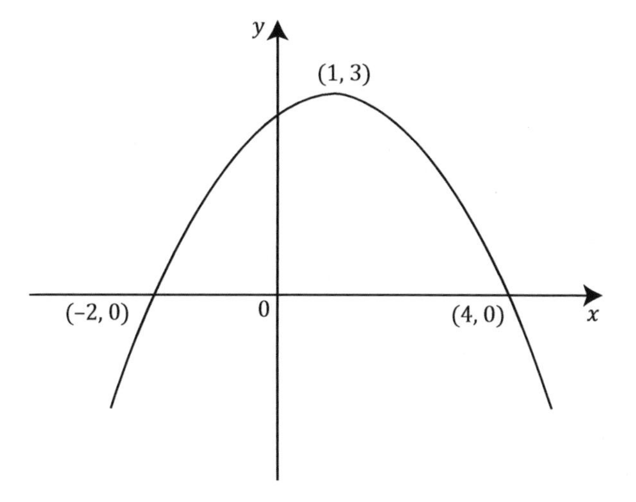

Sketch the graph of $y = -3f(x + 2)$, indicating the coordinates of the stationary point and the coordinates of the points of intersection of the graph with the x-axis. [3]

(WJEC C3 Jan 2011 Q8)

Answer

① There are three separate transformations:

Transformation 1:

$y = f(x)$ to $y = f(x + 2)$ represents a translation of -2 units parallel to the x-axis.

Transformation 2:

$y = f(x)$ to $y = 3f(x)$ represents a one-way stretch with scale factor 3 parallel to the y-axis.

Transformation 3:

$y = f(x)$ to $y = -f(x)$ represents a reflection in the x-axis.

Hence $y = -3f(x + 2)$ is a combination of all three transformations.

Transformation 1 means the whole graph will be shifted to the left by two units. Transformation 2 will stretch the y-coordinates by 3 (i.e. they will be multiplied by 3) leaving the x-coordinates unchanged.

Transformation 3 will reflect the whole graph in the x-axis.

These three transformations will produce the following curve.

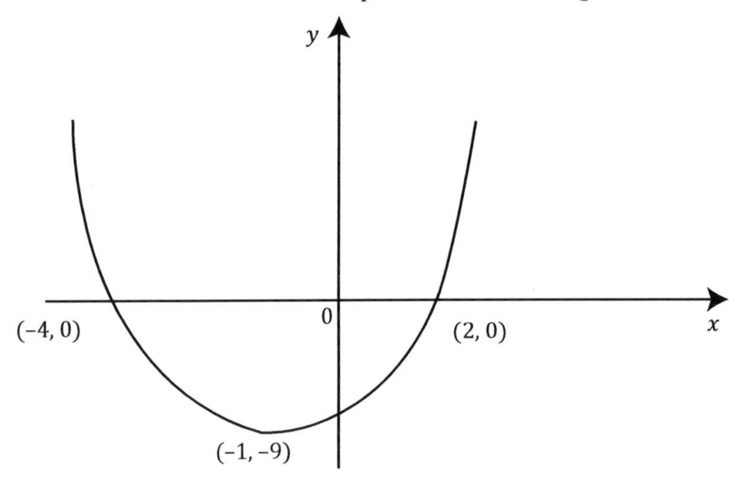

Example

② The function f is defined by $f(x) = |x|$.

(a) Sketch the graph of $y = f(x)$.

(b) On a separate set of axes, sketch the graph of $y = f(x - 5) + 3$. Mark on your sketch, the coordinates of the point on the graph where the y-coordinate is least and also the coordinates of the point where the graph crosses the y-axis.

Answer

② (a)

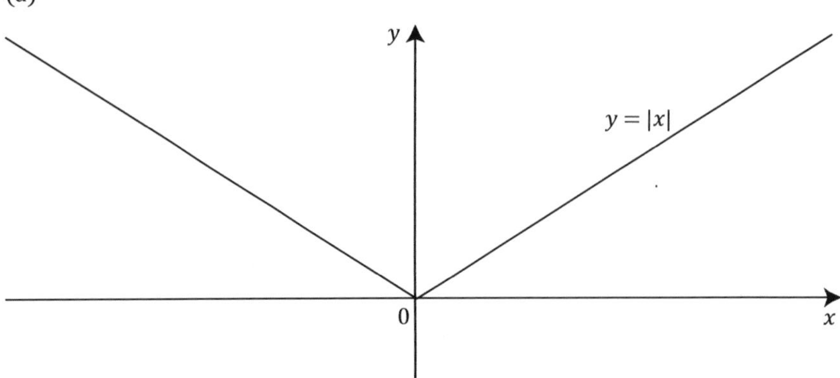

(b) The graph of $y = f(x - 5) + 3$ can be obtained from the graph in part (a) by applying a translation of 5 units parallel to the x-axis and then a translation of 3 units parallel to the y-axis.

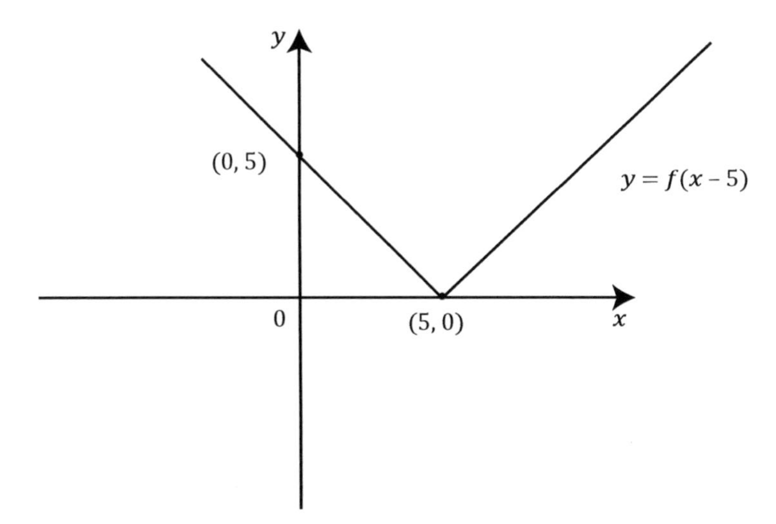

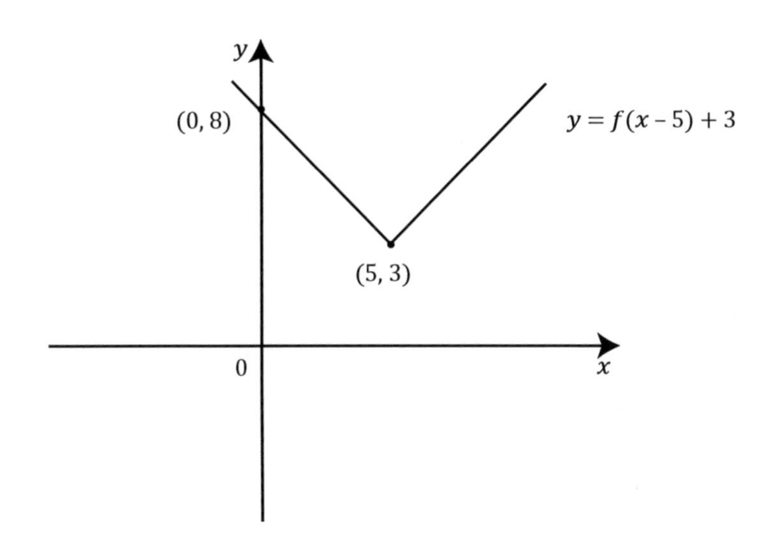

Examination style questions

① Solve the following

$7|x| - 2 = 8 - 3|x|$ [3]

Answer

① $7|x| - 2 = 8 - 3|x|$

$10|x| = 10$

$1|x| = 1$

$x = \pm 1$

② Solve the following

$|5x - 2| > 8$ [3]

Answer

② $|5x - 2| > 8$

$5x - 2 > 8$ or $5x - 2 < -8$

$5x > 10$ or $5x < -6$

$x > 2$ or $x < -\frac{6}{5}$

Alternative method

The following alternative method can also be used

$|5x - 2| > 8$

The modulus sign can be removed by squaring both sides.

Squaring both sides gives

$(5x - 2)^2 > 64$

$25x^2 - 20x + 4 > 64$

$25x^2 - 20x - 60 > 0$

Here the quadratic is divided by 5 to make the result easier to factorise.

$5x^2 - 4x - 12 > 0$

$(5x + 6)(x - 2) > 0$

Find the critical values by putting $(5x + 6)(x - 2) = 0$ and then solving.

Critical values are $x = -\frac{6}{5}$ and $x = 2$

If the graph of $y = (5x + 6)(x - 2)$ were plotted the curve would intersect the x-axis at $x = -\frac{6}{5}$ and $x = 2$. The graph would be ∪-shaped and the part of the graph above the x-axis would represent $(5x + 6)(x - 2) > 0$.

Hence $x < -\frac{6}{5}$ **or** $x > 2$.

A mark will be lost if 'and' is written instead of 'or' here. The reasoning for this is that x cannot be both less than $-\frac{6}{5}$ and greater than 2.

Test yourself

Answer the following questions and check your answers before moving on to the next topic.

① The function f has domain $x \leq -2$ and is defined by

$$f(x) = (x + 2)^2 - 1$$

(a) Find the range of f.

(b) Find an expression for $f^{-1}(x)$. State the domain and range of f^{-1}.

② The diagram shows a sketch of the graph of $y = f(x)$. The graph has its highest point at (3, 4) and intersects the x-axis at the points (1, 0) and (5, 0).

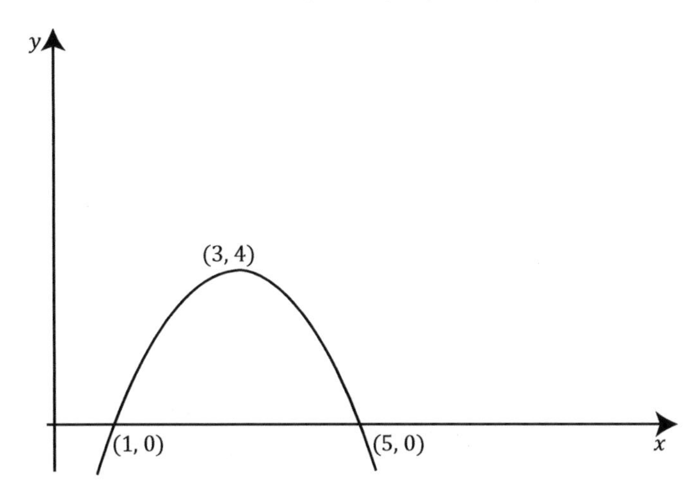

Sketch the graph of $y = 2f(x - 1)$, indicating the coordinates of three points on the graph.

③ Solve the following

(a) $3|x - 1| + 7 = 19$

(b) $6|x| - 3 = 2|x| + 5$

(Note: answers to Test yourself are found at the back of the book.)

1	Solve the following	
	$\|9x - 7\| \leq 3$	[3]
	$\sqrt{5\|x\|+1} = 3$	[2]
		(WJEC C3 June 2009 Q6)

Answer

1 (a) $|9x - 7| \leq 3$

$9x - 7 \leq 3$ and $9x - 7 \geq -3$

Note that the word 'and' should be included.

$9x \leq 10$ and $9x \geq 4$

$x \leq \frac{10}{9}$ and $x \geq \frac{4}{9}$

$\frac{4}{9} \leq x \leq \frac{10}{9}$

Alternative method

The following alternative method can also be used

$|9x - 7| \leq 3$

Squaring both sides gives

The modulus sign can be removed by squaring both sides.

$(9x - 7)^2 \leq 9$

$81x^2 - 126x + 49 \leq 9$

$81x^2 - 126x + 40 \leq 0$

$(9x - 10)(9x - 4) \leq 0$

At the critical points $x = \frac{10}{9}$ or $x = \frac{4}{9}$

If the curve $y = (9x - 10)(9x - 4)$ were plotted it would be ∪-shaped and would cut the x-axis at these two points. As we want the values of x for which $y \leq 0$, this is the part of the curve below the x-axis, i.e. the values of x that are between the two roots.

Hence $\frac{4}{9} \leq x \leq \frac{10}{9}$

(b) $\sqrt{5|x|+1} = 3$

Squaring both sides gives

$5|x| + 1 = 9$

$5|x| = 8$

$|x| = \frac{8}{5}$

$x = \pm\frac{8}{5}$

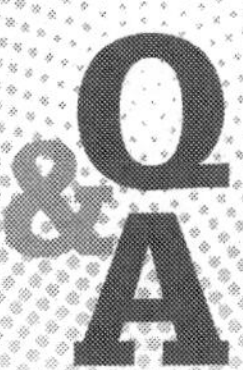

2 The function f has domain $x \leq 0$ and is defined by $f(x) = 5x^2 + 4$.

(a) Find an expression for $f^{-1}(x)$. [5]

(b) Write down the domain and range of f^{-1}. [1]

(WJEC C3 Jan 2009 Q9)

Answer

2 (a) Let $y = 5x^2 + 4$

$$\frac{y-4}{5} = x^2$$

Hence $x = \pm\sqrt{\frac{y-4}{5}}$

However, as $x \leq 0$, $x = -\sqrt{\frac{y-4}{5}}$

So $f^{-1}(x) = -\sqrt{\frac{x-4}{5}}$

(b) Domain of f^{-1}, $D(f^{-1}) = R(f) = [4, \infty]$ or $x \geq 4$

Range of f^{-1}, $R(f^{-1}) = D(f) = (-\infty, 0]$ or $f^{-1}(x) \leq 0$

> Rearrange the equation so that x becomes the subject.

> When square rooting you must remember to include $\pm$.

> Check with the domain of f to see which of the values is required. Note that the domain of f here only allows a value of x which is 0 or negative. Hence the positive sign cannot be used.

> The domain of f^{-1} is the same as the range of f, which is $[4, \infty]$.

3 (a) Solve the inequality $|3x + 1| \leq 5$. [3]

(b) The function f is defined by $f(x) = |x|$.

(i) Sketch the graph of $y = f(x)$.

(ii) On a separate set of axes, sketch the graph of $y = f(x - 3) + 2$. On your sketch, indicate the coordinates of the point on the graph where the value of the y-coordinate is least and the coordinates of the point where the graph crosses the y-axis. [4]

(WJEC C3 June 2010 Q7)

Answer

3 (a) $|3x + 1| \leq 5$

$3x + 1 \leq 5$ and $3x + 1 \geq -5$

$3x \leq 4$ and $3x \geq -6$

$x \leq \frac{4}{3}$ and $x \geq -2$, i.e. $-2 \leq x \leq \frac{4}{3}$

Alternative method

The following alternative method can also be used

$|3x + 1| \leq 5$

Squaring both sides means that the modulus sign can be removed.

$(3x + 1)^2 \leq 25$

$9x^2 + 6x + 1 \leq 25$

$9x^2 + 6x - 24 \leq 0$

Simplify the quadratic equation by dividing both sides by 3.

$3x^2 + 2x - 8 \leq 0$

$(3x - 4)(x + 2) \leq 0$

Critical values are $x = \frac{4}{3}$ and $x = -2$

Hence $-2 \leq x \leq \frac{4}{3}$

If a graph of $y = (3x - 4)(x + 2)$ were plotted it would be U-shaped and intersect the x-axis at the critical values. The required values of x would be all those for which the curve lies on or below the x-axis, i.e. the values of x between the two roots.

(b) (i)

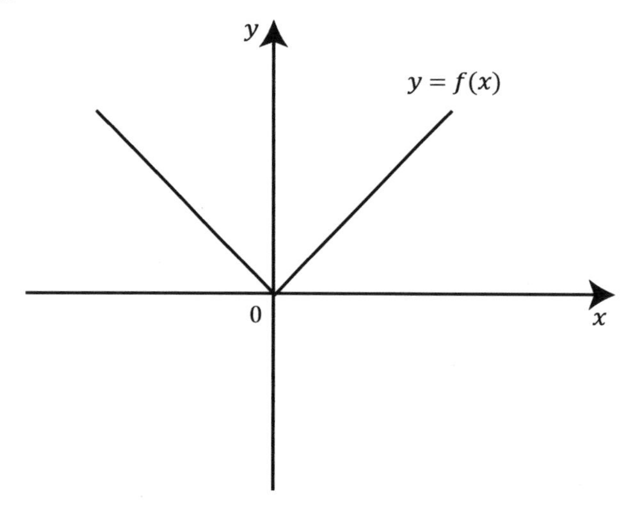

(ii)

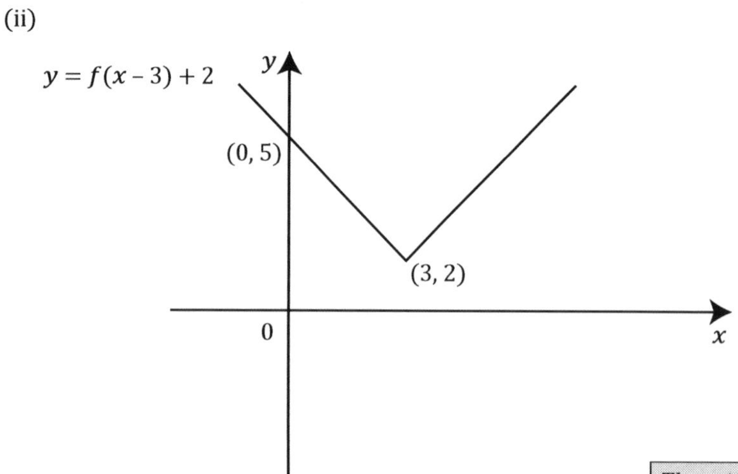

The original graph is translated three units to the right and two units up, i.e. a translation of $\binom{3}{2}$.

4

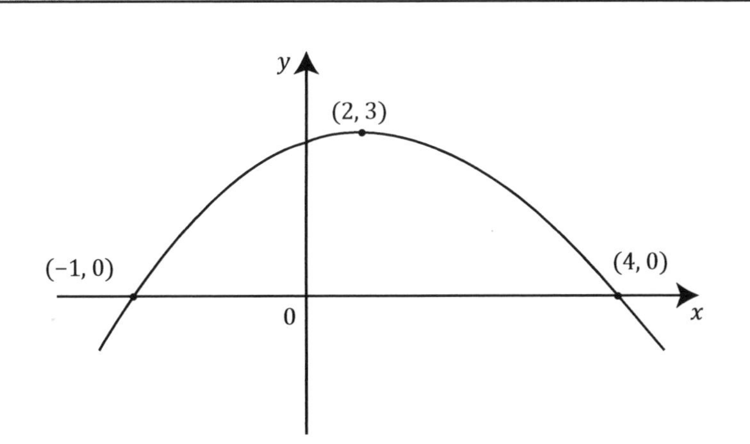

The diagram shows a sketch of the graph of $y = f(x)$. The graph has its highest point at (2, 3) and intersects the x-axis at the points (−1, 0) and (4, 0). Sketch the graph of $y = 3f(x - 2)$, indicating the coordinates of three points on the graph. [3]

(WJEC C3 June 2009 Q8)

Answer

4 $y = f(x)$ to $y = 3f(x - 2)$ represents two transformations. A translation to the right by 2 units and a one-way stretch of scale factor 3 parallel to the y-axis.

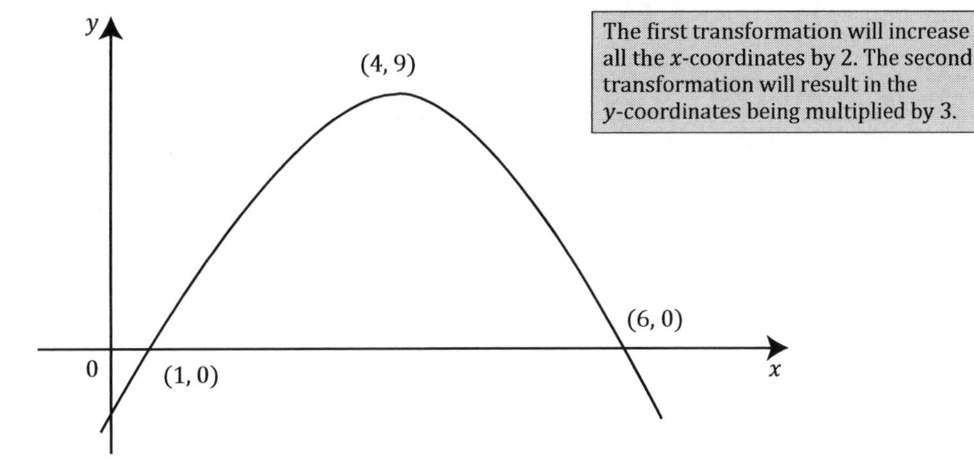

The first transformation will increase all the x-coordinates by 2. The second transformation will result in the y-coordinates being multiplied by 3.

Topic 2 Trigonometry

This topic covers the following:

- Secant, cosecant and cotangent functions and their graphs
- Solution of trigonometric equations making use of the identities $\sec^2 \theta = 1 + \tan^2 \theta$ and $\operatorname{cosec}^2 \theta = 1 + \cot^2 \theta$
- Inverse trigonometric functions $\sin^{-1}$, $\cos^{-1}$ and $\tan^{-1}$, their graphs and domains
- Showing by counter-example

Secant, cosecant and cotangent and their graphs

Sec θ

Sec θ is the reciprocal of cos θ so $\sec \theta = \frac{1}{\cos \theta}$

The graph of $y = \sec \theta$ is shown below. You can see from the graph that the curve $y = \sec \theta$ is defined for all values of θ other than $\theta = \pm\frac{\pi}{2}, \pm\frac{3\pi}{2}$, etc., since, at these values of θ, $\cos \theta = 0$. Notice that as θ approaches these values, the value of y approaches $\pm\infty$ (infinity) and the vertical lines, $\theta = \pm\frac{\pi}{2}, \pm\frac{3\pi}{2}$, etc., are called asymptotes to the curve.

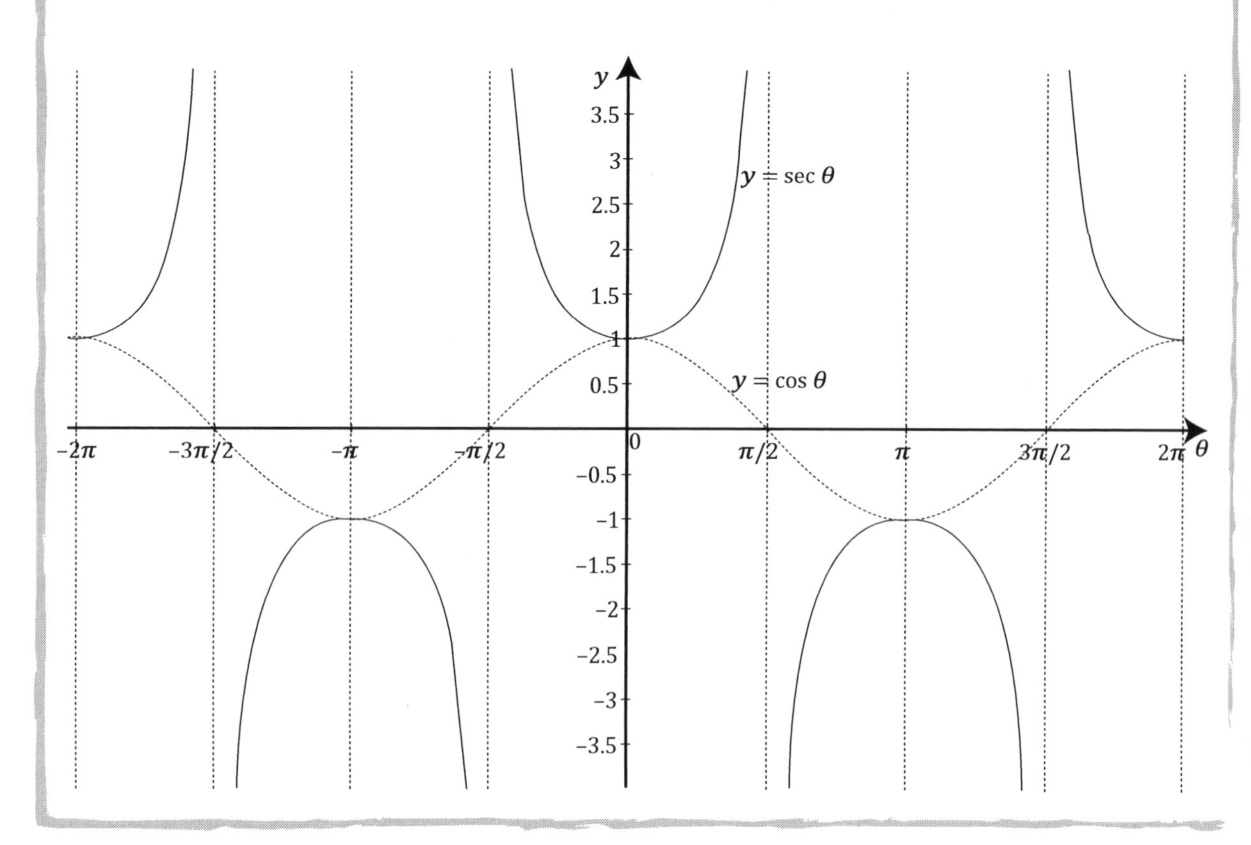

Cosec θ

Cosec θ is the reciprocal of sin θ, so $\operatorname{cosec}\theta = \dfrac{1}{\sin\theta}$

The graph of $y = \operatorname{cosec}\theta$ is shown below. The curve $y = \operatorname{cosec}\theta$ is defined for all values of θ other than where $\sin\theta = 0$, i.e. $\theta = 0, \pm\pi, \pm2\pi$, etc., which are asymptotes to the curve.

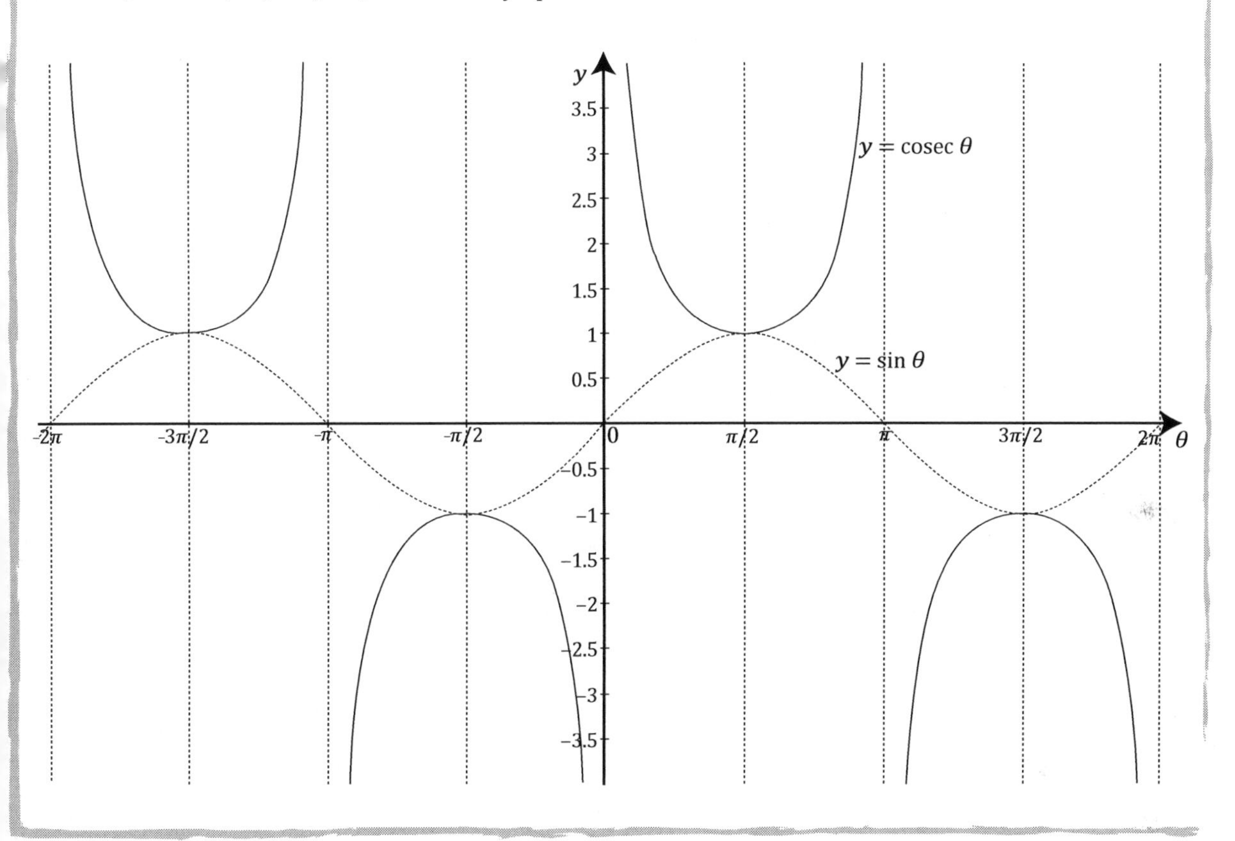

Cot θ

Cot θ is the reciprocal of tan θ so $\cot\theta = \dfrac{1}{\tan\theta}$

The graph of $y = \cot\theta$ is shown on the next page. The curve $y = \cot\theta$ is defined for all values of θ other than where $\tan\theta = 0$, i.e. $\theta = 0, \pm\pi, \pm2\pi$, etc., which are asymptotes to the curve.

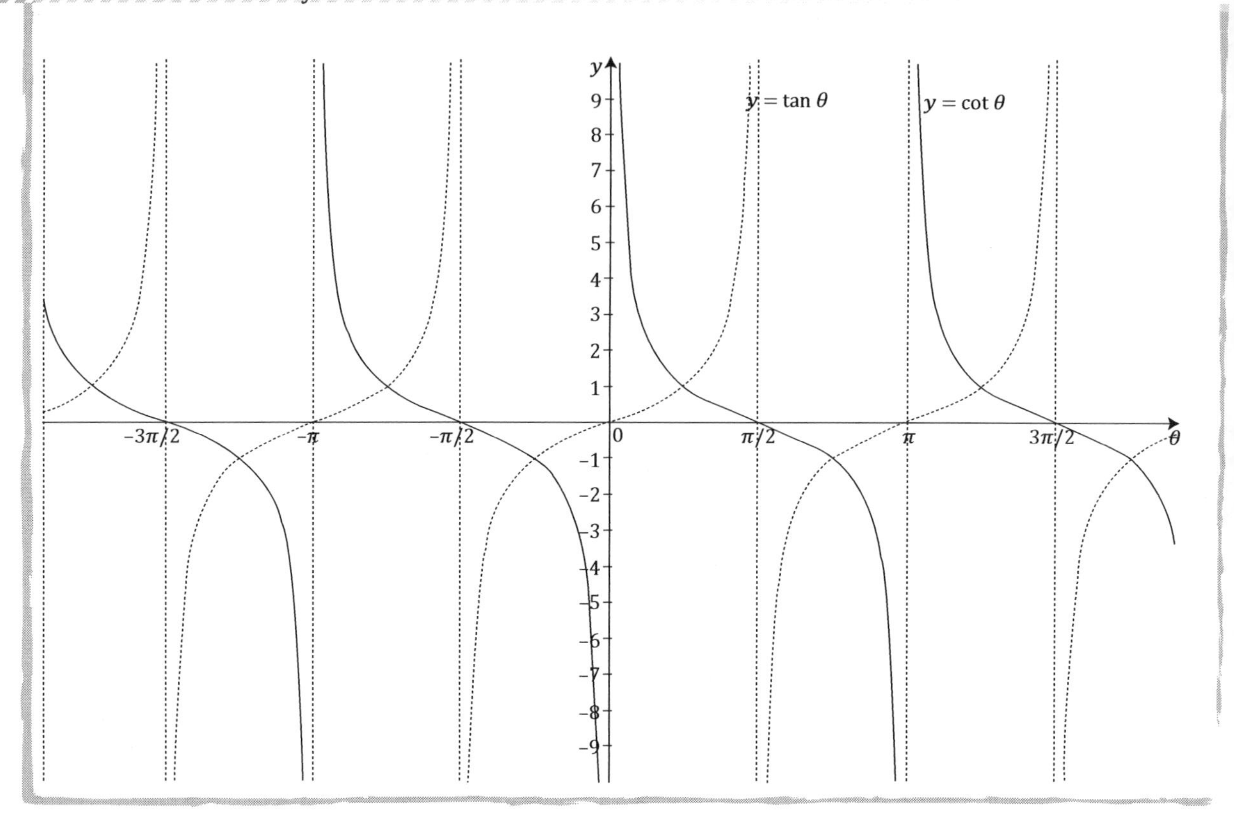

The new trigonometric identities to remember

Here are two more trigonometric identities you need to remember and use:

$\sec^2 \theta = 1 + \tan^2 \theta$

$\operatorname{cosec}^2 \theta = 1 + \cot^2 \theta$

> Both of these formulae must be remembered as they are not included in the formula booklet.

> You may see the identity sign ≡ being used in place of the equals sign.

Proof of the two trigonometric identities $\sec^2 \theta = 1 + \tan^2 \theta$ and $\operatorname{cosec}^2 \theta = 1 + \cot^2 \theta$

These two trigonometric identities may be proved in the following ways:

Using $\tan\theta = \dfrac{\sin\theta}{\cos\theta}$ and $\sin^2 \theta + \cos^2 \theta = 1$

Dividing through by $\cos^2 \theta$ gives:

$$\frac{\sin^2\theta}{\cos^2\theta} + 1 = \frac{1}{\cos^2\theta}$$

$$\left(\frac{\sin\theta}{\cos\theta}\right)^2 + 1 = \left(\frac{1}{\cos\theta}\right)^2$$

$\tan^2 \theta + 1 = \sec^2 \theta$

Similarly, dividing through by $\sin^2\theta$ gives:

$$\frac{\cos^2\theta}{\sin^2\theta}+1=\frac{1}{\sin^2\theta}$$

$$\left(\frac{\cos\theta}{\sin\theta}\right)^2+1=\left(\frac{1}{\sin\theta}\right)^2$$

$$\cot^2\theta+1=\operatorname{cosec}^2\theta$$

Solution of trigonometric equations making use of the identities $\sec^2\theta = 1 + \tan^2\theta$ and $\operatorname{cosec}^2\theta = 1 + \cot^2\theta$

You will frequently be asked to solve equations where you have to make use of the trigonometric identities $\sec^2\theta = 1 + \tan^2\theta$ and $\operatorname{cosec}^2\theta = 1 + \cot^2\theta$. In many of these questions, you need to form a quadratic equation in terms of just one trigonometric function before solving it, using factorisation where possible. The following examples will explain this technique.

Example

① Find the values of θ in the range $0° \leq \theta \leq 360°$ that satisfy the equation

$\sec^2\theta + 5 = 5\tan\theta$

giving your answers to 1 decimal place

In this type of question, retain the term which is to the power 1 (i.e. $\tan\theta$).

Answer

Use $\sec^2\theta = 1 + \tan^2\theta$ to give the equation just in terms of $\tan\theta$.

① $\sec^2\theta + 5 = 5\tan\theta$

$(1 + \tan^2\theta) + 5 = 5\tan\theta$

$\tan^2\theta - 5\tan\theta + 6 = 0$

$(\tan\theta - 3)(\tan\theta - 2) = 0$

A quadratic equation in terms of $\tan\theta$ is formed which is then factorised and solved to determine the values of θ in the range specified in the question.

Solving gives $\tan\theta = 3$ or $\tan\theta = 2$

$\theta = \tan^{-1}(3)$

giving $\theta = 71.6°$ or $251.6°$ (correct to one decimal place)

The graph of $y = \tan\theta$ has a period of 180°, so once a solution is found another solution may be found by adding 180°.

or $\theta = \tan^{-1}(2)$

giving $\theta = 63.4°$ or $243.4°$ (correct to one decimal place)

Another way to find the values of θ is to use the CAST method. $\tan\theta$ is positive in the first and third quadrants.

$\theta = 63.4°$ or $71.6°$, $243.4°$ or $251.6°$ (all correct to 1 decimal place)

Always list all your solutions in numerical order as a final answer.

Example

② Find the values of θ in the range $0^\circ \leq \theta \leq 360^\circ$ that satisfy the equation

$2\tan^2\theta = 6\sec\theta - 6$ [6]

Answer

② $2(\sec^2\theta - 1) = 6\sec\theta - 6$

$2\sec^2\theta - 2 = 6\sec\theta - 6$

$2\sec^2\theta - 6\sec\theta + 4 = 0$

$(2\sec\theta - 4)(\sec\theta - 1) = 0$

$\sec\theta = 2$ or $\sec\theta = 1$

$\frac{1}{\cos\theta} = 2$ or $\frac{1}{\cos\theta} = 1$

$\cos\theta = \frac{1}{2}$ giving $\theta = 60^\circ$ or 300°

$\cos\theta = 1$ giving $\theta = 0^\circ$ or 360°

Hence $\theta = 0^\circ, 60^\circ, 300^\circ$ or 360°

Retain the term which is to the power 1 (i.e. $\sec\theta$).

Use the formula $\sec\theta = \frac{1}{\cos\theta}$
You must remember this.

Use a graph of $y = \cos\theta$ or the CAST method to find the angles in the required range. Using the CAST method $\cos\theta$ is positive in the 1st and 4th quadrants. As $\cos^{-1}\left(\frac{1}{2}\right) = 60^\circ$ and this is in the 1st quadrant, the other angle in the range will be $360^\circ - 60^\circ = 300^\circ$. The angles which give $\cos\theta = 1$, can be worked out in a similar way.

Inverse trigonometric functions $\sin^{-1}$, $\cos^{-1}$ and $\tan^{-1}$ and their graphs and domains

The graph of $y = \sin^{-1}\theta$

To obtain the graph of $y = \sin^{-1}\theta$, first take the graph of $y = \sin\theta$ in the region between $\theta = -\frac{\pi}{2}$ and $\theta = \frac{\pi}{2}$ and reflect it in the line $y = \theta$.

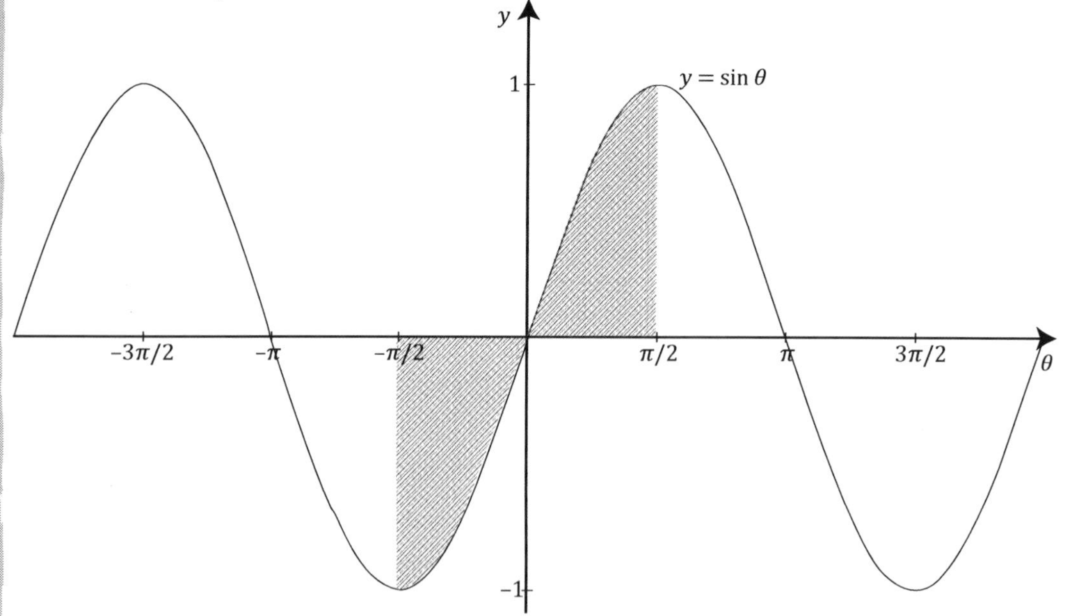

If you look at the curve for $y = \sin\theta$, one value of y corresponds to many values of θ. However, to find an inverse it is necessary that one value of y corresponds to only one value of θ, and this is known as one-to-one. For this reason, the values of θ are restricted to the interval between $-\frac{\pi}{2}$ and $\frac{\pi}{2}$.

The graph for $y = \sin^{-1}\theta$ is obtained by reflecting the graph of $y = \sin\theta$ in the line $y = \theta$.

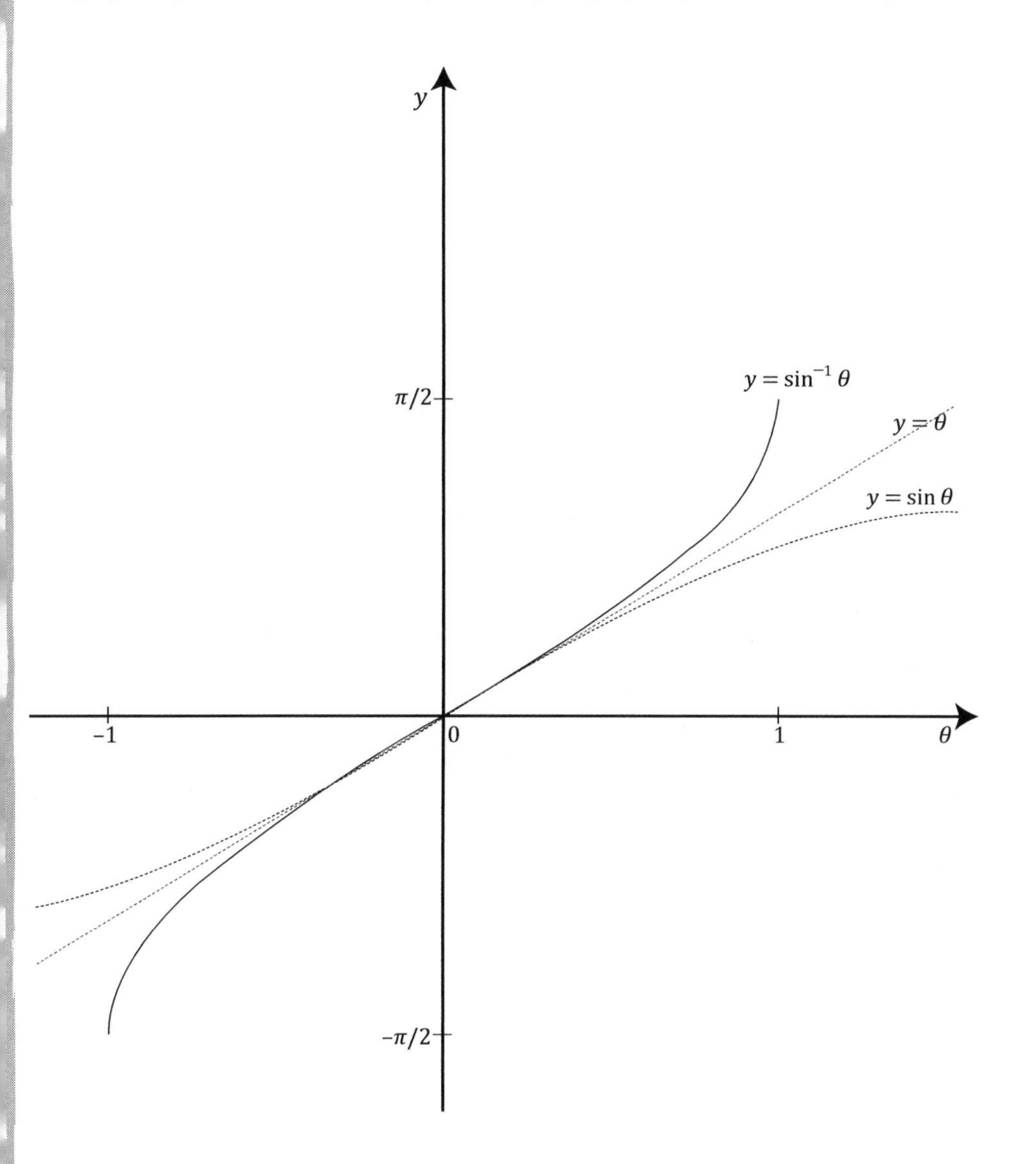

Notice from the graph that, for $y = \sin^{-1}\theta$, the only allowable values of θ lie in the interval $[-1, 1]$, i.e. $-1 \leq \theta \leq 1$. The set of allowable values that can be entered into a function is called the domain.

The range is the corresponding set of y-values the function can have.

The range here is $-\frac{\pi}{2} \leq \theta \leq \frac{\pi}{2}$.

The graph of $y = \cos^{-1} \theta$

To obtain the graph of $y = \cos^{-1} \theta$, first take the graph of $y = \cos \theta$ in the region between $\theta = 0$ and $\theta = \pi$ and reflect it in the line $y = \theta$.

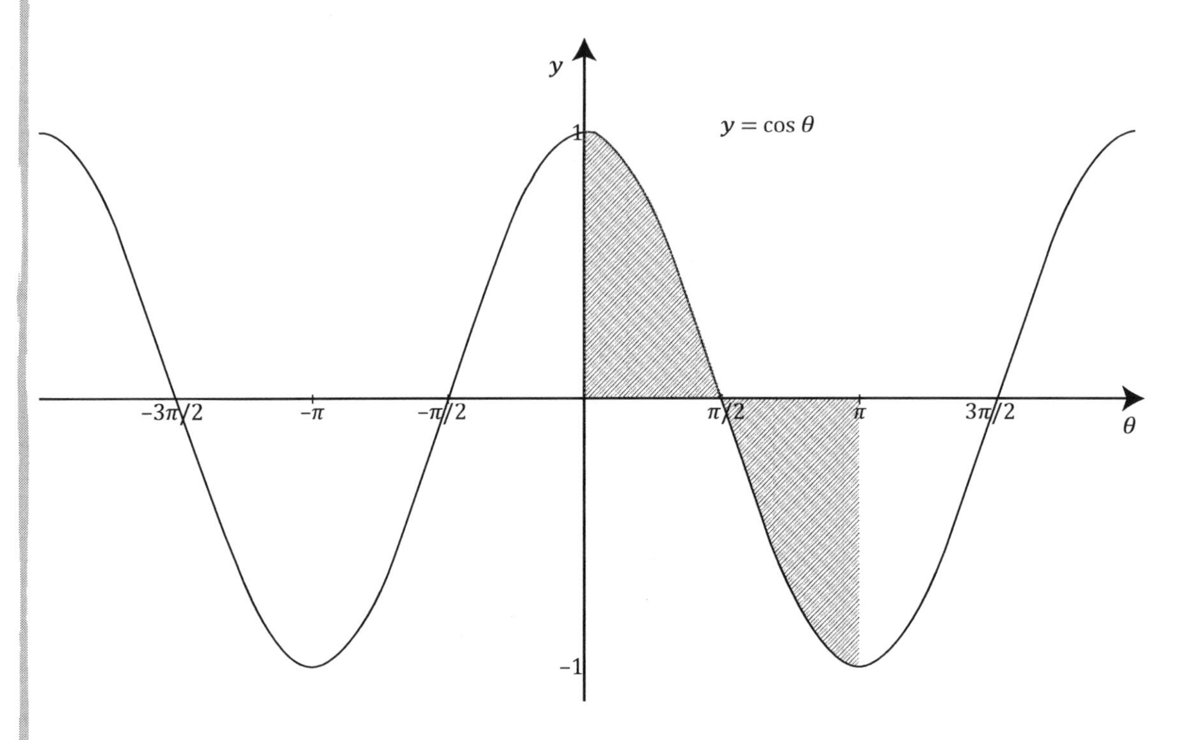

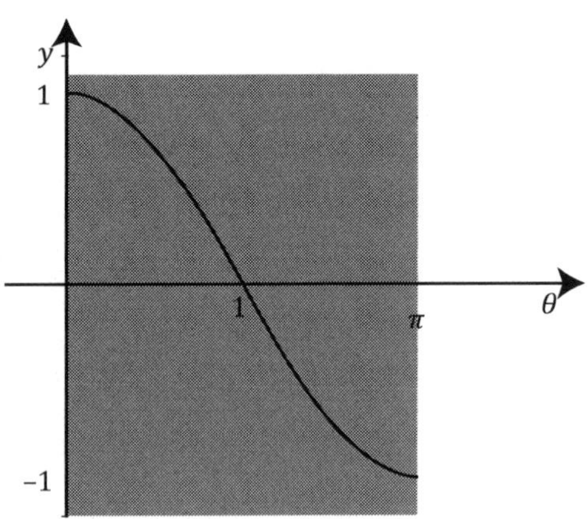

So that the original function is one to one, the domain is restricted to $0 \leq \theta \leq \pi$.

When the function ($y = \cos \theta$) is reflected in the line $y = \theta$, the graph of the inverse function

$y = \cos^{-1} \theta$ is obtained as shown here:

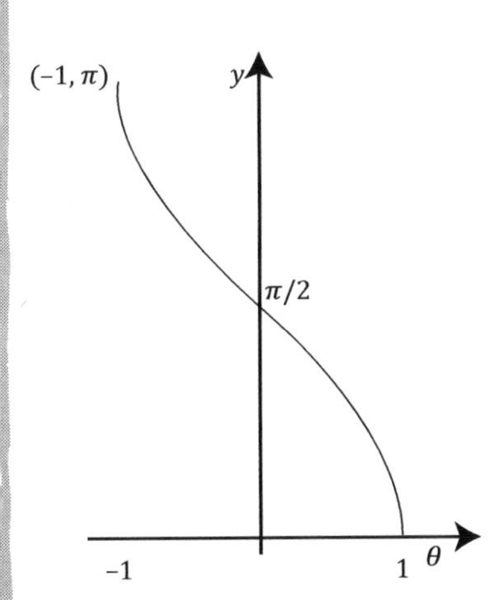

The domain of the original function (i.e. $0 \leq \theta \leq \pi$) becomes the range of the inverse function and the range of the original function (i.e. $-1 \leq \cos\theta \leq 1$) will become the domain of the inverse function.

The domain of $y = \cos^{-1}\theta$ is $[-1, 1]$, i.e. $-1 \leq \theta \leq 1$

The range of $y = \cos^{-1}\theta$ is $[0, \pi]$, i.e. $0 \leq \cos^{-1}\theta \leq \pi$

The graph of $y = \tan^{-1}\theta$

Here the graph of $y = \tan\theta$ is reflected in the line $y = \theta$ to produce the graph of the inverse function $y = \tan^{-1}\theta$.

Again, only part of the graph is used so that each y-value has only one possible x-value.

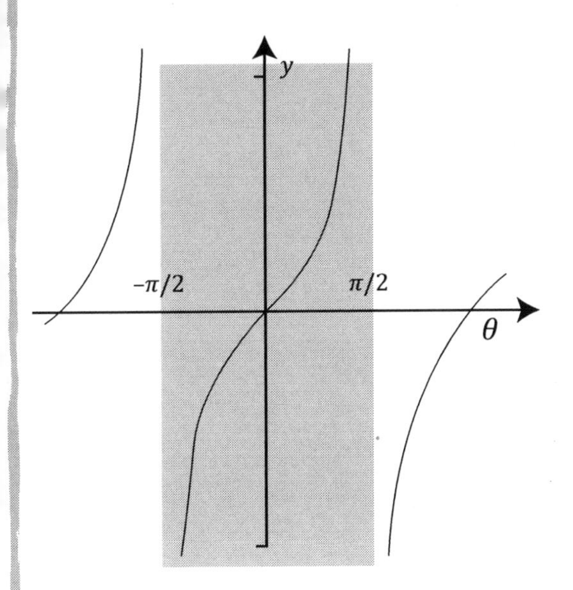

The graph of $y = \tan^{-1}\theta$ is shown here:

The domain of $y = \tan^{-1}\theta$ is the set of all real numbers.

The range of $y = \tan^{-1}\theta$ is $\left[-\frac{\pi}{2}, \frac{\pi}{2}\right]$, i.e. $-\frac{\pi}{2} \leq \tan^{-1}\theta \leq \frac{\pi}{2}$

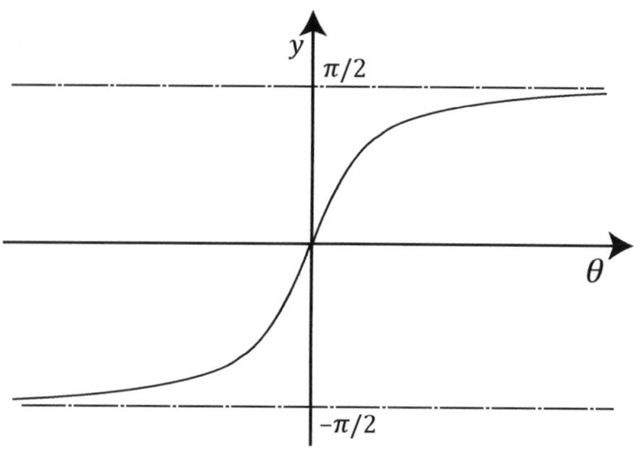

Showing by counter-example

To prove that a given statement is false, you need to find *just one case* for which the statement is not true. This is called a counter-example. In order to show by counter-example that two trigonometric expressions are not equivalent to each other, you can substitute a value into each expression. If the two expressions are not equal, then you have proved that they are not equivalent. You can substitute any value, but it is easier to use a value that gives a simple known result. For example, when substituting for θ into any of the trigonometric functions, $\sin\theta$, $\cos\theta$ or $\tan\theta$, choose a value such as $0, \pi, \frac{\pi}{2}, \frac{\pi}{4}$, etc.

It should be noted that counter-example questions do not always involve trigonometric expressions.

Example

① Show by counter-example, that the statement

$\operatorname{cosec}^2\theta \equiv 1 + \sec^2\theta$

is false.

Answer

Let $\theta = \frac{\pi}{2}$

$$\text{LHS} = \operatorname{cosec}^2\theta = \frac{1}{\sin^2\theta} = \frac{1}{\sin^2\frac{\pi}{2}} = \frac{1}{1} = 1$$

$\sin\frac{\pi}{2} = 1$ so $\sin^2\frac{\pi}{2} = 1 \times 1 = 1$

$$\text{RHS} = 1 + \sec^2\theta = 1 + \frac{1}{\cos^2\theta} = 1 + \frac{1}{\cos^2\frac{\pi}{2}} = 1 + \frac{1}{0} = \infty$$

Note $\frac{1}{0} = \infty$ and adding 1 still makes it ∞

$1 \neq \infty$ so the statement $\operatorname{cosec}^2\theta \equiv 1 + \sec^2\theta$ is false.

② Show that the statement $|a + b| \equiv |a| + |b|$ is false.

Answer

② Let $a = 1, b = -1$

LHS $= |1 - 1| = |0| = 0$

RHS $= |1| + |-1| = 1 + 1 = 2$

$0 \neq 2$ so the statement $|a + b| \equiv |a| + |b|$ is false.

Examination style questions

① Find the values of θ in the range $0° \leq \theta \leq 360°$ that satisfy the equation

$4 \sec^2 \theta = 7 - 11 \tan \theta$

giving your answer to 1 decimal place. [5]

Answer

① $4 \sec^2 \theta = 7 - 11 \tan \theta$

$4(1 + \tan^2 \theta) = 7 - 11 \tan \theta$

$4 + 4 \tan^2 \theta = 7 - 11 \tan \theta$

$4 \tan^2 \theta + 11 \tan \theta - 3 = 0$

$(4 \tan \theta - 1)(\tan \theta + 3) = 0$

$\tan \theta = \frac{1}{4}$ or $\tan \theta = -3$

When $\tan \theta = \frac{1}{4}$, $\theta = 14.0°$ or $194.0°$

When $\tan \theta = -3$, $\theta = 180 - 71.6° = 108.4°$ or $\theta = 360 - 71.6° = 288.4°$

Hence $\theta = 14.0°, 108.4°, 194.0°$ or $288.4°$ correct to one decimal place.

Use $\sec^2 \theta = 1 + \tan^2 \theta$ to give the equation just in terms of $\tan \theta$. You have to recognise that the resulting equation is a quadratic equation.

The tan function has a period of 180°. Once you have found $\tan^{-1} \frac{1}{4}$, which is 14°, you add 180° to this to find the next solution. The solution beyond this lies outside the range.

tan is negative in the second and fourth quadrants, so $\theta = 180 - 71.6$ or $360 - 71.6$

Alternatively, using the fact that the tan function has a period of 180°, once you have found one solution, i.e. 108.4°, you add 180° to find the next solution.

② Show, by counter-example, that the statement

$\sin 2\theta \equiv 2 \sin^2 \theta - \cos \theta$

is false. [2]

You can let θ be any value but it makes sense to use a value where the sine and cosine of θ are known.

Answer

② Let $\theta = \frac{\pi}{2}$

LHS $= \sin 2\theta = \sin 2 \times \frac{\pi}{2} = \sin \pi = 0$

RHS $= 2\sin^2\theta - \cos\theta = 2\sin^2\frac{\pi}{2} - \cos\frac{\pi}{2} = 2 - 0 = 2$

Note that $\sin\frac{\pi}{2} = 1$ and $\cos\frac{\pi}{2} = 0$

$0 \neq 2$ so the statement $\sin 2\theta \equiv 2\sin^2\theta - \cos\theta$ is false.

③ Show, by counter example, that for real numbers a, b the statement $(a + b)^3 \equiv a^3 + b^3$ is false.

Answer

Let $a = 1, b = 1$

LHS $= (1 + 1)^3 = 2^3 = 8$

and RHS $= 1^3 + 1^3 = 1 + 1$

$8 \neq 1$ and the statement $(a + b)^3 \equiv a^3 + b^3$ is false.

Test yourself

Answer the following questions and check your answers before moving on to the next topic.

① Show, by counter-example, that the statement

$\cos 4\theta \equiv 4\cos^3\theta - 3\cos\theta$

is false

② Find all values of θ in the range $0° \leq \theta \leq 360°$ satisfying

$2\sec^2\theta + \tan\theta = 8$

③ (a) Show, by counter-example, that the statement

$$\tan 2\theta \equiv \frac{2\tan\theta}{1 + \tan^2\theta}$$

is false.

(b) Find all values of θ in the range $0° \leq \theta \leq 360°$ satisfying

$2\sec\theta + \tan^2\theta = 7$

(Note: answers to Test yourself are found at the back of the book.)

1 (a) Show, by counter-example, that the statement

$\sec^2\theta \equiv 1 - \operatorname{cosec}^2\theta$

is false. [2]

(b) Find all the values of θ in the range $0° \le \theta \le 360°$ satisfying

$3\operatorname{cosec}^2\theta = 11 - 2\cot\theta$ [6]

(WJEC C3 Jan 2011 Q2)

Answer

1 (a) Let $\theta = \frac{\pi}{4}$

$$\text{LHS} = \sec^2\theta = \frac{1}{\cos^2\theta} = \frac{1}{\cos^2\frac{\pi}{4}} = \frac{1}{\left(\frac{1}{\sqrt{2}}\right)^2} = 2$$

$$\text{RHS} = 1 - \operatorname{cosec}^2\theta = 1 - \frac{1}{\sin^2\theta} = 1 - \frac{1}{\sin^2\frac{\pi}{4}} = 1 - \frac{1}{\left(\frac{1}{\sqrt{2}}\right)^2} = 1 - 2 = -1$$

$2 \ne -1$ so the statement $\sec^2\theta \equiv 1 - \operatorname{cosec}^2\theta$ is false.

(b) $3\operatorname{cosec}^2\theta = 11 - 2\cot\theta$

Use $\operatorname{cosec}^2\theta = 1 + \cot^2\theta$ to write the equation in terms of $\cot\theta$.

$3(1 + \cot^2\theta) = 11 - 2\cot\theta$

$3 + 3\cot^2\theta = 11 - 2\cot\theta$

$3\cot^2\theta + 2\cot\theta - 8 = 0$

$(3\cot\theta - 4)(\cot\theta + 2) = 0$

Hence $\cot\theta = \frac{4}{3}$ or $\cot\theta = -2$

Remember that the tan function has a period of 180° (i.e. π). So from the first angle (e.g. 36.9°) the other angle can be found by adding 180° to it (i.e. $180 + 36.9 = 216.9°$).

$\cot\theta = \frac{1}{\tan\theta}$ so $\tan\theta = \frac{3}{4}$ giving $\theta = 36.9°$ or 216.9°

$\tan\theta$ is negative in the second and fourth quadrants, so $\theta = 180 - 26.6 = 153.4°$ or $\theta = 360 - 26.6 = 333.4°$.

$\cot\theta = \frac{1}{\tan\theta}$ so $\tan\theta = -\frac{1}{2}$ giving $\theta = 153.4°$ or $333.4°$

Check that all the angles you have found lie in the range $0° \le \theta \le 360°$ specified in the question.

Topic 3 Exponential and logarithmic functions

This topic covers the following:

- The function e^x and its graph
- The function ln x and its graph
- ln x as the inverse function of e^x

The function e^x and its graph

The function $y = e^x$ has a domain of all real numbers and is a one-to-one function meaning that one value of y corresponds to only one value of x. Hence, e^x has an inverse function. The graph of $y = e^x$ is shown below.

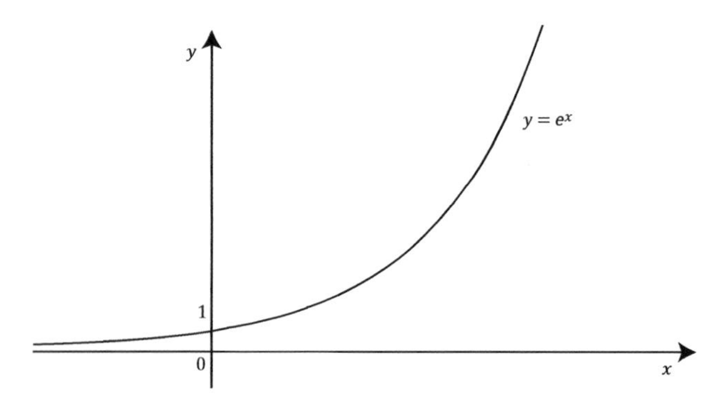

Notice that:

- the graph of $y = e^x$ cuts the y-axis at $y = 1$ (because when $x = 0$, $y = e^0 = 1$)
- for large negative values of x, y approaches zero from above, i.e. the x-axis is an asymptote (since as $x \to -\infty$, $y \to e^{-\infty} = \frac{1}{e^{\infty}} = \frac{1}{\infty} = 0$)
- for large positive values of x, y also takes large positive values (since as $x \to \infty$, $y \to e^{\infty} = \infty$).

Notice also if $f(x) = e^x$ then:

- the domain of f is the set of all real numbers, which can be written as $D(f) = (-\infty, \infty)$
- the range of f is the set of all positive real numbers, (i.e. $f(x) > 0$), which can be written as $R(f) = (0, \infty)$.

Remember from your AS studies, that the statements $y = a^x$ and $x = \log_a y$ are equivalent power and logarithm versions of the same relationship.

Substituting e for a leads to the statements $y = e^x$ and $x = \log_e y$ being equivalent.

If $y = f(x) = e^x$, then to find the inverse we change the subject of the formula from y to x.

From the rules of logarithms we have $x = \log_e y$.

The logarithm to base e is also known as the natural logarithm and can be written as ln y intead of $\log_e y$

So $x = \ln y$

Hence $f^{-1}(x) = \ln x$

Remember, to find the inverse of a function, follow these steps:

Let the function equal y.

Rearrange the resulting equation to make x the subject.

Replace x with $f^{-1}(x)$ and replace y with x.

The function ln x and its graph

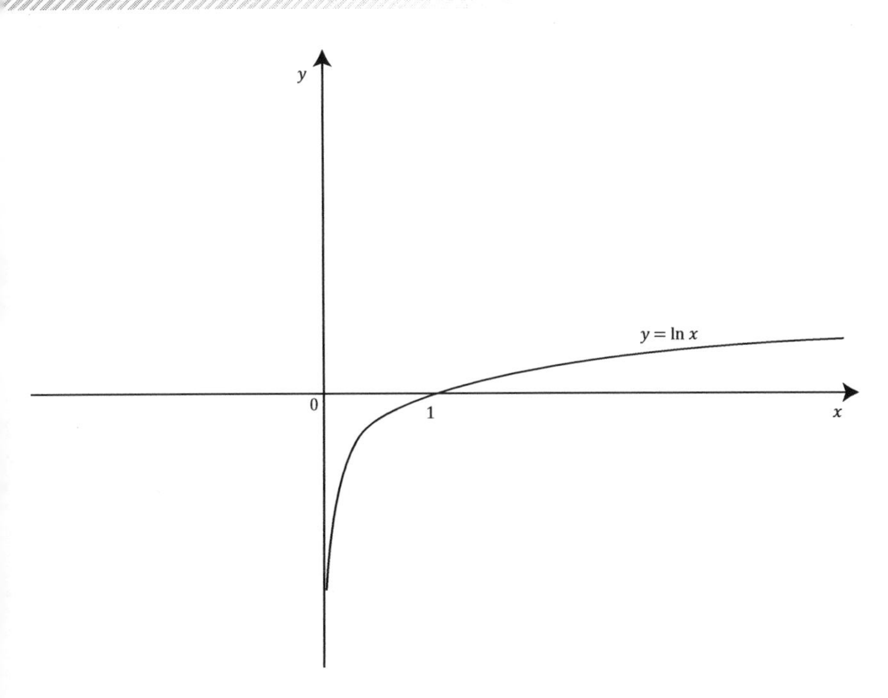

Notice that:

- the graph of $y = \ln x$ cuts the x-axis at $x = 1$. This is because when $y = 0$, $\ln x = 0$ and $\ln 1 = 0$.
- for large positive values of x, the y-values become large and positive (i.e. as $x \to \infty$, $y = \ln x \to \infty$)
- for small values of x, the y-values become large and negative (i.e. as $x \to 0$, $y = \ln x \to -\infty$), so the y-axis is an asymptote.

Notice also if $f(x) = \ln x$:

- the domain of f is the set of all positive real numbers, i.e. $x > 0$, which can be written as $D(f) = (0, \infty)$
- the range of f is the set of all real numbers, i.e. $-\infty < x < \infty$, which can be written as $R(f) = (-\infty, \infty)$.

$\ln x$ as the inverse function of e^x

The inverse of a function will produce the input value from the output value. The inverse of $y = e^x$ is $y = \ln x$.

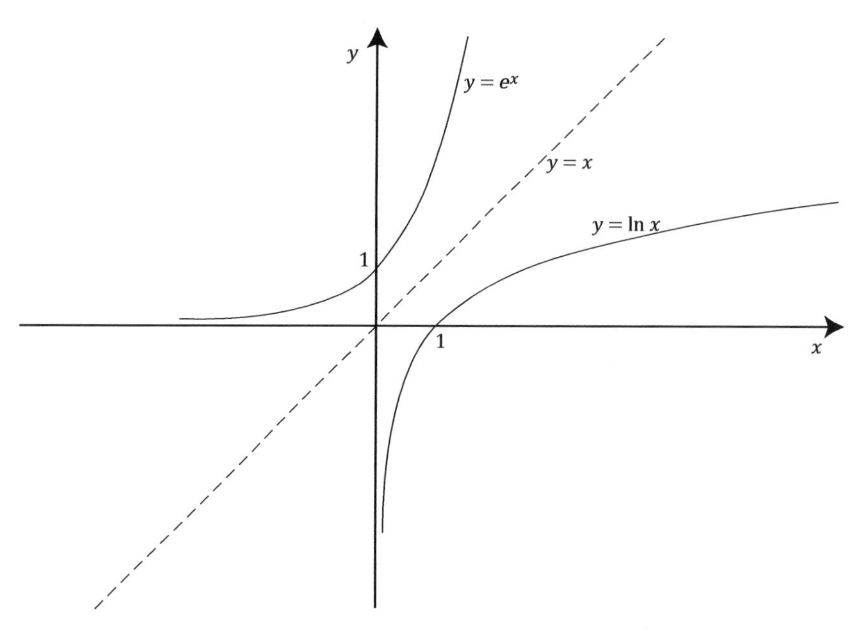

The graph of $y = \ln x$ can be obtained by reflecting the graph of $y = e^x$ in the line $y = x$

When reflecting in the line $y = x$, you need to ensure that the scales on both axes are the same.

Notice also that:

The x-axis is an asymptote to the curve $y = e^x$.

The y-axis is an asymptote to the curve $y = \ln x$.

Since the action of an inverse function reverses the effect of the function, then two useful results follow: $e^{\ln x} = x$ and $\ln e^x = x$.

Example

① The function f has domain $(-\infty, \infty)$ and is defined by

$$f(x) = 3e^{2x}$$

The function g has domain $(0, \infty)$ and is defined by

$$g(x) = \ln 4x$$

(a) Write down the domain and range of fg. [2]

(b) Solve the equation

$$fg(x) = 12.$$ [5]

(WJEC C3 June 2009 Q9)

Answer

①

The domain of a composite function fg is the domain of g.

(a) Domain of fg is the domain of g, i.e. $(0, \infty)$

Note that $e^{\ln g(x)} = g(x)$

$fg(x) = 3e^{2g(x)} = 3e^{2\ln 4x}$

$fg(x) = 3e^{\ln(4x)^2}$

In order to find the range of fg, find the composite function and then, by substituting values from the domain, find its maximum and minimum values.

$fg(x) = 3e^{\ln 16x^2}$

$fg(x) = 3(16x^2)$

$fg(x) = 48x^2$

Now $D(fg) = (0, \infty)$.

$fg(0) = 48(0)^2 = 0$ and as $x \to \infty$, $fg(x) \to 48(\infty)^2 = \infty$

Hence $R(fg) = (0, \infty)$

(b) $fg(x) = 48x^2$

Now $fg(x) = 12$

So $48x^2 = 12$

$x^2 = \frac{1}{4}$

It is important to check these values against the domain of the composite function to see if both values are allowable.

$x = \pm\frac{1}{2}$

However as the domain is $(0, \infty)$ $\quad x \neq -\frac{1}{2}$

Hence solution is $x = \frac{1}{2}$

Example

② Given that $f(x) = \ln x$, sketch the graphs of $y = f(x)$ and $y = -f(x + 1)$ on the same diagram. Label the coordinates of the points of intersection with the x-axis and indicate the behaviour of the graphs for large positive and negative values of y. [5]

(WJEC C3 Jan 2009 Q8)

Answer

②

You need to be able to reproduce the graph of $y = \ln x$, showing the point of intersection with the x-axis ($\ln 1 = 0$) and the y-axis as an asymptote.

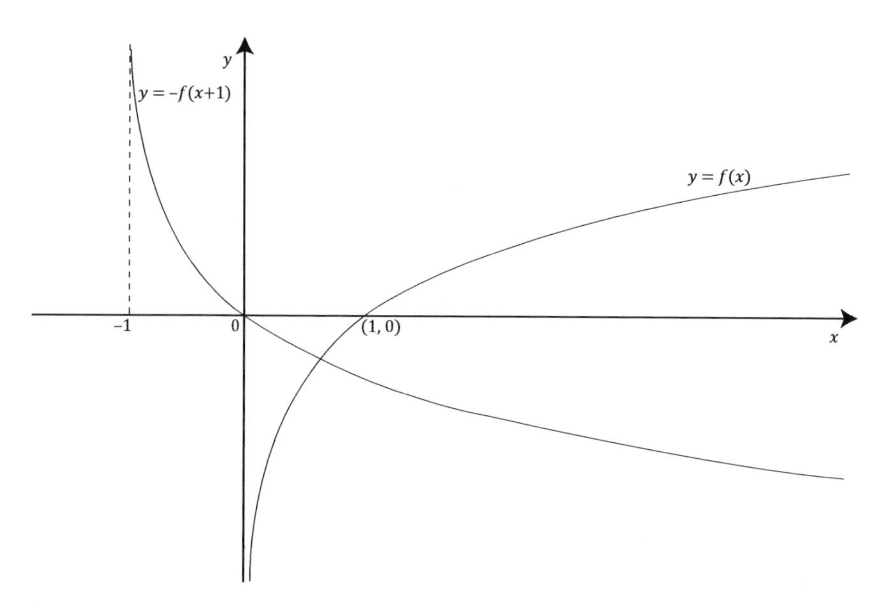

Note the above graph would be hand-drawn in the exam.

For $y = f(x) = \ln x$

The curve passes through the point (1, 0), since $\ln 1 = 0$.

For large positive values of x, there are large positive values of y.

For negative values of x, the function $f(x) = \ln x$ does not exist.

For values of x between 0 and 1, $f(x) = \ln x$ is negative.

As x approaches 0 from above, the negative values of y become larger, (i.e. as $x \to 0$, $\ln x \to -\infty$), so the y-axis is an asymptote.

For $y = -f(x + 1)$,

the curve passes through the point (0, 0),

the line $x = -1$ is an asymptote.

$y = -f(x+1)$ represents a translation of $y = f(x)$ by one unit to the left followed by reflection in the x-axis.

Examination style questions

① Given that $f(x) = e^x$, sketch on the same diagram, the graphs of $y = f(x)$ and $y = -f(x) + 1$. Label the coordinates of the points of intersection of each of the graphs with the axes. Indicate the behaviour of each of the graphs for large positive and negative values of x. [5]

Answer

① Note that in the exam this graph would be hand-drawn.

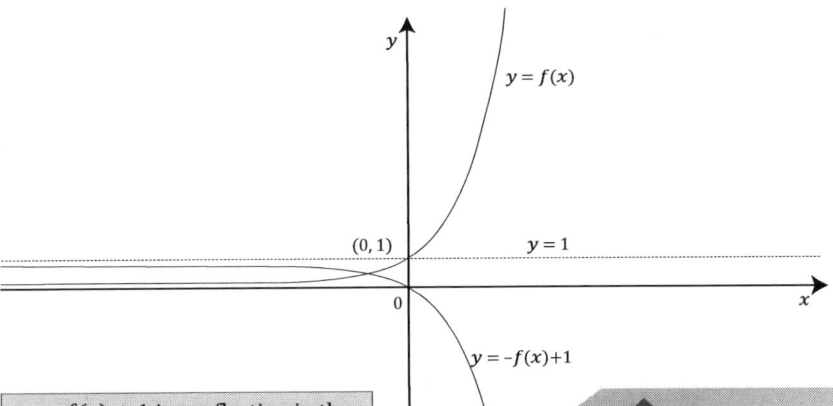

$y = -f(x) + 1$ is a reflection in the x-axis and a translation by $+1$ in the positive y direction.

Grade boost

Make sure you have labelled the curve, any points of intersection asked for in the question, any asymptotes and the axes.

$y = f(x) = e^x$ cuts the y-axis at (0, 1), since $e^0 = 1$.

The curve has an asymptote of $y = 0$ (or the x-axis), since as $x \to -\infty$, $e^x \to e^{-\infty} = \frac{1}{e^{\infty}} = 0$. When $x \to +\infty$, the y-values also become large and positive (i.e. $y \to +\infty$).

$y = -f(x) + 1$ cuts the y-axis at (0, 0) and has an asymptote of $y = 1$ (i.e. as $x \to -\infty$, $y \to 1$).

When $x \to +\infty$, the y-values become large and negative (i.e. $y \to -\infty$).

② The function f has domain $(-\infty, \infty)$ and is defined by

$$f(x) = 3e^{2x}$$

The function g has domain $[1, \infty)$ and is defined by

$$g(x) = 2 \ln x$$

(a) Explain why $gf(-1)$ does not exist. [2]

(b) Find in its simplest form an expression for $fg(x)$. [2]

Answer

② (a) $f(-1) = 3e^{-2} < 1$ so that $f(-1)$ is not in the domain of g, i.e. not in $[1, \infty)$.

Hence $gf(-1)$ does not exist.

(b) $fg(x) = 3e^{2g(x)}$

$= 3e^{2(2 \ln x)}$

$= 3e^{4 \ln x}$

Use this law of logarithms: $k \log_a x = \log_a x^k$

$= 3e^{\ln x^4}$

Use $e^{\ln a} = a$

$= 3x^4$

Test yourself

Answer the following questions and check your answers before moving on to the next topic.

① Given that $f(x) = e^x$, sketch on the same diagram, the graphs of $y = f(x)$ and $y = 2f(x) - 2$. Label the coordinates of the points of intersection of each of the graphs with the x-axis. Indicate the behaviour of each of the graphs for large positive and negative values of x.

② The function f has domain $(-\infty, \infty)$ and is defined by

$f(x) = 2e^{3x}$

The function g has domain $(0, \infty)$ and is defined by

$g(x) = \ln 2x$

(a) Write down the domain and range of fg.

(b) Solve the equation

$fg(x) = 128$.

1 The function f has domain $[1, \infty)$ and is defined by

$$f(x) = \ln(3x-2) + 5$$

(a) Find an expression for $f^{-1}(x)$. [4]

(b) State the domain of f^{-1}. [1]

(WJEC C3 June 2010 Q9)

Answer

Rearrange the equation to make x the subject of the equation. Then replace y with x and replace the subject of the equation by $f^{-1}(x)$.

Convert from the logarithmic to the index form of this relationship.

1 (a) Let $y = \ln(3x-2) + 5$

$$y - 5 = \ln(3x - 2)$$

$$e^{y-5} = 3x - 2$$

$$e^{y-5} + 2 = 3x$$

$$x = \frac{e^{y-5}+2}{3}$$

$$f^{-1}(x) = \frac{e^{x-5}+2}{3}$$

(b) The domain of f^{-1} is the same as the range of f.

$R(f) = [5, \infty)$

Hence $D(f^{-1}) = [5, \infty)$

2 The functions f and g have domains $[0, \infty)$ and $(-\infty, \infty)$ respectively and are defined by

$$f(x) = e^x,$$

$$g(x) = 4x^3 + 7$$

(a) Find and simplify an expression for $gf(x)$ [2]

(b) Find the domain and range of gf. [2]

(c) (i) Solve the equation $gf(x) = 18$. Give your answer correct to three decimal places.

(ii) Giving a reason, write down a value for k so that $gf(x) = k$ has no solutions. [3]

(WJEC C3 Jan 2011 Q10)

Answer

2 (a) $gf(x) = 4[f(x)]^3 + 7 = 4(e^x)^3 + 7$
$= 4e^{3x} + 7$

(b) $D(gf) = [0, \infty)$

> The domain of gf is the set of all x in the domain of f for which $f(x)$ is in the domain of g. f has domain $[0, \infty)$ and range $[1, \infty)$ and g has domain $(-\infty, \infty)$. The domain of gf is the domain of f.

When $x = 0$, $gf(0) = 4e^0 + 7 = 11$

As $x \to \infty$, $gf(x) \to \infty$

Hence $R(gf) = [11, \infty)$

> Substitute values from the domain into $gf(x)$ to find its maximum and minimum values.

(c) (i) $gf(x) = 18$

$4e^{3x} + 7 = 18$

$4e^{3x} = 11$

$e^{3x} = \frac{11}{4}$

$3x = \ln\frac{11}{4}$

$3x = 1.0116$

$x = 0.3372$

$x = 0.337$ (correct to three decimal places)

(ii) $R(gf) = [11, \infty)$, these are the maximum and minimum y-values if a graph of the composite function were drawn.

There is no y-value for the function outside this range.

$k = 8$ would be one of the many values that would yield no solution.

> As the range is $[11, \infty)$, the line $y = k$ would not have any solutions for values of k outside the range. Any value of k less than 11 would suffice.

Topic 4 Differentiation

This topic covers the following:

- Differentiation of e^x, $\ln x$, $\sin x$, $\cos x$ and $\tan x$
- Differentiation using the Chain rule
- Use of $\frac{dy}{dx} = \frac{1}{\left(\frac{dx}{dy}\right)}$ to differentiate $\sin^{-1}x$, $\cos^{-1}x$, $\tan^{-1}x$
- Differentiation using the Product and Quotient rules
- Differentiation of simple functions defined implicitly
- Differentiation of simple functions defined parametrically

Differentiation of e^x, $\ln x$, $\sin x$, $\cos x$ and $\tan x$

The following derivatives will be used in this topic and these will need to be remembered as they are **not** included in the formula booklet

$$\frac{d(e^x)}{dx} = e^x$$

$$\frac{d(\ln x)}{dx} = \frac{1}{x}$$

$$\frac{d(\sin x)}{dx} = \cos x$$

$$\frac{d(\cos x)}{dx} = -\sin x$$

$$\frac{d(\tan x)}{dx} = \sec^2 x$$

Here are some important results that you need to know that are not included in the formula booklet:

Note that in all the results shown here, a must be an ordinary number.

$$\frac{d(e^{ax})}{dx} = ae^x$$

$$\frac{d(\sin ax)}{dx} = a\cos ax$$

$$\frac{d(\cos ax)}{dx} = -a\sin ax$$

$$\frac{d(\tan ax)}{dx} = a\sec^2 ax$$

Examples

① If $y = e^{4x}$, find $\frac{dy}{dx}$

Answer

① $y = e^{4x}$,

$\frac{dy}{dx} = 4e^{4x}$

Use $\frac{d\left(e^{ax}\right)}{dx} = ae^{x}$

② If $y = \sin 2x$, find $\frac{dy}{dx}$.

Answer

② $y = \sin 2x$

$\frac{dy}{dx} = 2\cos 2x$

Use $\frac{d(\sin ax)}{dx} = a\cos ax$

③ If $y = \tan\frac{x}{2}$, find $\frac{dy}{dx}$.

Answer

③ $\frac{dy}{dx} = \frac{1}{2}\sec^2\frac{x}{2}$

Use $\frac{d(\tan ax)}{dx} = a\sec^2 ax$

The Chain rule

Using the Chain rule, you can differentiate a composite function (sometimes called a function of a function). Suppose y is a function of u and u is a function of x, then the Chain rule states:

$$\frac{dy}{dx} = \frac{dy}{du} \times \frac{du}{dx}$$

For example if $y = \sin(x^9 + 2x + 1)$ then $y = \sin u$ where $u = x^9 + 2x + 1$.

Example

① Differentiate each of the following

(a) $y = (4x^2 - 1)^3$

(b) $y = \sqrt{3x^2 + 1}$

(c) $y = \ln(5x^2 + 3)$

(d) $y = \cos(x^3 + x + 5)$

(e) $y = \tan 3x$

Answer

① (a) $y = (4x^2 - 1)^3$

Here the variable u is put equal to the contents inside the bracket.

Let $u = 4x^2 - 1$ $\quad\left(\frac{du}{dx} = 8x\right)$

so that $y = u^3$ $\quad\left(\frac{dy}{du} = 3u^2\right)$

The Chain rule is used here. You have to remember it as it is not given in the formula booklet.

Then $\frac{dy}{dx} = \frac{dy}{du} \times \frac{du}{dx} = 3u^2 \times 8x$

Substitute $u = 4x^2 - 1$ back into the equation so that the result just contains x only.

$= 3(4x^2 - 1)^2 \times 8x$

$= 24x\,(4x^2 - 1)^2$

(b) $y = \sqrt{3x^2 + 1} = (3x^2 + 1)^{\frac{1}{2}}$

Any terms containing roots need to be written in index form.

Let $u = 3x^2 + 1$ $\quad\left(\frac{du}{dx} = 6x\right)$

So that $y = u^{\frac{1}{2}}$ $\quad\left(\frac{dy}{du} = \frac{1}{2}u^{-\frac{1}{2}}\right)$

Then $\frac{dy}{dx} = \frac{dy}{du} \times \frac{du}{dx} = \frac{1}{2}u^{-\frac{1}{2}} \times 6x$

Remember that $u^{-\frac{1}{2}} = \frac{1}{\sqrt{u}}$ and then substitute u back as $3x^2 + 1$.

$= \frac{1}{2\sqrt{3x^2 + 1}} \times 6x$

$= \frac{3x}{\sqrt{3x^2 + 1}}$

(c) $y = \ln(5x^2 + 3)$

Let $u = 5x^2 + 3$ $\left(\frac{du}{dx} = 10x\right)$

so that $y = \ln u$ $\left(\frac{dy}{du} = \frac{1}{u}\text{, see differentiation of the ln function on page 53}\right)$

Then $\frac{dy}{dx} = \frac{dy}{du} \times \frac{du}{dx}$

$= \frac{1}{u} \times 10x$

$= \frac{10x}{5x^2 + 3}$

Substitute for u in the final result.

(d) $y = \cos(x^3 + x + 5)$

Let $u = x^3 + x + 5$ $\left(\frac{du}{dx} = 3x^2 + 1\right)$

so that $y = \cos u$ $\left(\frac{dy}{du} = -\sin u\right)$

Then $\frac{dy}{dx} = \frac{dy}{du} \times \frac{du}{dx} = -\sin u \times (3x^2 + 1)$

Substitute for u to obtain the final result.

$= -(3x^2 + 1)\sin(x^3 + x + 5)$

(e) $y = \tan 3x$

Let $u = 3x$ $\left(\frac{du}{dx} = 3\right)$

So that $y = \tan u$ $\left(\frac{dy}{du} = \sec^2 u\right)$

Substitute for u to obtain the final result.

Then $\frac{dy}{dx} = \frac{dy}{du} \times \frac{du}{dx} = \sec^2 u \times 3$

$= 3\sec^2 3x$

We are able to summarise the work in this example by producing a generalised form of the table given on the first page of this topic. The results can be obtained in each case by writing

$u = f(x)$ and noting that $\frac{du}{dx} = f'(x)$

$$\frac{d}{dx}\left((f(x))^n\right) = n(f(x))^{n-1} \times f'(x)$$

$$\frac{d}{dx}((\sin x))^n = n\sin^{n-1} x \times \cos x$$

$$\frac{d}{dx}\left(e^{f(x)}\right) = e^{f(x)} f'(x)$$

$$\frac{d}{dx}\left(e^{x^3+1}\right) = e^{x^3+1} \times 3x^2$$

$$\frac{d}{dx}\left(\ln\left(f(x)\right)\right) = \frac{1}{f(x)} \times f'(x)$$

$$\frac{d}{dx}\left(\ln\left(x^5 + x\right)\right) = \frac{1}{x^5 + x} \times \left(5x^4 + 1\right)$$

$$\frac{d}{dx}\left(\sin\left(f(x)\right)\right) = \cos f(x) \times f'(x)$$

$$\frac{d}{dx}(\sin 3x) = \cos 3x \times 3$$

$$\frac{d}{dx}\left(\cos\left(f(x)\right)\right) = -\sin f(x) \times f'(x)$$

$$\frac{d}{dx}\left(\cos\left(x^9 + x + 1\right)\right) = -\sin\left(x^9 + x + 1\right) \times \left(9x^8 + 1\right)$$

$$\frac{d}{dx}\left(\tan\left(f(x)\right)\right) = \sec^2 f(x) \times f'(x)$$

$$\frac{d}{dx}(\tan 5x) = \sec^2 5x \times 5$$

Note

Note the following result in relation to the differentiation of particular logarithmic functions.

If $y = \ln ax$ where a is any constant, then

$$\frac{dy}{dx} = \frac{1}{ax} \times a = \frac{1}{x}$$

$f(x) = ax, \qquad f'(x) = a$

which is the same result we obtain if we differentiate $\ln x$.

The result occurs because

$$y = \ln(ax) = \ln a + \ln x \qquad \text{(using the law of logarithms)}$$

and $\frac{d}{dx} = (\ln a + \ln x) = \frac{d}{dx}(\ln x) = \frac{1}{x}$, since $\ln a$ disappears when differentiated.

Examples

① If $y = \ln 3x$, find $\frac{dy}{dx}$.

Answer

① $\frac{dy}{dx} = \frac{1}{3x} \times 3 = \frac{1}{x}$

② If $y = \ln\left(\frac{x}{2}\right)$, find $\frac{dy}{dx}$.

Answer

② $\frac{dy}{dx} = \frac{1}{\frac{x}{2}} \times \frac{1}{2}$

$$= \frac{2}{x} \times \frac{1}{2} = \frac{1}{x}$$

Differentiation of $\sin^{-1} x$, $\cos^{-1} x$, $\tan^{-1} x$

Remember that $y = \sin^{-1} x$ is equivalent to $\sin y = x$, that $y = \cos^{-1} x$ is equivalent to $\cos y = x$ and that $y = \tan^{-1} x$ is equivalent to $\tan y = x$.

To differentiate these inverse trigonometric functions, we note that

$$\frac{dy}{dx} = \frac{1}{\left(\frac{dx}{dy}\right)}$$

Proving $\frac{d}{dx}(\sin^{-1} x) = \frac{1}{\sqrt{1-x^2}}$

Given that $y = \sin^{-1} x$,

$$\sin y = x$$

Differentiate with respect to y

$$\cos y = \frac{dx}{dy}$$

$$y = \sin^{-1} x$$

Then $\frac{dy}{dx} = \frac{1}{\left(\frac{dx}{dy}\right)} = \frac{1}{\cos y}$

$$= \frac{1}{\pm\sqrt{1-\sin^2 y}}$$

Remember that $\sin^2 x + \cos^2 x = 1$

$$= \frac{1}{\pm\sqrt{1-x^2}}$$

$\sin y = x$

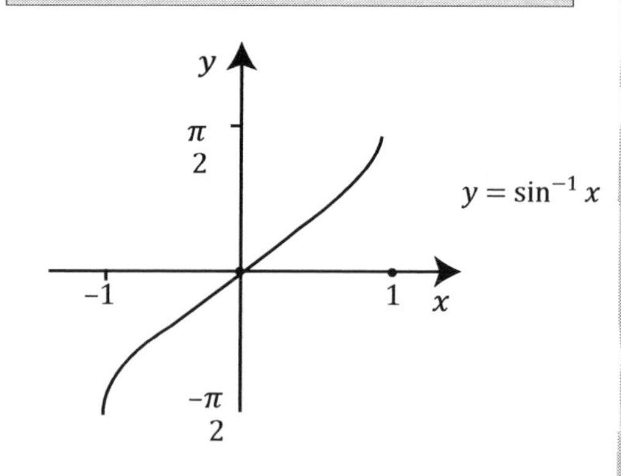

Since $\frac{dy}{dx} > 0$, $\frac{dy}{dx} = \frac{1}{\sqrt{1-x^2}}$

For $y = \sin^{-1} x$, $\frac{dy}{dx} > 0$.

Proving $\frac{d}{dx}(\cos^{-1}x)=\frac{-1}{\sqrt{1-x^2}}$

Given that $y=\cos^{-1}x$,

$$\cos y = x$$

Differentiate with respect to y

$$-\sin y=\frac{dx}{dy}$$

Then $\frac{dy}{dx}=\frac{1}{\left(\frac{dx}{dy}\right)}=\frac{-1}{\sin y}$

$$=\frac{-1}{\pm\sqrt{1-\cos^2 y}}$$

Remember that $\sin^2 x+\cos^2 x=1$

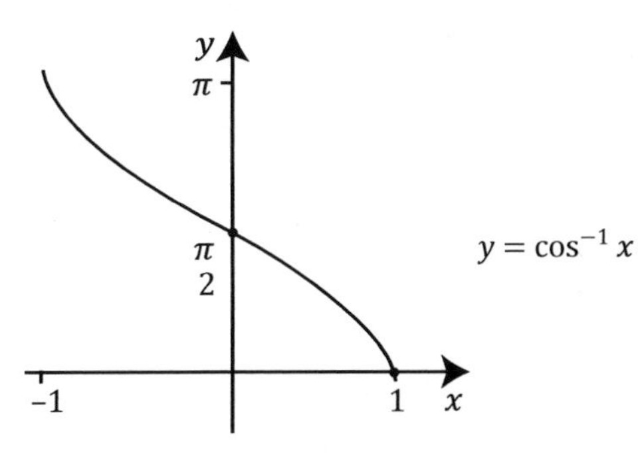

For $y=\cos x$, $\frac{dy}{dx}<0$.

Since $\frac{dy}{dx}<0$,

$$\frac{dy}{dx}=\frac{-1}{\sqrt{1-x^2}}$$

We leave the derivation of $\frac{d}{dx}(\tan^{-1}x)=\frac{1}{1+x^2}$ as a later exercise.

To summarise

$$\frac{d(\sin^{-1}x)}{dx}=\frac{1}{\sqrt{1+x^2}}$$

$$\frac{d(\cos^{-1}x)}{dx}=-\frac{1}{\sqrt{1-x^2}}$$

$$\frac{d(\tan^{-1}x)}{dx}=\frac{1}{1+x^2}$$

These results can be generalised by taking $u = f(x)$ and using the Chain rule.

$$\frac{d}{dx}\left(\sin^{-1}(f(x))\right) = \frac{1}{\sqrt{1-(f(x))^2}} \times f'(x)$$

$$\frac{d}{dx}\left(\sin^{-1}(x^3)\right) = \frac{1}{\sqrt{1-(x^3)^2}} \times 3x^2$$
$$= \frac{3x^2}{\sqrt{1-x^6}}$$

$$\frac{d}{dx}\left(\cos^{-1}(f(x))\right) = \frac{-1}{\sqrt{1-(f(x))^2}} \times f'(x)$$

$$\frac{d}{dx}\left(\cos^{-1}(5x)\right)$$
$$= \frac{-1}{\sqrt{1-(5x)^2}} \times 5$$
$$= \frac{-5}{\sqrt{1-25x^2}}$$

$$\frac{d}{dx}\left(\tan^{-1}(f(x))\right) = \frac{1}{1+(f(x))^2} \times f'(x)$$

$$\frac{d}{dx}\left(\tan(x^4)\right)$$
$$= \frac{1}{1+(x^4)^2} \times 4x^3$$
$$= \frac{4x^3}{1+x^8}$$

Examples

① Differentiate each of the following

(a) $y = \cos^{-1} 4x$

(b) $y = \sin^{-1} \dfrac{x}{2}$

(c) $y = 3\tan^{-1} 2x$

Answers

① (a) $y = \cos^{-1} 4x$

$$\frac{dy}{dx} = -\frac{4}{\sqrt{1-(4x)^2}} = -\frac{4}{\sqrt{1-16x^2}}$$

(b) $y = \sin^{-1} \dfrac{x}{2}$

$$\frac{dy}{dx} = \frac{\frac{1}{2}}{\sqrt{1-\left(\frac{x}{2}\right)^2}} = \frac{1}{2\sqrt{1-\frac{x^2}{4}}} = \frac{1}{\sqrt{4-x^2}}$$

(c) $y = 3\tan^{-1}2x$

$$\frac{dy}{dx} = \frac{3\times 2}{1+(2x)^2} = \frac{6}{1+4x^2}$$

Differentiation using the Product and the Quotient rule

The Product rule

The Product rule is used when you differentiate two different functions of x that are multiplied together.

The Product rule states:

If $y = f(x)g(x)$, $\frac{dy}{dx} = f(x)g'(x) + g(x)f'(x)$

$f(x)g(x)$ means a function f of x multiplied by a function g of x. f' and g' are the derivatives of f and g respectively.

You will need to remember the Product rule as it is not given in the formula booklet.

You can remember it as the first term multiplied by the derivative of the second and then added to the second multiplied by the derivative of the first.

Example

① Differentiate the following with respect to x, simplifying your answer wherever possible.

(a) x^2e^{2x}

(b) $3x^2 \sin 2x$

(c) $(x^3 + 4x^2 - 3) \tan 3x$

All these are the product of one function and another so they need to be differentiated using the Product rule.

Answer

① (a) Let $y = x^2e^{2x}$

$$\frac{dy}{dx} = f(x)g'(x) + g(x)f'(x)$$

$$= x^2(2e^{2x}) + e^{2x}(2x)$$

$$= 2x^2e^{2x} + 2xe^{2x} = 2xe^{2x}(x + 1)$$

Note that the Product rule must be remembered and note the use of the Chain rule.

(b) Let $y = 3x^2 \sin 2x$

$$\frac{dy}{dx} = f(x)g'(x) + g(x)f'(x)$$

$$= 3x^2(2\cos 2x) + \sin 2x\,(6x)$$

$$= 6x^2\cos 2x + 6x \sin 2x$$

$$= 6x\,(x \cos 2x + \sin 2x)$$

The derivatives of sin and cos cannot be obtained from the formula booklet so they must be remembered.

(c) Let $y = (x^3 + 4x^2 - 3) \tan 3x$

$$\frac{dy}{dx} = f(x)g'(x) + g(x) f'(x)$$

$$\frac{dy}{dx} = (x^3 + 4x^2 - 3)3 \sec^2 3x + \tan 3x (3x^2 + 8x)$$

$$\frac{dy}{dx} = 3(x^3 + 4x^2 - 3) \sec^2 3x + (3x^2 + 8x) \tan 3x$$

The derivative of $\tan x$ is included in the formula booklet and can be looked up.

The Chain rule is used to differentiate $\tan 3x$.

The Quotient rule

The Quotient rule is used when you differentiate two different functions of x when one is divided by the other. The Quotient rule states:

If $= \frac{f(x)}{g(x)}$, $\frac{dy}{dx} = \frac{f'(x)g(x) - f(x)g'(x)}{(g(x))^2}$

You do not need to remember this formula as it can be looked up in the formula booklet.

Example

① Differentiate the following with respect to x, simplifying your answer wherever possible.

(a) $\frac{x^3 + 2x^2}{x^2 - 1}$

(b) $\frac{\sin 2x}{\cos x}$

(c) $\frac{e^{5x}}{x^2 + 3}$

Answer

① (a) Let $y = \frac{f(x)}{g(x)} = \frac{x^3 + 2x^2}{x^2 - 1}$

$$\frac{dy}{dx} = \frac{f'(x)g(x) - f(x)g'(x)}{(g(x))^2}$$

$$\frac{dy}{dx} = \frac{(3x^2 + 4x)(x^2 - 1) - (x^3 + 2x^2)(2x)}{(x^2 - 1)^2}$$

$$\frac{dy}{dx} = \frac{3x^4 - 3x^2 + 4x^3 - 4x - 2x^4 - 4x^3}{(x^2 - 1)^2}$$

$$\frac{dy}{dx} = \frac{x^4 - 3x^2 - 4x}{(x^2 - 1)^2} = \frac{x(x^3 - 3x - 4)}{(x - 1)^2}$$

(b) Let $y = \frac{f(x)}{g(x)} = \frac{\sin 2x}{\cos x}$

$$\frac{dy}{dx} = \frac{f'(x)g(x) - f(x)g'(x)}{(g(x))^2}$$

$$\frac{dy}{dx} = \frac{2\cos 2x(\cos x) - \sin 2x(-\sin x)}{\cos^2 x}$$

The Chain rule is used to differentiate sin 2*x*.

$$\frac{dy}{dx} = \frac{2\cos 2x \cos x + \sin 2x \sin x}{\cos^2 x}$$

(c) Let $y = \frac{f(x)}{g(x)} = \frac{e^{5x}}{x^2 + 3}$

$$\frac{dy}{dx} = \frac{f'(x)g(x) - f(x)g'(x)}{(g(x))^2}$$

$$\frac{dy}{dx} = \frac{5e^{5x}(x^2+3) - e^{5x}(2x)}{(x^2+3)^2}$$

The Chain rule is used to differentiate e^{5x}.

$$\frac{dy}{dx} = \frac{5x^2e^{5x} + 15e^{5x} - 2xe^{5x}}{(x^2+3)^2}$$

$$\frac{dy}{dx} = \frac{e^{5x}(5x^2 - 2x + 15)}{(x^2+3)^2}$$

Examples

① (a) Differentiate each of the following with respect to x, simplifying your answer wherever possible.

(i) $\sqrt{2+5x^3}$ (ii) $x^2 \sin 3x$ (iii) $\frac{e^{2x}}{x^4}$ [8]

(b) By first writing $y = \tan^{-1} x$ as $x = \tan y$, find $\frac{dy}{dx}$ in terms of x. [4]

(WJEC C3 Jan 2011 Q5)

Answer

① (a) (i) $y = \sqrt{2+5x^3}$

You have to recognise that this is a function of a function and therefore needs to be differentiated using the Chain rule.

$$y = (2+5x^3)^{\frac{1}{2}}$$

$y = (f(x))^n$ with $f(x) = (2 + 5x^3)$, $n = \frac{1}{2}$.

$$\frac{dy}{dx} = \left(\frac{1}{2}\right)(2+5x^3)^{-\frac{1}{2}}(15x^2)$$

$$\frac{dy}{dx} = \frac{15x^2}{2\sqrt{2+5x^3}}$$

(ii) $y = x^2 \sin 3x$

$$\frac{dy}{dx} = x^2\, 3\cos 3x + \sin 3x \times 2x$$

The Product rule is used here.

$$\frac{dy}{dx} = 3x^2 \cos 3x + 2x \sin 3x = x\,(3x \cos 3x + 2 \sin 3x)$$

(iii) $y = \dfrac{e^{2x}}{x^4}$

This is the Quotient rule and can be obtained from the formula booklet.

$$\frac{f(x)}{g(x)} = \frac{f'(x)g(x) - f(x)g'(x)}{(g(x))^2}$$

$$\frac{dy}{dx} = \frac{2e^{2x}(x^4) - e^{2x}(4x^3)}{(x^4)^2}$$

$$\frac{dy}{dx} = \frac{2x^4e^{2x} - 4x^3e^{2x}}{x^8}$$

$$\frac{dy}{dx} = \frac{2x^3e^{2x}(x-2)}{x^8}$$

The top and bottom of this fraction is divided by x^3.

$$\frac{dy}{dx} = \frac{2e^{2x}(x-2)}{x^5}$$

(b) $x = \tan y$

$$\frac{dx}{dy} = \sec^2 y$$

$\sec^2 y = 1 + \tan^2 y$ (note: this should be remembered from Topic 1 as it is not given in the formula booklet).

$$\frac{dx}{dy} = 1 + \tan^2 y$$

Substitute $x = \tan y$ into this equation.

$$\frac{dx}{dy} = 1 + x^2$$

Now $\dfrac{dy}{dx} = \dfrac{1}{\left(\dfrac{dx}{dy}\right)} = \dfrac{1}{1+x^2}$

② (a) Differentiate each of the following with respect to x, simplifying your answer wherever possible.

(i) $(7 + 2x)^{13}$ (ii) $\sin^{-1} 5x$ (iii) $x^3 e^{4x}$ [7]

(b) By first writing $\tan x = \dfrac{\sin x}{\cos x}$, show that

$$\frac{d}{dx}(\tan x) = \sec^2 x$$ [3]

(WJEC C3 June 2010 Q5)

Answer

② (a) (i) $y = (7 + 2x)^{13}$

$$\frac{dy}{dx} = 13(7 + 2x)^{12}(2)$$

$$\frac{dy}{dx} = 26(7 + 2x)^{12}$$

(ii) $y = \sin^{-1} 5x$

From the formula booklet we have derivative of $\sin^{-1} x = \frac{1}{\sqrt{1-x^2}}$

$$d\left(\sin^{-1} x\right) = \frac{1}{\sqrt{1-x^2}}$$

Use the Chain rule with $u = 5x$, or use $\frac{d}{dx}\left(\sin^{-1} g(x)\right) = \frac{g'(x)}{\sqrt{1-(g(x))^2}}$

$$\frac{d\left(\sin^{-1} 5x\right)}{dx} = \frac{5}{\sqrt{1-(5x)^2}}$$

$$= \frac{5}{\sqrt{1-25x^2}}$$

(iii) $y = x^3 e^{4x}$

$$\frac{dy}{dx} = x^3(4e^{4x}) + e^{4x}(3x^2)$$

This is a product so the Product rule is used. The Product rule is not in the formula booklet.

$$= 4x^3e^{4x} + 3x^2e^{4x}$$

$$= x^2e^{4x}(4x + 3)$$

(b) $\frac{d}{dx}(\tan x) = \frac{d}{dx}\left(\frac{\sin x}{\cos x}\right)$

This is a quotient so the Quotient rule is used to find the derivative.

$$= \frac{\cos x(\cos x) - \sin x(-\sin x)}{\cos^2 x}$$

$$= \frac{\cos^2 x + \sin^2 x}{\cos^2 x}$$

$\sin^2 x + \cos^2 x = 1$. You need to remember this from your AS studies as it is not included in the formula booklet.

$$= \frac{1}{\cos^2 x}$$

$$= \sec^2 x$$

Remember that $\frac{1}{\cos\theta} = \sec\theta$.

Differentiation of simple functions defined implicitly

Finding $\frac{dy}{dx}$ in terms of both x and y is called implicit differentiation.

Here are some of the basics:

$$\frac{d(3x^2)}{dx} = 6x$$

Terms involving x or constant terms are differentiated as normal.

and $$\frac{d(6y^3)}{dx} = 18y^2 \times \frac{dy}{dx}$$

Differentiate with respect to y and then multiply the result by $\frac{dy}{dx}$.

$$\frac{d(y)}{dx} = 1 \times \frac{dy}{dx}$$

$$\frac{d(x^2y^3)}{dx} = (x^2)\left(3y^2 \times \frac{dy}{dx}\right) + (y^3)(2x)$$

$$= 3x^2y^2\frac{dy}{dx} + 2xy^3$$

Because there are two terms here, the Product rule is used. Notice the need to include $\frac{dy}{dx}$ when the term involving y is differentiated.

Examples

① Find $\frac{dy}{dx}$ for the equation $2x^2 + xy + y^3 = 15$

The Product rule needs to be used to differentiate the middle term xy.

Answer

Differentiating with respect to x we obtain

$$4x + (x)(1)\frac{dy}{dx} + (y)(1) + 3y^2\frac{dy}{dx} = 0$$

$$4x + x\left(\frac{dy}{dx}\right) + y + 3y^2\frac{dy}{dx} = 0$$

$$x\left(\frac{dy}{dx}\right) + 3y^2\frac{dy}{dx} = -y - 4x$$

$$\frac{dy}{dx}(x + 3y^2) = -y - 4x$$

$$\frac{dy}{dx} = \frac{-y-4x}{x+3y^2}$$

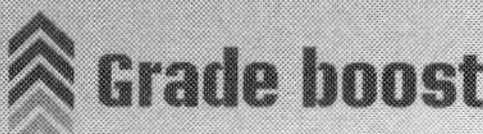

It is a common mistake for students to forget to differentiate the right-hand side of the equation, especially if it is just a number.

Collect all the terms containing $\frac{dy}{dx}$ on one side of the equation and all the other terms on the other.

Take $\frac{dy}{dx}$ out of the brackets as a factor.

Differentiation of simple functions defined parametrically

x and y can be defined in terms of a third variable called a parameter. The equation of a curve can be expressed in parametric form by using $x = f(t)$, $y = g(t)$ where t is the parameter being used.

The formulae for differentiating parametric forms are:

$$\frac{dy}{dx} = \frac{dy}{dt} \bigg/ \frac{dx}{dt} = \frac{dy}{dt} \times \frac{dt}{dx}$$

and $$\frac{d^2y}{dx^2} = \frac{d}{dt}\left(\frac{dy}{dx}\right) \bigg/ \frac{dx}{dt} = \frac{d}{dt}\left(\frac{dy}{dx}\right) \times \frac{dt}{dx}$$

An example of the parametric equation of a curve is

$x = t^2, \quad y = 2t$

To determine the gradient of the tangent to a curve defined parametrically we use the formula for $\frac{dy}{dx}$ given above.

$$\frac{dx}{dt} = 2t \text{ so } \frac{dt}{dx} = \frac{1}{2t}$$

$$\frac{dy}{dt} = 2$$

$$\frac{dy}{dx} = \frac{dy}{dt} \times \frac{dt}{dx}$$

$$= 2 \times \frac{1}{2t}$$

$$= \frac{1}{t}$$

Remember to invert $\frac{dx}{dt}$ in this equation.

If a value of t is known then this can be substituted in so that the gradient can be expressed as a number.

Examples

① Given that $x = 2t^2 + 1$, $y = \frac{4t+1}{t+1}$, find

(a) $\frac{dy}{dt}$

(b) $\frac{dy}{dx}$

Answer

① (a) $$\frac{dy}{dt} = \frac{4(t+1) - (4t+1)(1)}{(t+1)^2}$$

The Quotient rule is used here.

$$\frac{dy}{dt} = \frac{4t + 4 - 4t - 1}{(t+1)^2}$$

$$\frac{dy}{dt} = \frac{3}{(t+1)^2}$$

(b) $\frac{dx}{dt} = 4t$

$$\frac{dy}{dx} = \frac{dy}{dt} \times \frac{dt}{dx}$$

$$= \frac{3}{(t+1)^2} \times \frac{1}{4t}$$

$$= \frac{3}{4t(t+1)^2}$$

$\frac{dx}{dt}$ is inverted to give $\frac{dt}{dx}$.

② Given that $x = \ln t$, $y = 3t^4 - 2t$,

(a) find an expression for $\frac{dy}{dx}$ in terms of t,

(b) find the value of $\frac{d^2y}{dx^2}$ when $t = \frac{1}{2}$.

Answer

② (a) $x = \ln t$

$$\frac{dx}{dt} = \frac{1}{t}$$

$$y = 3t^4 - 2t$$

$$\frac{dy}{dt} = 12t^3 - 2$$

$$\frac{dy}{dx} = \frac{dy}{dt} \times \frac{dt}{dx}$$

$$\frac{dy}{dx} = (12t^3 - 2)t$$

$$\frac{dy}{dx} = 12t^4 - 2t$$

$$\frac{dy}{dx} = 2t(6t^3 - 1)$$

$\frac{dt}{dx} = \frac{1}{\frac{1}{t}} = t$

(b) $\frac{d^2y}{dx^2} = \frac{d}{dt}(12t^4 - 2t) \times \frac{dt}{dx}$

$$= (48t^3 - 2)t$$

$$= 2t(24t^3 - 1)$$

When $= \frac{1}{2}$, $\frac{d^2y}{dx^2} = 2\left(\frac{1}{2}\right)\left(24 \times \left(\frac{1}{2}\right)^3 - 1\right) = 1(3-1) = 2$

The first derivative is differentiated again to find the second derivative.

③ (a) Given that

$$x^4 + 3x^2y - 2y^2 = 15,$$

find an expression for $\frac{dy}{dx}$ in terms of x and y. [4]

(b) Given that $x = \ln t$, $y = t^3 - 7t$,

(i) find an expression for $\frac{dy}{dx}$ in terms of t,

(ii) find the value of $\frac{d^2y}{dx^2}$ when $t = \frac{1}{3}$. [8]

(WJEC C3 Jan 2011 Q3)

Answer

③ (a) Differentiating implicitly with respect to x, we obtain

$$4x^3 + 3x^2\frac{dy}{dx} + 6xy - 4y\frac{dy}{dx} = 0$$

$$3x^2\frac{dy}{dx} - 4y\frac{dy}{dx} = -4x^3 - 6xy$$

$$\frac{dy}{dx}\left(3x^2 - 4y\right) = -4x^3 - 6xy$$

$$\frac{dy}{dx} = \frac{-4x^3 - 6xy}{3x^2 - 4y}$$

Multiply the top and bottom by -1

$$\frac{dy}{dx} = \frac{4x^3 + 6xy}{4y - 3x^2}$$

(b) (i) $x = \ln t$

$$\frac{dx}{dt} = \frac{1}{t}$$

$$y = t^3 - 7t$$

$$\frac{dy}{dt} = 3t^2 - 7$$

$$\frac{dy}{dx} = \frac{dy}{dt} \times \frac{dt}{dx}$$

$$\frac{dy}{dx} = \left(3t^2 - 7\right)t$$

$$\frac{dy}{dx} = 3t^3 - 7t$$

(ii) $$\frac{d^2y}{dx^2} = \frac{\frac{d}{dt}\left(\frac{dy}{dx}\right)}{\frac{dx}{dt}}$$

The Chain rule is used here to find the second derivative.

$$\frac{d^2y}{dx^2} = \frac{d}{dt}\left(\frac{dy}{dx}\right) \times \frac{dt}{dx}$$

$$\frac{d^2y}{dx^2} = \frac{d}{dt}\left(3t^3 - 7t\right) \times t$$

As $\frac{dx}{dt} = \frac{1}{t}$, $\frac{dt}{dx} = \frac{1}{\frac{dx}{dt}} = \frac{1}{\frac{1}{t}} = t$

$$= (9t^2 - 7)t$$

$$= 9t^3 - 7t$$

When $x = \frac{1}{3}$, $\frac{d^2y}{dx^2} = 9\left(\frac{1}{3}\right)^3 - 7\left(\frac{1}{3}\right) = -2$

Examination style questions

① Differentiate each of the following with respect to x, simplifying your answer wherever possible.

(a) $\tan^{-1} 5x$ [2]

(b) $\ln(3x^2 + 5x - 1)$ [2]

(c) $e^{3x} \cos x$ [3]

(d) $\dfrac{1+\sin x}{1-\sin x}$ [3]

Answers

① (a) $y = \tan^{-1} 5x$

$$\frac{dy}{dx} = \frac{5}{1+(5x)^2}$$

$$\frac{dy}{dx} = \frac{5}{1+25x^2}$$

Use $\dfrac{d(\tan^{-1} x)}{dx} = \dfrac{1}{1+x^2}$ obtained from the formula booklet. Then either use the Chain rule or remember that $\dfrac{d(\tan^{-1} ax)}{dx} = \dfrac{a}{1+(ax)^2}$.

(b) $y = \ln(3x^2 + 5x - 1)$

$$\frac{dy}{dx} = \frac{6x+5}{3x^2+5x-1}$$

To differentiate a ln function, differentiate the function and then divide by the original function.

(c) $y = e^{3x} \cos x$

$$\frac{dy}{dx} = e^{3x}(-\sin x) + \cos x\left(3e^{3x}\right)$$

$$\frac{dy}{dx} = -e^{3x}\sin x + 3e^{3x}\cos x$$

$$= e^{3x}(-\sin x + 3\cos x)$$

This represents a product so the Product rule is used.

The Product rule is not included in the formula booklet.

(d) $y = \dfrac{1+\sin x}{1-\sin x}$

$$\frac{dy}{dx} = \frac{(\cos x)(1-\sin x) - (1+\sin x)(-\cos x)}{(1-\sin x)^2}$$

$$\frac{dy}{dx} = \frac{2\cos x}{(1-\sin x)^2}$$

This is a quotient so the Quotient rule is used. The Quotient rule can be looked up in the formula booklet. The formula for the Quotient rule is as follows:

If $y = \dfrac{f(x)}{g(x)}$, $\dfrac{dy}{dx} = \dfrac{f'(x)g(x) - f(x)g'(x)}{(g(x))^2}$

You must remember the derivatives of $\sin x$ and $\cos x$ as they are not given in the formula booklet.

② Differentiate each of the following with respect to x and simplify your answers where possible.

(a) $(1 + 3x)^{11}$ [2]

(b) $\ln(3 + x^3)$ [2]

(c) $\dfrac{\cos x}{1 - \sin x}$ [3]

(d) $\tan^{-1}(4x)$ [2]

(e) $x^4 \tan x$ [2]

Answers

② (a) Let $y = (1 + 3x)^{11}$

$$\frac{dy}{dx} = 11(1+3x)^{10}(3)$$

$$= 33(1 + 3x)^{10}$$

Use $\frac{d}{dx}\left((f(x))^n\right) = n(f(x))^{n-1} \times f'(x)$ with $f(x) = 1 + 3x$, $n = 11$.

(b) Let $y = \ln(3 + x^3)$

$$\frac{dy}{dx} = \frac{3x^2}{3+x^3}$$

Use $\frac{d(\ln(f(x)))}{dx} = \frac{f'(x)}{f(x)}$

(c) Let $y = \dfrac{\cos x}{1 - \sin x}$

This is a quotient, so the Quotient rule is used to differentiate.

$$\frac{dy}{dx} = \frac{(-\sin x)(1 - \sin x) - (\cos x)(-\cos x)}{(1 - \sin x)^2}$$

$$\frac{dy}{dx} = \frac{-\sin x + \sin^2 x + \cos^2 x}{(1 - \sin x)^2}$$

Use $\sin^2 x + \cos^2 x = 1$.

$$\frac{dy}{dx} = \frac{\sin^2 x + \cos^2 x - \sin x}{(1 - \sin x)^2}$$

$$\frac{dy}{dx} = \frac{1 - \sin x}{(1 - \sin x)^2}$$

Divide top and bottom by $(1 - \sin x)$.

$$= \frac{1}{1 - \sin x}$$

(d) Let $y = \tan^{-1}(4x)$

$$\frac{dy}{dx} = \frac{4}{1 + (4x)^2}$$

$$\frac{dy}{dx} = \frac{4}{1 + 16x^2}$$

Use the formula: $\frac{d(\tan^{-1} x)}{dx} = \frac{1}{1+x^2}$ which can be looked up in the formula booklet and let $u = 4x$.

(e) Let $y = x^4 \tan x$

$$\frac{dy}{dx} = f(x)g'(x) + f'(x)g(x)$$

$$= x^4 \sec^2 x + (\tan x) \times (4x^3)$$

$$= x^4 \sec^2 x + 4x^3 \tan x$$

$$= x^3(x \sec^2 x + 4 \tan x)$$

③ Given that $x = 2t - \sin 2t$, $y = \cos 3t$, show that $\frac{dy}{dx} = \frac{3}{4}$ when $t = \frac{\pi}{2}$. [5]

Answer

③ $x = 2t - \sin 2t$

First differentiate the parametric equations by means of the Chain rule.

$$\frac{dx}{dt} = 2 - 2\cos 2t$$

$y = \cos 3t$

$$\frac{dy}{dt} = -3\sin 3t$$

$$\frac{dy}{dx} = \frac{dy}{dt} \times \frac{dt}{dx}$$

$$\frac{dy}{dx} = \frac{(-3\sin 3t)}{(2 - 2\cos 2t)}$$

When $t = \frac{\pi}{2}$,

$$\frac{dy}{dx} = \frac{\left(-3\sin\frac{3\pi}{2}\right)}{\left(2 - 2\cos\frac{2\pi}{2}\right)}$$

$$= \frac{3}{4}$$

$\sin\frac{3\pi}{2} = -1$ and $\cos \pi = -1$

④ The function f is defined by $f(x) = x^2e^x$.

(a) Show that $f'(x) = xe^x(x + 2)$ [2]

(b) Find the value of $f'(x)$ in terms of e when $x = 1$. [1]

Answer

④ (a) $f(x) = x^2e^x$

This is a product, so the Product rule is used.

$f'(x) = x^2e^x + e^x(2x)$

$f'(x) = xe^x(x + 2)$

(b) $f'(1) = 1e^1(1 + 2) = 3e$

Test yourself

Answer the following questions and check your answers before moving on to the next topic.

① If $y = (4x^3 + 3x)^3$, find $\frac{dy}{dx}$.

② If $y = (3 - 2x)^{10}$, find $\frac{dy}{dx}$.

③ A function is defined parametrically by $= 3t^2$, $y = t^4$

Find $\frac{dy}{dx}$ in terms of t.

④ Find $\frac{dy}{dx}$ in terms of x and y for the curve

$$4x^3 - 6x^2 + 3xy = 5$$

⑤ Differentiate each of the following with respect to x, simplifying your answer wherever possible.

(a) $\ln(x^3)$

(b) $\sin^{-1} 2x$

(c) $\ln(\sin x)$

(Note: answers to Test yourself are found at the back of the book.)

1 Differentiate each of the following with respect to x, simplifying your answer wherever possible.

(a) $(2x^2 - 1)^3$ [2]

(b) $x^3 \sin 2x$ [2]

(c) $\dfrac{3x^2+4}{x^2+6}$ [2]

Answer

1 (a) $y = (2x^2 - 1)^3$

$$\frac{dy}{dx} = 3(2x^2-1)^2(4x)$$

$$\frac{dy}{dx} = 12x(2x^2-1)^2$$

Use the Chain rule with $u = 2x^2 - 1$ or use table on page 56 with $f(x) = 2x^2 - 1, n = 3$.

(b) $y = x^3 \sin 2x$

$$\frac{dy}{dx} = x^3 2\cos 2x + \sin 2x\,(3x^2)$$

$$\frac{dy}{dx} = 2x^3\cos 2x + 3x^2 \sin 2x = x^2(2x\cos 2x + 3\sin 2x)$$

This is the product of two functions so the Product rule must be used when differentiating.

(c) $y = \dfrac{3x^2+4}{x^2+6}$

This is one function divided by another function so the Quotient rule must be used when differentiating.

$$\frac{dy}{dx} = \frac{(6x)(x^2+6)-(3x^2+4)(2x)}{(x^2+6)^2}$$

$$\frac{dy}{dx} = \frac{6x^3+36x-6x^3-8x}{(x^2+6)^2}$$

Look up the Quotient rule in the formula booklet.

$$\frac{dy}{dx} = \frac{28x}{(x^2+6)^2}$$

2 Find $\frac{dy}{dx}$ for the equation $x^3 + 6xy^2 = y^3$

Answer

2 Differentiating implicitly with respect to x, we obtain

$$3x^2 + (6x)(2y)\left(\frac{dy}{dx}\right) + y^2(6) = 3y^2\frac{dy}{dx}$$

The term $6xy^2$ is differentiated using the Product rule.

$$3x^2 + 12xy\left(\frac{dy}{dx}\right) + 6y^2 = 3y^2\frac{dy}{dx}$$

$$(12xy - 3y^2)\left(\frac{dy}{dx}\right) = -3x^2 - 6y^2$$

$$\frac{dy}{dx} = \frac{-3x^2 - 6y^2}{12xy - 3y^2} = \frac{-3(x^2 + 2y^2)}{3y(4x - y)} = \frac{-(x^2 + 2y^2)}{y(4x - y)}$$

3 If $y = \ln(2 + 5x^2)$, find $\frac{dy}{dx}$.

Answer

3 $y = \ln(2 + 5x^2)$

$$\frac{dy}{dx} = \frac{10x}{(2 + 5x^2)}$$

Topic 5 Integration

This topic covers the following:

- Integration of x^n $(n \neq -1)$, e^x, $\frac{1}{x}$, $\sin x$, $\cos x$
- Integration of $(ax+b)^n$ $(n \neq -1)$, e^{ax+b}, $\frac{1}{ax+b}$, $\sin(ax+b)$, $\cos(ax+b)$
- Integration by substitution

Integration of x^n $(n \neq -1)$, e^x, $\frac{1}{x}$, $\sin x$, $\cos x$

Integration is the reverse process to differentiation and this fact can be used to help remember the integrals of the functions covered in this section as the formulae for these integrals are not included in the formula booklet. Always remember, if you integrate without using limits you must include a constant of integration, c.

Integration of $x^n (n \neq -1)$

$$\int x^n \mathrm{d}x = \frac{x^{n+1}}{n+1} + c$$

See C2.

Integration of e^x

$$\int e^x \mathrm{d}x = e^x + c$$

Integration of $\frac{1}{x}$

$$\int \frac{1}{x} \mathrm{d}x = \ln|x| + c$$

You cannot find the ln of a negative number so the modulus sign is included here.

Integration of $\sin x$

$$\int \sin x \,\mathrm{d}x = -\cos x + c$$

Note that the derivative of $\cos x$ is $-\sin x$ so that the integral of $\sin x$ is $-\cos x$, as integration is the opposite process of differentiation.

Integration of $\cos x$

$$\int \cos x \,\mathrm{d}x = \sin x + c$$

If you differentiate $\sin x$ you obtain $\cos x$.

Integration of $(ax+b)^n$ $(n \neq -1)$, e^{ax+b}, $\frac{1}{ax+b}$, $\sin(ax+b)$, $\cos(ax+b)$

The results in the table earlier on are modified when x is replaced by the linear expression $ax + b$, where a and b are constants. Thus, for example,

when, $n \neq -1$, $\frac{d}{dx}\left((ax+b)^{n+1}\right) = (n+1)(ax+b)^n(a)$

Using the Chain rule.

so that $\int (n+1)(ax+b)^n(a)\,dx = (ax+b)^{n+1}$

Omitting the constant of integration.

or on division of both sides by the constant $(n + 1)a$,

$$\int (ax+b)^n\,dx = \frac{(ax+b)^{n+1}}{(n+1)a} + c$$

Similarly, since

$$\frac{d}{dx}\left(e^{ax+b}\right) = \left(e^{ax+b}\right)(a) + c$$

we have $\int e^{ax+b}dx = \frac{e^{ax+b}}{a} + c$

Using the Chain rule and omitting the constant of integration.

The full table is then as follows:

$$\int (ax+b)^n\,dx = \frac{(ax+b)^{n+1}}{(n+1)a} + c \qquad (n \neq -1)$$

$$\int e^{ax+b}\,dx = \frac{e^{ax+b}}{a} + c$$

You will be required to remember these results as they are not given in the formula booklet.

$$\int \frac{1}{ax+b}\,dx = \frac{1}{a}\ln|ax+b| + c$$

$$\int \sin(ax+b)\,dx = \frac{-\cos(ax+b)}{a} + c$$

$$\int \cos(ax+b)\,dx = \frac{\sin(ax+b)}{a} + c$$

It is appropriate to draw attention to two aspects of the modification of the first table to the second table. Firstly, the results in the second table are obtained from those of the first by

(i) replacing x by $ax + b$

(ii) introducing a factor of $\frac{1}{a}$.

First table is given on page 77.

Secondly, it is important to notice that the relatively simple modification occurs because the derivative of $ax + b$ is a.

Thus, note that

$\int (ax^2+b)^n \, dx$ is not equal to $\dfrac{(ax^2+b)^{n+1}}{(n+1)\,2ax}+c$

If you differentiate $\dfrac{(ax^2+b)^{n+1}}{(n+1)\,2ax}$ you will not obtain $(ax^2 + b)^n$. Remember the Quotient rule.

Examples

① Where possible, use the second table to integrate the following. If not, explain why you cannot use the second table.

(a) e^{4x+5} (b) $\sin(x^3)$ (c) $\cos 3x$ (d) $\dfrac{1}{5x^2+7}$

Answers

① (a) $4x + 5$ is of the form $ax + b$, where $a = 4$, $b = 5$.

Then $\int \dfrac{1}{4x+5}\,dx = \dfrac{1}{4}\ln|4x+5| + c$

(b) The table cannot be used to find $\int \sin(x^3)\,dx$ because x^3 is not of the form $ax + b$.

(c) $3x$ is of the form $ax + b$ where $a = 3$, $b = 0$.

Then $\int \cos 3x \; dx = \dfrac{\sin 3x}{3} + c$

(d) $5x^2 + 7$ is not of the form $ax + b$, so the table cannot be used.

② Integrate

(a) e^{2x} (b) $\sin(7x + 5)$ (c) $\dfrac{1}{7x+1}$ (d) $\cos\left(\dfrac{x}{3}\right)$

Answers

② (a) $\dfrac{e^{2x}}{2} + c$

e^{ax+b} with $a = 2$, $b = 0$.

(b) $\dfrac{-\cos(7x+5)}{7} + c$

$\sin(ax + b)$ with $a = 7$, $b = 5$.

(c) $\dfrac{1}{7}\ln|7x+1| + c$

$\dfrac{1}{ax+b}$ with $a = 7$, $b = 1$.

(d) $\dfrac{\sin\left(\dfrac{x}{3}\right)}{\dfrac{1}{3}} + c = 3\sin\left(\dfrac{x}{3}\right) + c$

$\cos(ax + b)$ with $a = \dfrac{1}{3}$, $b = 0$.

We note also that $\int k(ax+b)\mathrm{d}x = k\int (ax+b)\mathrm{d}x$ and that definite integrals are evaluated as in C2.

Examples

① Integrate

(a) $6e^{-2x}$ (b) $\frac{8}{4x+1}$ (c) $7\sin(2x+3)$ (d) $15\cos(3x+2)$

Answers

① (a) $\int 6e^{-2x}\mathrm{d}x = 6\int e^{-2x}\mathrm{d}x$

$$= 6 \times \frac{e^{-2x}}{-2} + c$$

$$= -3e^{-2x} + c$$

e^{ax+b} with $a = -2, b = 0$.

(b) $\int \frac{8}{4x+1}\mathrm{d}x = 8\int \frac{1}{4x+1}\mathrm{d}x$

$$= 8 \times \frac{1}{4}\ln|4x+1| + c$$

$$= 2\ln|4x+1| + c$$

$\frac{1}{ax+b}$ with $a = 4, b = 1$.

(c) $\int 7\sin(2x+3)\mathrm{d}x = 7\int \sin(2x+3) + c$

$$= -\frac{7}{2}\cos(2x+3) + c$$

$\sin(ax+b)$ with $a = 2, b = 3$.

(d) $\int 15\cos(3x+2)\mathrm{d}x = 15\int \cos(3x+2)\mathrm{d}x$

$$= 15 \times \frac{1}{3}\sin(3x+2) + c$$

$$= 5\sin(3x+2) + c$$

$\cos(ax+b)$ with $a = 3, b = 2$.

② Find the values of

(a) $\int_2^4 \frac{8}{(3x-4)^3}\mathrm{d}x$

(b) $\int_0^{\frac{\pi}{6}} 3\sin\left(4x + \frac{\pi}{6}\right)\mathrm{d}x$

Answers

② (a) $\int_2^4 \frac{8}{(3x-4)^3}\mathrm{d}x = 8\int_2^4 (3x-4)^{-3}\mathrm{d}x$

$$= 8\left[\frac{(3x-4)^{-2}}{(-2)\times 3}\right]_2^4$$

$(ax+b)^n$ with $a = 3, b = -4$ and $n = -3$.

$$= -\frac{8}{6}\left[(3x-4)^{-2}\right]_2^4$$

$$= -\frac{4}{3}\left[(12-4)^{-2} - (6-4)^{-2}\right]$$

$$= -\frac{4}{3}\left[\frac{1}{64} - \frac{1}{4}\right]$$

$$= -\frac{4}{3} \times \left(-\frac{15}{64}\right)$$

$$= \frac{5}{16}$$

(b) $\int_0^{\frac{\pi}{6}} 3 \sin\left(4x + \frac{\pi}{6}\right) \mathrm{d}x = 3\int_0^{\frac{\pi}{6}} \sin\left(4x + \frac{\pi}{6}\right) \mathrm{d}x$

sin $(ax + b)$ with $a = 4, b = \frac{\pi}{6}$.

$$= 3\left[-\frac{1}{4}\cos\left(4x + \frac{\pi}{6}\right)\right]_0^{\frac{\pi}{6}}$$

$$= 3\left[-\frac{1}{4}\cos\frac{5\pi}{6} + \frac{1}{4}\cos\frac{\pi}{6}\right]$$

$\cos\frac{5\pi}{6} = -\cos\frac{\pi}{6}$.

$$= 3\left[\frac{1}{4}\cos\frac{\pi}{6} + \frac{1}{4}\cos\frac{\pi}{6}\right]$$

$$= 3 \times \frac{1}{2}\cos\frac{\pi}{6}$$

$$= 3 \times \frac{1}{2} \times \frac{\sqrt{3}}{2}$$

$$= \frac{3\sqrt{3}}{4}$$

$= 1.299$ (correct to three decimal places)

Examination style questions

① Evaluate $\int_0^{\frac{\pi}{3}} \cos\left(6x+\frac{\pi}{3}\right)\mathrm{d}x$ [4]

Answer

① $\int_0^{\frac{\pi}{3}} \cos\left(6x+\frac{\pi}{3}\right)\mathrm{d}x$

$=\left[\frac{1}{6}\sin\left(6x+\frac{\pi}{3}\right)\right]_0^{\frac{\pi}{3}}$

$\cos(ax+b)$ with $a=6$, $b=\frac{\pi}{3}$.

$=\frac{1}{6}\left[\sin\left(6x+\frac{\pi}{3}\right)\right]_0^{\frac{\pi}{3}}$

$=\frac{1}{6}\left[\left(\sin\frac{7\pi}{3}\right)-\left(\sin\frac{\pi}{3}\right)\right]$

$=\frac{1}{6}\left[\frac{\sqrt{3}}{2}-\frac{\sqrt{3}}{2}\right]$

$=0$

② Find

(a) $\int\frac{1}{1-2x}\mathrm{d}x$ [2]

(b) $\int e^{6x}\mathrm{d}x$ [2]

(c) $\int(4x-3)^4\,\mathrm{d}x$ [2]

Answer

② (a) $\int\frac{1}{1-2x}\mathrm{d}x$

$\frac{1}{ax+b}$ with $a=-2$, $b=1$.

$=-\frac{1}{2}\ln|1-2x|+c$

(b) $\int e^{6x}\mathrm{d}x$

e^{ax+b} with $a=6$, $b=0$.

$=\frac{1}{6}e^{6x}+c$

(c) $\int(4x-3)^4\,\mathrm{d}x$

$(ax+b)^n$ with $a=4$, $b=-3$, $n=4$.

$=\frac{(4\mathrm{x}-3)^5}{4\times5}+c$

$=\frac{1}{20}(4x-3)^5+c$

Test yourself

Answer the following questions and check your answers before moving on to the next topic.

① Find

(a) $\int \frac{6}{5x+1} \, dx$

(b) $\int \cos 7x \, dx$

(c) $\int \frac{4}{(3x+1)^3} \, dx$

② Find

(a) $\int \sin 4x \, dx$

(b) $\int \frac{1}{2x+1} \, dx$

(c) $\int \frac{1}{(2x+1)^5} \, dx$

③ Evaluate $\int_0^2 \frac{1}{(2x+1)^3} \, dx$

④ Evaluate $\int_0^3 \frac{1}{5x+1} \, dx$, expressing your answer as a logarithm.

(Note: answers to Test yourself are found at the back of the book.)

1 (a) Find

(i) $\int \cos 4x \, dx$ (ii) $\int 5e^{2-3x} \, dx$ (iii) $\int \frac{3}{(6x-7)^5} \, dx$ [6]

(b) Evaluate $\int_1^4 \frac{9}{2x+5} \, dx$, giving your answer correct to three decimal places. [4]

(WJEC C3 Jan 2011 Q6)

Answer

1 (a)(i) $\int \cos 4x \, dx = \frac{1}{4} \sin 4x + c$

(ii) $\int 5e^{2-3x} \, dx = \frac{5}{-3} e^{2-3x} + c = -\frac{5}{3} e^{2-3x} + c$

(iii) $\int \frac{3}{(6x-7)^5} \, dx = 3\int (6x-7)^{-5} \, dx$

$$= \frac{3}{-4 \times 6}(6x-7)^{-4} + c$$

$$= -\frac{1}{8}(6x-7)^{-4} + c$$

(b) $\int_1^4 \frac{9}{2x+5} \, dx = \frac{9}{2}\left[\ln|2x+5|\right]_1^4$

$$= \frac{9}{2}[\ln 13 - \ln 7]$$

$$= \frac{9}{2} \ln \frac{13}{7}$$

= 2.786 (correct to three decimal places)

Use one of the three laws of logarithms:
$\log_a x - \log_a y = \log_a \frac{x}{y}$

2 (a) Find

(i) $\int \frac{1}{4x-7}\,dx$ (ii) $\int e^{3x-1}\,dx$ (iii) $\int \frac{5}{(2x+3)^4}\,dx$ [6]

(b) Evaluate $\int_0^{\frac{\pi}{4}} \sin\left(2x+\frac{\pi}{4}\right) dx$, expressing your answer in surd form. [4]

(WJEC C3 Jan 2010 Q6)

Answer

2 (a)(i) $\int \frac{1}{4x-7}\,dx$

$$= \frac{1}{4}\log|4x-7| + c$$

(ii) $\int e^{3x-1}\,dx$

$$= \frac{1}{3}e^{3x-1} + c$$

(iii) $\int \frac{5}{(2x+3)^4}\,dx$

$$= 5\int (2x+3)^{-4}\,dx$$

$$= -\frac{5}{6}(2x+3)^{-3} + c$$

(b) $\int_0^{\frac{\pi}{4}} \sin\left(2x+\frac{\pi}{4}\right) dx = \left[-\frac{1}{2}\cos\left(2x+\frac{\pi}{4}\right)\right]_0^{\frac{\pi}{4}}$

$$= \left(-\frac{1}{2}\cos\frac{3\pi}{4}\right) - \left(-\frac{1}{2}\cos\frac{\pi}{4}\right)$$

$$= \left(\frac{1}{2\sqrt{2}}\right) - \left(-\frac{1}{2\sqrt{2}}\right)$$

$$= \frac{2}{2\sqrt{2}}$$

$$= \frac{1}{\sqrt{2}}$$

$$= \frac{\sqrt{2}}{2}$$

$\cos\frac{\pi}{4} = \frac{1}{\sqrt{2}}$ and $\cos\frac{3\pi}{4} = -\frac{1}{\sqrt{2}}$ You must be able to write commonly used trigonometric values in surd form.

Multiply the top and bottom by $\sqrt{2}$ in order to remove the surd from the denominator.

Topic 6 Roots, iterative methods and numerical integrations

This topic covers the following:

- Location of roots of $f(x) = 0$, considering changes of sign of $f(x)$
- Sequences generated by a simple recurrence relation of the form $x_{n+1} = f(x_n)$
- Approximate solutions of equations using simple iterative methods
- Numerical integration of functions using Simpson's Rule

Location of roots of $f(x) = 0$ considering changes of sign of $f(x)$

If $f(x)$ can take any value between a and b, then if there is a change of sign between $f(a)$ and $f(b)$, then a root of $f(x) = 0$ lies between a and b.

It is assumed that the graph of $y = f(x)$ is an unbroken line between $x = a$, $x = b$.

Example

Show that the equation

$$9x^3 - 9x + 1 = 0$$

has a root α between 0 and 0.2

Answer

Let $f(x) = 9x^3 - 9x + 1$

Insert both values in turn into the function and if there is a sign change, then the root lies between the two values.

$$f(0) = 1$$

$$f(0.2) = 9(0.2)^3 - 9(0.2) + 1 = 0.072 - 1.8 + 1 = -0.728$$

As there is a sign change, the root α must lie between 0 and 0.2

Sequences generated by a simple recurrence relation of the form $x_{n+1} = f(x_n)$

The following relation is called a recurrence relation,

$$x_{n+1} = x_n^3 + \frac{1}{9}.$$

This recurrence relation can be used to generate a sequence by substituting a starting value called x_0 into the relation to calculate the next term in the sequence, called x_1. The value of x_1 is then substituted for x_n into the relation to calculate x_2. The process is repeated until the desired number of terms of the sequence have been found.

Example

① A sequence is generated using the recurrence relation

$$x_{n+1} = x_n^3 + \frac{1}{9}$$

Starting with $x_0 = 0.1$, find and record x_1, x_2, x_3.

Answer

① $x_0 = 0.1$

$$x_1 = x_0^3 + \frac{1}{9} = (0.1)^3 + \frac{1}{9} = 0.1121111111$$

Do not round off any of your values. Write down the full calculator display.

$$x_2 = x_1^3 + \frac{1}{9} = (0.1121111111)^3 + \frac{1}{9} = 0.1125202246$$

$$x_3 = x_2^3 + \frac{1}{9} = (0.1125202246)^3 + \frac{1}{9} = 0.1125357073$$

Approximate solutions of equations using simple iterative methods

To find an approximate solution to an equation by iteration, you first start with an approximate value to the root and then substitute this into a recurrence relation. The result is then substituted back into the recurrence relation and the process is repeated until a value to the desired degree of accuracy is obtained.

This technique can be seen in the following example.

Example

① You may assume that the equation $6x^4 + 7x - 3 = 0$ has a root α between 0 and 1.

The recurrence relation with $x_0 = 0.4$ can be used to find

$$x_{n+1} = \frac{3 - 6x_n^4}{7}$$

Find and record the values of x_1, x_2, x_3, x_4. Write down the value of x_4 correct to four decimal places and show this is the value of α correct to four decimal places. [5]

(WJEC C3 Jan 2011 Q4)

Answer

① $x_{n+1} = \dfrac{3 - 6x_n^4}{7}$

This is the iterative formula and is given in the question. This is the formula into which the starting value and subsequent values are entered.

$x_0 = 0.4$

x_0 is the starting value and is given in the question. This value is substituted into the formula to obtain the next value x_1

$$x_1 = \frac{3 - 6x_0^4}{7} = \frac{3 - 6(0.4)^4}{7} = 0.406628571$$

$$x_2 = \frac{3 - 6x_1^4}{7} = \frac{3 - 6(0.406628571)^4}{7} = 0.405137517$$

$$x_3 = \frac{3 - 6x_2^4}{7} = \frac{3 - 6(0.405137517)^4}{7} = 0.405479348$$

$$x_4 = \frac{3 - 6x_3^4}{7} = \frac{3 - 6(0.405479348)^4}{7} = 0.405401314$$

Hence $x_4 = 0.4054$ (correct to four decimal places)

Here we need to look at the value of α either side of the value of $x_4 = 0.4054$ (i.e. at 0.40535 and at 0.40545). If there is a sign change when these values are put into $6x^4 + 7x - 3$, then α is the root correct to 4 d.p.

Let $f(x) = 6x^4 + 7x - 3$

$f(0.40535) = 6(0.40535)^4 + 7(0.40535) - 3 = -5.66 \times 10^{-4}$

$f(0.40545) = 6(0.40545)^4 + 7(0.40545) - 3 = 2.94 \times 10^{-4}$

As there is a sign change, $\alpha = 0.4054$ correct to four decimal places.

Example

② Show that the equation

$x - \sin x - 0.2 = 0,$

where x is measured in radians, has a root α between 1 and 2.

The recurrence relation

$x_{n+1} = \sin x_n + 0.2$

with $x_1 = 1.1$ can be used to find α. Find and record the values of x_1, x_2, x_3, x_4.

Write down the value of x_4 correct to three decimal places and show this is the value of α correct to three decimal places.

Answer

②

x	$x - \sin x - 0.2$
1	-4.15×10^{-2}
2	8.9×10^{-1}

Since there is a change of sign, there is a root between 1 and 2.

$x_1 = \sin(1.1) + 0.2 = 1.09120736$

$x_2 = \sin(1.09120736) + 0.2 = 1.087184654$

$x_3 = \sin(1.087184654) + 0.2 = 1.085321346$

$x_4 = 1.084453409$

Hence $x_4 \approx 1.084$ (correct to three decimal places)

Now we check 1.0835 and 1.0845 in the original equation (not in the recurrence relation).

x	$x - \sin x - 0.2$
1.0835	-1.02×10^{-4}
1.0845	4.3×10^{-4}

Since there is a change of sign, the root is 1.084 correct to three decimal places.

Numerical integration of functions using Simpson's Rule

You learnt about the Trapezium Rule in C2 of the AS course. This rule approximated the value of $\int_a^b y\,dx$ by using a formula which made use of dividing the area under the curve into a series of strips (in the shape of trapeziums).

There is another formula that can be used to provide an approximation to $\int_a^b y\,dx$ using an even number of strips, called Simpson's Rule.

Simpson's Rule:

$$\int_a^b y\,dx \approx \frac{1}{3}h\{(y_o + y_n) + 4(y_1 + y_3 + \ldots + y_{n-1}) + 2(y_2 + y_4 + \ldots + y_{n-2})\}$$

where $h = \frac{b-a}{n}$ and n is even

With Simpson's Rule the number of strips, n, must be even and this means that the number of ordinates will be odd. Remember that n is always one less than the number of ordinates used.

Example

① Use Simpson's Rule with five ordinates to find an approximate value for the integral

$$\int_4^6 \frac{1}{3-\sqrt{x}}\,dx.$$

Show your working and give your answer correct to three decimal places. [4]

(WJEC C3 Jan 2011 Q1)

Answer

$$\int_a^b y\,dx = \int_4^6 \frac{1}{3-\sqrt{x}}\,dx$$

It is important to note that n is the number of strips and not the number of ordinates. Here there are 5 ordinates, so there will be 4 strips. Hence $n = 4$.

$$h = \frac{b-a}{n} = \frac{6-4}{4} = 0.5$$

This means that you start at the value of a (i.e. 4 in this case) and go up in steps of h (0.5 here) until the value of b is reached (6 in this case).

When $x = 4$, $y_0 = \frac{1}{3-\sqrt{4}} = 1$

$x = 4{\cdot}5$, $y_1 = \frac{1}{3-\sqrt{4.5}} = 1.138071187$

Always work to at least one decimal place beyond that you are asked to find the answer to.

$x = 5$, $y_2 = \frac{1}{3-\sqrt{5}} = 1.309016994$

$x = 5{\cdot}5$, $y_3 = \frac{1}{3-\sqrt{5.5}} = 1.527202251$

$x = 6$, $y_4 = \frac{1}{3-\sqrt{6}} = 1.816496581$

The formula for Simpson's Rule is obtained from the formula booklet. You do not have to remember it.

$$\int_a^b y\,dx \approx \frac{1}{3}h\{(y_o + y_n) + 4(y_1 + y_3 + \ldots + y_{n-1}) + 2(y_2 + y_4 + \ldots + y_{n-2})\}$$

$n = 4$

$$\approx \frac{0.5}{3} \times \{(1 + 1.816496581) + 4\,(1.138071187 + 1.527202251\,) + 2(1.309016994)\}$$

≈ 2.682604054

≈ 2.683 (correct to three decimal places)

Remember to give your answer to the required number of decimal places or significant figures specified in the question.

A useful check of your working which tests the reasonableness of your answer is to calculate the middle y value $\times$ range of integration. In this case the middle y value is $y_2 = 1.309016994$ and the range of integration is $6 - 4 = 2$.

The integral is approximately $2 \times 1.309016994 \approx 2.618$ which compares with 2.683.

Important note

You need to be aware that examination questions in solution of equations and Simpson's Rule sometimes involve knowledge from other parts of the course.

Examination style questions

① Show that the function given by

$f(x) = x^4 + 4x^2 - 32x + 5$

has a stationary point when x satisfies the equation

$x^3 + 2x - 8 = 0$

Show that the equation

$x^3 + 2x - 8 = 0$

has a root α between 1 and 2.

The recurrence relation

$x_{n+1} = (8 - 2x_n)^{\frac{1}{3}}$

with $x_0 = 1.7$ may be used to find α. Find and record the values of x_1, x_2, x_3, x_4. Write down the value of x_4 correct to four decimal places.

Answer

① The stationary point occurs when $f' = 0$, i.e. when

$4x^3 + 8x - 32 = 0$

$\therefore \quad x^3 + 2x - 8 = 0$

Let $f(x) = x^3 + 2x - 8$

$f(1) = (1)^3 + 2(1) - 8 = -5$

$f(2) = (2)^3 + 2(2) - 8 = 4$

The sign change indicates a root α between 1 and 2.

The two values between which the root is supposed to lie are entered in turn into the function.

A sign change indicates that the root lies between the two values.

$x_0 = 1.7$

$x_1 = (8 - 2x_0)^{\frac{1}{3}} = (8 - 2(1.7))^{\frac{1}{3}} = 1.663103499$

$x_2 = (8 - 2x_1)^{\frac{1}{3}} = (8 - 2(1.663103499))^{\frac{1}{3}} = 1.671949509$

$x_3 = (8 - 2x_2)^{\frac{1}{3}} = (8 - 2(1.671949509))^{\frac{1}{3}} = 1.669837194$

$x_4 = (8 - 2x_3)^{\frac{1}{3}} = (8 - 2(1.669837194))^{\frac{1}{3}} = 1.670342073$

Hence $x_4 = 1.6703$ (correct to 4 decimal places)

Always round your final answer to the required number of decimal places or significant figures.

② Use Simpson's Rule with five ordinates to find an approximate value for

$$\int_1^2 \ln x \, dx$$

Show your working and give your answer correct to three decimal places.

Deduce an approximate value for $\int_1^2 \ln(x^2) \, dx$.

Answer

② $h = \dfrac{b-a}{n} = \dfrac{2-1}{4} = 0.25$

When $x = 1$, $y_0 = \ln 1 = 0$

When $x = 1.25$, $y_1 = \ln 1.25 = 0.223143551$

When $x = 1.50$, $y_2 = \ln 1.50 = 0.405465108$

When $x = 1.75$, $y_3 = \ln 1.75 = 0.559615788$

When $x = 2$, $y_4 = \ln 2 = 0.693147181$

$$\int_a^b y \, dx \approx \frac{1}{3}h\{(y_o + y_n) + 4(y_1 + y_3 + \dots + y_{n-1}) + 2(y_2 + y_4 + \dots + y_{n-2})\}$$

$$\approx \frac{0.25}{3} \times \{(0 + 0.693147181) + 4(0.223143551 + 0.559615788) + 2(0.405465108)\}$$

≈ 0.3862595628

≈ 0.386 (correct to 3 decimal places)

Since $\int_1^2 \ln(x^2) \, dx = \int_1^2 2 \ln x \, dx$

Property of logs $\ln(x^n) = n \ln x$

$= 2\int_1^2 \ln x \, dx = 2 \times 0.3862595628$

$= 0.773$ (correct to three decimal places)

Checking answer to $\int_1^2 \ln x \, dx$

Approximate value = middle y value $\times$ range of integration

$= y_2 \times (2 - 1)$

$= 0.405465 \times 1$

≈ 0.405 (correct to three decimal places)

This compares with 0.386.

Test yourself

Answer the following questions and check your answers before moving on to the next topic.

① Use Simpson's Rule with five ordinates to find an approximate value for the integral

$$\int_0^1 \frac{1}{1+x^2}\,dx$$

Show your working and give your answer correct to three decimal places.

② You may assume that the equation $(x-1)e^{2x}-1=0$ has a root α between 1 and 2. The recurrence relation

$$x_{n+1}=1+e^{-2x_n}$$

with $x_0 = 1.1$ can be used to find α. Find and record the values of x_1, x_2, x_3. Write down the value of x_3 correct to four decimal places and prove that this value is the value of α correct to four decimal places.

(Note: answers to Test yourself are found at the back of the book.)

1 Use Simpson's Rule with five ordinates to find an approximate value for

$$\int_0^{0.8} \frac{1}{1+e^{2x}}\, dx$$

Show your working and give your answer correct to four decimal places. [4]

(WJEC C3 June 2010 Q1)

Answer

1 $\int_a^b y\, dx = \int_0^{0.8} \frac{1}{1+e^{2x}}\, dx$

$$h = \frac{b-a}{n} = \frac{0.8-0}{4} = 0.2$$

When $x = 0,\ y_0 = \frac{1}{1+e^0} = 0.5$

$x = 0.2,\ y_1 = \frac{1}{1+e^{0.4}} = 0.401312339$

$x = 0.4,\ y_2 = \frac{1}{1+e^{0.8}} = 0.310025518$

$x = 0.6,\ y_3 = \frac{1}{1+e^{1.2}} = 0.231475216$

$x = 0.8,\ y_4 = \frac{1}{1+e^{1.6}} = 0.167981614$

The following formulae for Simpson's Rule and the value of h are obtained from the formula booklet.

$$\int_a^b y\, dx \approx \frac{1}{3}h\{(y_o + y_n) + 4(y_1 + y_3 + \ldots + y_{n-1}) + 2(y_2 + y_4 + \ldots + y_{n-2})\}$$

$$h = \frac{b-a}{n}$$

Keep all the decimal places and do not round off to four decimal places until the end.

Grade boost

It is so easy to make an arithmetic error when doing these calculations so always check your answer.

$$\int_a^b y\, dx \approx \frac{1}{3}h\{(y_o + y_n) + 4(y_1 + y_3 + \ldots + y_{n-1}) + 2(y_2 + y_4 + \ldots + y_{n-2})\}$$

$$\int_0^{0.8} \frac{1}{1+e^{2x}}\, dx \approx \frac{1}{3} \times 0.2\{(0.5 + 0.167981614) + 4(0.401312339 + 0.231475216) + 2(0.310025518)\}$$

≈ 0.254612191

≈ 0.2546 (correct to four decimal places)

Check $y_2 \times$ range of integration $= 0.310025518 \times 0.8 = 0.2480$.

2 Show that the equation

$4x^3 - 2x - 5 = 0$

has a root α between 1 and 2.

The recurrence relation

$$x_{n+1} = \left(\frac{2x_n + 5}{4}\right)^{\frac{1}{3}},$$

with $x_0 = 1.2$, may be used to find α. Find and record the values of x_1, x_2, x_3, x_4. Write down the value of x_4 correct to five decimal places and prove that this value is the value of α correct to five decimal places. [7]

(WJEC C3 June 2010 Q4)

Answer

2 Let $f(x) = 4x^3 - 2x - 5$

$f(1) = 4(1)^3 - 2(1) - 5 = -3$

$f(2) = 4(2)^3 - 2(2) - 5 = 23$

Both values between which the solution lies are entered in turn for x. If there is a sign change, then the solution lies between these two values.

There is a change in sign between 1 and 2. Hence there is a root between these two values.

$$x_{n+1} = \left(\frac{2x_n + 5}{4}\right)^{\frac{1}{3}}$$

$x_0 = 1.2$

Do not round off these numbers yet.

$$x_1 = \left(\frac{2x_0 + 5}{4}\right)^{\frac{1}{3}} = \left(\frac{2(1.2) + 5}{4}\right)^{\frac{1}{3}} = 1.227601026$$

$$x_2 = \left(\frac{2x_1 + 5}{4}\right)^{\frac{1}{3}} = \left(\frac{2(1.227601026) + 5}{4}\right)^{\frac{1}{3}} = 1.230645994$$

$$x_3 = \left(\frac{2x_2 + 5}{4}\right)^{\frac{1}{3}} = \left(\frac{2(1.230645994) + 5}{4}\right)^{\frac{1}{3}} = 1.230980996$$

$$x_4 = \left(\frac{2x_3 + 5}{4}\right)^{\frac{1}{3}} = \left(\frac{2(1.230980996) + 5}{4}\right)^{\frac{1}{3}} = 1.231017841$$

$x_4 = 1.23102$ (correct to five decimal places)

Round off the final answer to the required number of decimal places.

Here we need to look at the value of α either side of the value of $x_4 = 1.23102$ (i.e. at 1.231015 and at 1.231025).

$f(1.231015) = 4(1.231015)^3 - 2(1.231015) - 5 = -0.000119667$

Enter both of these values into the $f(x)$ to see if there is a sign change.

$f(1.231025) = 4(1.231025)^3 - 2(1.231025) - 5 = 0.000042182$

As there is a sign change, $\alpha = 1.23102$ correct to five decimal places.

Q&A 3

3 (a) Sketch the graphs of $y = x^3$ and $y = x + 2$. Deduce the number of real roots of the equation

$$x^3 - x - 2 = 0$$

(b) The cubic equation $x^3 - x - 2 = 0$ has a root α between 1 and 2.

The recurrence relation

$$x_{n+1} = (x_n + 2)^{\frac{1}{3}}$$

with $x_0 = 1.5$, can be used to find α. Calculate x_4, giving your answer correct to three decimal places. Prove that this value is also the value of α correct to three decimal places.

Answer

3 (a)

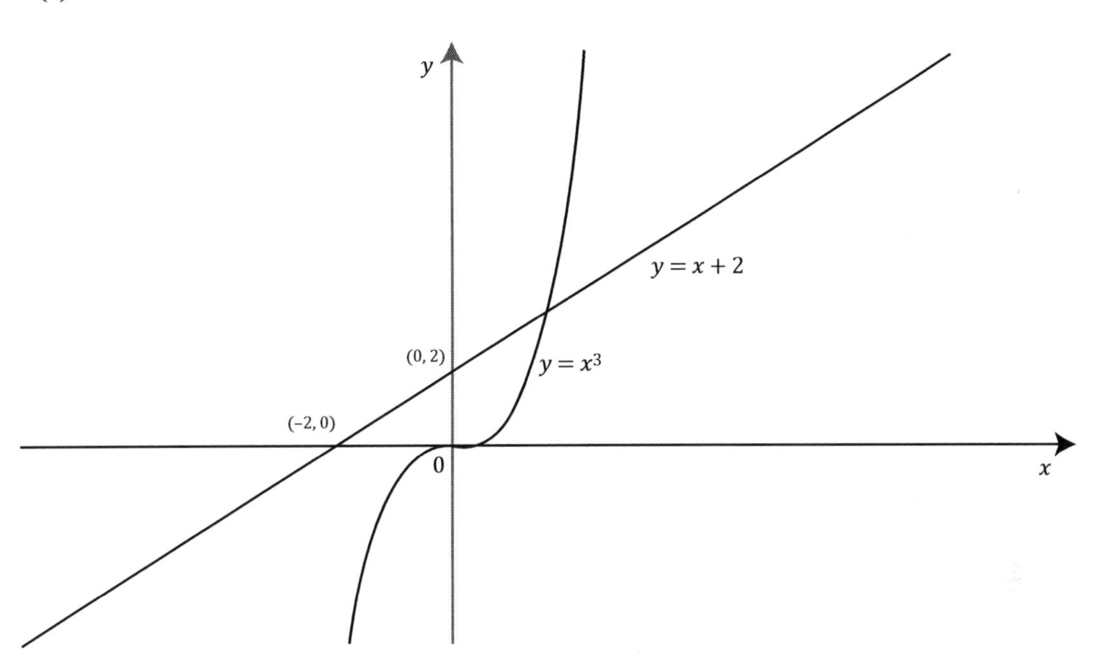

There is a real root of $x^3 - x - 2 = 0$ where the graphs of $y = x^3$ and $y = x + 2$ intersect. The graphs intersect once so there is one real root of the equation

$$x^3 - x - 2 = 0$$

(b) $x_1 = 1.5182945$

$x_2 = 1.5209353$

$x_3 = 1.5213157$

$x_4 = 1.5213705 \approx 1.521$ (correct to three decimal places)

Check value of $x^3 - x - 2$ for $x = 1.5205, 1.5215$

x	$f(x)$
1.5205	-0.0052
1.5215	0.0007

Since there is a change of sign, the root is 1.521 correct to three decimal places.

Summary C3

1 Functions

A function is a relation between a set of inputs and a set of outputs such that each input is related to exactly one output.

The domain and range of a function

The domain is the set of input values that can be entered into a function.

The range is the set of output values from a function.

Composition of functions

Composition of functions involves applying two or more functions in succession.

The composite function $fg(x)$ means $f(g(x))$ and is the result of performing the function g first and then f.

One-to-one functions

A function where one output value would correspond to only one possible input value.

To find $f^{-1}(x)$ given $f(x)$

First check that $f(x)$ is a one-to-one function. Let y equal the function and rearrange so that x is the subject of the equation. Replace x on the left with $f^{-1}(x)$ and on the right replace all occurrences of y with x.

Domain and range of inverse functions

The range of $f^{-1}(x)$ is the same as the domain of $f(x)$.

The domain of $f^{-1}(x)$ is the same as the range of $f(x)$.

Graphs of inverse functions

The graph of $y = f^{-1}(x)$ is obtain by reflecting the graph of $y = f(x)$ in the line $y = x$.

The modulus function

The modulus of x is written as $|x|$ and means the numerical value of x (ignoring the sign).

So whether x is positive or negative, $|x|$ is always positive (or zero).

Graphs of modulus functions

First plot the graph of $y = f(x)$ and reflect any part of the graph below the x-axis in the x-axis. The resulting graph will be $y = |f(x)|$.

Combinations of transformations

If a graph of $y = f(x)$ is drawn, then the graph of $y = f(x - a) + b$ can be obtained by applying the translation $\begin{pmatrix} a \\ b \end{pmatrix}$ to the original graph.

If a graph of $y = f(x)$ is drawn, then the graph of $y = af(x - b)$ can be obtained by applying the following two transformations in either order: a stretch parallel to the y-axis with scale factor a and a translation of $\begin{pmatrix} b \\ 0 \end{pmatrix}$.

If a graph of $y = f(x)$ is drawn, then the graph of $y = f(ax)$ can be obtain by scaling the x values by $\frac{1}{a}$.

2 Trigonometry

Sec, cosec and cot

$$\sec\theta = \frac{1}{\cos\theta}$$

$$\text{cosec}\ \theta = \frac{1}{\sin\theta}$$

$$\cot\theta = \frac{1}{\tan\theta}$$

Trig identities

$\sec^2\theta = 1 + \tan^2\theta$

$\text{cosec}^2\theta = 1 + \cot^2\theta$

3 Exponential and logarithmic functions

The function e^x and its graph

$y = e^x$

e^x is a one-to-one function and had an inverse $\ln x$.

The graph of $y = e^x$ cuts the y-axis at $y = 1$ and has the x-axis as an asymptote.

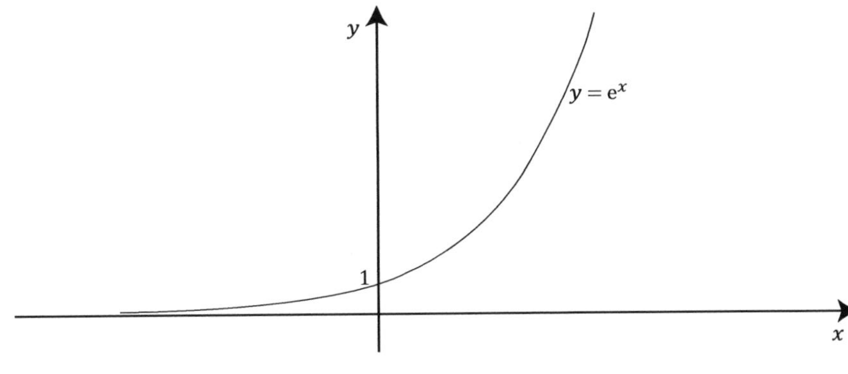

$D(f) = (-\infty, \infty)$

$R(f) = (0, \infty)$

The function ln x and its graph

$y = \ln x$

ln x is a one-to-one function and has an inverse e^x.

The graph of $y = \ln x$ cuts the x-axis at $x = 1$ and has the y-axis as an asymptote.

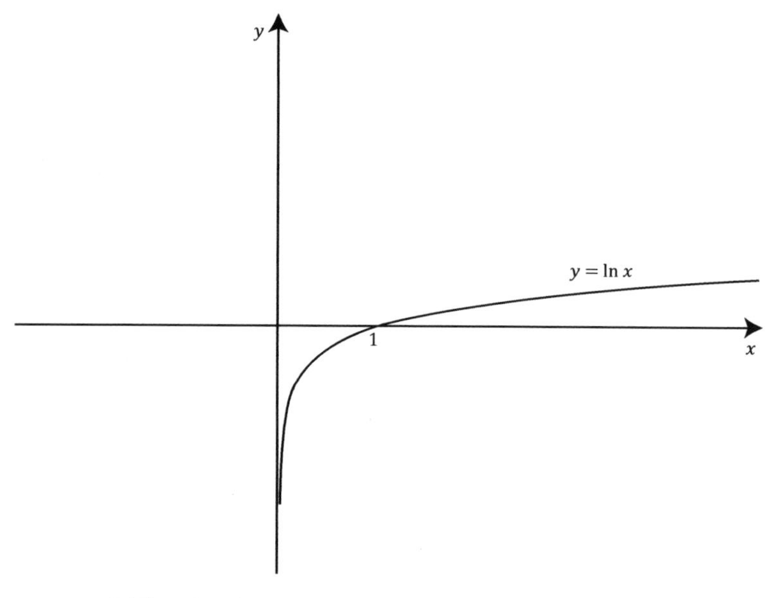

$D(f) = (0, \infty)$

$R(f) = (-\infty, \infty)$

The functions $y = \ln x$ and $y = e^x$ are inverse functions.

So, the graphs of $y = \ln x$ and $y = e^x$ are reflections of each other in the line $y = x$.

Also, $e^{\ln x} = x$ and $\ln e^x = x$.

4 Differentiation

Differentiation of e^x, $\ln x$, $\sin x$, $\cos x$ and $\tan x$

$$\frac{d(e^x)}{dx} = e^x$$

$$\frac{d(\ln x)}{dx} = \frac{1}{x}$$

$$\frac{d(\sin x)}{dx} = \cos x$$

$$\frac{d(\cos x)}{dx} = -\sin x$$

$$\frac{d(\tan x)}{dx} = \sec^2 x$$

The Chain rule

If y is a function of u and u is a function of x, then the chain rule states:

$$\frac{dy}{dx} = \frac{dy}{du} \times \frac{du}{dx}$$

Differentiation of $\sin^{-1} x$, $\cos^{-1} x$ and $\tan^{-1} x$

$$\frac{d\left(\sin^{-1} x\right)}{dx} = \frac{1}{\sqrt{1-x^2}}$$

$$\frac{d\left(\cos^{-1} x\right)}{dx} = \frac{-1}{\sqrt{1-x^2}}$$

$$\frac{d\left(\tan^{-1} x\right)}{dx} = \frac{1}{1+x^2}$$

The Product rule

If $y = f(x)g(x)$, $\dfrac{dy}{dx} = f(x)g'(x) + g(x)f'(x)$

The Quotient rule

If $y = \dfrac{f(x)}{g(x)}$, $\dfrac{dy}{dx} = \dfrac{f'(x)g(x) - f(x)g'(x)}{(g(x))^2}$

Differentiating logarithmic functions

To differentiate the natural logarithm of a function you differentiate the function and then divide by the function.

This can be expressed mathematically as:

$$\frac{d(\ln(f(x)))}{dx} = \frac{f'(x)}{f(x)}$$

Differentiation of simple functions defined implicitly

Finding $\dfrac{dy}{dx}$ in terms of both x and y is called implicit differentiation.

Here are the rules for differentiating implicitly:

- Terms involving x or constant terms are differentiated as normal.
- For terms just involving y, (e.g. $3y$, $5y^3$, etc.) differentiate with respect to y and then multiply the result by $\dfrac{dy}{dx}$.
- For terms involving both x and y (e.g. xy, $5x^2y^3$, etc.) the product rule is used because there are two terms multiplied together. Note the need to include $\dfrac{dy}{dx}$ when the term involving y is differentiated.

Differentiation of functions defined parametrically

The equation of a curve can be expressed in parametric form by using $x = f(t)$, $y = g(t)$ where t is the parameter being used.

The formulae for differentiating parametric forms are:

$$\frac{dy}{dx} = \frac{dy}{dt} \bigg/ \frac{dx}{dt} = \frac{dy}{dt} \times \frac{dt}{dx}$$

and $$\frac{d^2y}{dx^2} = \frac{d}{dt}\left(\frac{dy}{dx}\right) \bigg/ \frac{dx}{dt} = \frac{d}{dt}\left(\frac{dy}{dx}\right) \times \frac{dt}{dx}$$

5 Integration

$$\int x^n \, dx = \frac{x^{n+1}}{n+1} + c \quad (n \neq -1)$$

$$\int (ax+b)^n \, dx = \frac{(ax+b)^{n+1}}{(n+1)a} + c \quad (n \neq -1)$$

$$\int e^x \, dx = e^x + c$$

$$\int e^{ax+b} \, dx = \frac{e^{ax+b}}{a} + c$$

$$\int \sin x \, dx = -\cos x + c$$

$$\int \sin(ax+b) \, dx = \frac{-\cos(ax+b)}{a} + c$$

$$\int \cos x \, dx = \sin x + c$$

$$\int \cos(ax+b) \, dx = \frac{\sin(ax+b)}{a} + c$$

$$\int \frac{1}{x} \, dx = \ln|x| + c$$

$$\int \frac{1}{ax+b} \, dx = \frac{1}{a}\ln|ax+b| + c$$

6 Roots, iterative methods and numerical integrations

Location of roots of $f(x) = 0$ considering changes of sign of $f(x)$

If $f(x)$ can take any value between a and b, then if there is a change of sign between $f(a)$ and $f(b)$, then a root of $f(x) = 0$ lies between a and b.

Simpson's Rule

$$\int_a^b y \, dx \approx \frac{1}{3}h\{(y_o + y_n) + 4(y_1 + y_3 + ... + y_{n-1}) + 2(y_2 + y_4 + ... + y_{n-2})\}$$

where $h = \dfrac{b-a}{n}$ and n is even

Unit C4 Pure Mathematics 4

Unit C4 covers Pure Mathematics and seeks to build on your knowledge, skills and understanding obtained from units C1, C2 and C3. You must be proficient in the use of mathematical theories and techniques and you will probably need to look back at previous work.

Revision checklist

Tick column 1 when you have completed all the notes.
Tick column 2 when you think you have a good grasp of the topic.
Tick column 3 during the final revision when you feel you have mastery of the topic.

		1	2	3	Notes
	1 Binomial series				
p109	Binomial expansion for positive integral indices				
p110	The binomial theorem for other values of n				
p113	Partial fractions				
	2 Trigonometry				
p122	Knowledge and use of $\sin(A \pm B)$, $\cos(A \pm B)$ and $\tan(A \pm B)$				
p125	Expressions for $a \cos \theta + b \sin \theta$ in the equivalent forms $R \cos(\theta \pm \alpha)$ or $R \sin(\theta \pm \alpha)$				
	3 Cartesian and parametric equations of curves				
p137	Parametric equations				
p140	Using the Chain rule to find the first and second derivatives				
p141	Implicit differentiation				
	4 Simple differential equations and exponential growth				
p148	Formation of simple differential equations				
p148	Exponential growth and decay				
	5 Integration				
p154	Evaluation of volume of revolution				
p156	Integration by substitution and integration by parts				
p162	Integration using partial fractions				
p164	Analytical solution of first order differential equations with separable variables				

		1	2	3	Notes
	6 Vectors				
p171	Scalars and vectors				
p172	Vectors in two and three dimensions				
p173	The magnitude of a vector				
p174	Algebraic operations of vector addition, subtraction and multiplication by scalars, and their geometrical interpretations				
p176	Position vectors				
p177	The distance between two points				
p177	Vector equation of a line				
p180	Scalar product				
p181	Condition for vectors to be perpendicular to each other				
p183	The position vector of a point dividing a line in a given ratio				

Topic 1 Binomial expansions, simplification of expressions and partial fractions

This topic covers the following:

- Binomial expansion for positive integral values of n
- The binomial expansion for other values of n
- Partial fractions

Binomial expansion for positive integral indices

The binomial expansion was covered in AS C1, so if you are unsure on the basics you should look back at Topic 4 of the AS book.

There are several formulae you need to use. All these formulae are included in the formula booklet.

Binomial expansion is the expansion of the expression $(a + b)^n$ where n is a positive integer.

The formula for the expansion will be given in the formula booklet and is shown here:

$$(a+b)^n = a^n + \binom{n}{1}a^{n-1}b + \binom{n}{2}a^{n-2}b^2 + \ldots + \binom{n}{r}a^{n-r}b^r + \ldots + b^n$$

where $\binom{n}{r} = {}^nC_r = \dfrac{n!}{r!(n-r)!}$

You do not need to memorise these formulae as they are given in the formula booklet.

$n!$ means n factorial. If $n = 5$ then $5! = 1 \times 2 \times 3 \times 4 \times 5$ which you may also see written as 1.2.3.4.5

Note that $0! = 1$.

Using Pascal's triangle to work out the coefficients of the terms

You can also find the coefficients in the expansion of $(a + b)^n$ by using Pascal's triangle.

Suppose you want to expand the expression from the previous example, $(a + b)^4$ using Pascal's triangle.

You would write down Pascal's triangle and look for the line starting 1 and then 4 (because n is 4 here). The line 1, 4, 6, 4, 1 gives the coefficients. This avoids the calculation involving the factorials for each coefficient but you will have to remember how to construct Pascal's triangle.

Notice that all the rows start and end with a 1. Notice also that the other numbers are found by adding the pairs of numbers immediately above. For example if we have 1 3 in the line above then the number to be entered between these numbers on the next line is a 4.

1

1 1

1 2 1

1 3 3 1

1 4 6 4 1

1 5 10 10 5 1

Grade boost

If you intend to use Pascal's triangle you must remember how to construct it and also how to decide which line should be used. You will not be given Pascal's triangle in the formula booklet.

Hence inserting the coefficients 1, 4, 6, 4 ,1 we have the following expansion:

$(a + b)^4 = a^4 + 4a^3b + 6a^2b^2 + 4ab^3 + b^4$

The binomial expansion where $a = 1$

When the first term in the bracket (i.e. a) is 1 and b is replaced by x the binomial expansion when n is a positive integer, becomes:

$$(1+x)^n = 1 + nx + \frac{n(n-1)x^2}{2!} + \frac{n(n-1)(n-2)x^3}{3!} + \ldots$$

Again this formula is given in the formula booklet so you don't need to memorise it.

The binomial theorem for other values of n

In the previous section, which referred to the binomial expansion covered in C1, it should be noted that the index n was a positive integer.

However, the expansion

$$(1+x)^n = 1 + nx + \frac{n(n-1)x^2}{1.2} + \frac{n(n-1)(n-2)x^3}{1.2.3} + \ldots$$

holds for negative or fractional values of n, provided that x lies between ± 1, i.e. $|x| < 1$.

For this range of values of x the series is convergent; because as x is raised to increasing powers, the values of successive terms decrease rapidly. As a result, once the first few terms have been added, subsequent terms become small and insignificant and the sum of the series approaches a final steady value. If $|x| < 1$ did not apply, the subsequent terms would get larger and larger and it would be impossible to determine an approximation to the series.

Examples

Here are the values of x for which the expansions of each of the following are convergent.

① $(1+x)^{-1}$ expansion is convergent for $|x| < 1$.

② $\left(1+\frac{x}{3}\right)^{-1}$ $\left|\frac{x}{3}\right| < 1$ so expansion is convergent for $|x| < 3$.

③ $(1-x)^{-1}$ expansion is convergent for $|x| < 1$.

The condition for convergence when two binomial expansions are combined

Suppose the following two binomial expansions are added together:

$$(1+2x)^5 + \left(1-\frac{x}{2}\right)^4$$

$\mathbf{(1+2x)^5}$ We require $|2x| < 1$, so this expansion is convergent for $|x| < \frac{1}{2}$.

$\left(\mathbf{1}-\frac{x}{\mathbf{2}}\right)^{\mathbf{4}}$ We require $\frac{x}{2} < 1$, so this expansion is convergent for $|x| < 2$.

Now the value of x has to satisfy both conditions and as $|x| < \frac{1}{2}$ lies inside $|x| < 2$, the condition for the combined convergence is $|x| < \frac{1}{2}$ or $-\frac{1}{2} < x < \frac{1}{2}$.

Examples

① Expand $(2-x)^{\frac{1}{2}}$ in ascending powers of x up to and including the term in x^2.

State the range of values of x for which the expansion is valid.

Answer

① $$(2-x)^{\frac{1}{2}} = \left[2\left(1-\frac{x}{2}\right)\right]^{\frac{1}{2}}$$
$$= 2^{\frac{1}{2}}\left(1-\frac{x}{2}\right)^{\frac{1}{2}}$$
$$= \sqrt{2}\left[1+\left(\frac{1}{2}\right)\left(\frac{-x}{2}\right)+\frac{\left(\frac{1}{2}\right)\left(-\frac{1}{2}\right)\left(\frac{-x}{2}\right)^2}{2!}+\ldots\right]$$
$$= \sqrt{2}\left(1-\frac{x}{4}-\frac{x^2}{32}+\ldots\right)$$

Notice how the 2 is removed out of the bracket. It is important to note that this 2 is raised to the power $\frac{1}{2}$.

Use the formula for the binomial expansion $(1+x)^n = 1+nx+\frac{n(n-1)x^2}{2!}+\ldots$ obtained from the formula booklet with $n=\frac{1}{2}$ and x replaced by $-\frac{x}{2}$.

For the expansion of $\left(1-\frac{x}{2}\right)^{\frac{1}{2}}$ to converge, we require $\left|\frac{x}{2}\right| < 1$ i.e. $|x| < 2$ or $-2 < x < 2$.

② Expand $\left(1-\frac{x}{4}\right)^{\frac{1}{2}}$ in ascending powers of x up to and including the term in x^2.

State the range of values of x for which your expansion is valid.

Hence, by writing $x = 1$ in your expansion, show that

$\sqrt{3} = \frac{111}{64}$ [5]

(WJEC C4 June 2010 Q1)

Answer

② Now $(1+x)^n = 1+nx+\frac{n(n-1)x^2}{2!}+\frac{n(n-1)(n-2)x^3}{3!}+\ldots$

This formula for the binomial expansion is given in the formula booklet so you don't need to memorise it.

Here $n = \frac{1}{2}$ and x is replaced with $-\frac{x}{4}$, so

$$\left(1-\frac{x}{4}\right)^{\frac{1}{2}} = 1+\left(\frac{1}{2}\right)\left(-\frac{x}{4}\right)+\frac{\frac{1}{2}\left(-\frac{1}{2}\right)}{1\times 2}\left(\frac{x^2}{16}\right)+\ldots$$
$$= 1-\frac{x}{8}-\frac{x^2}{128}+\ldots$$

Notice the +... here. It means that the series continues.

When n is negative or fractional, the $(1+x)^n$ expansion is valid for $|x| < 1$

This is shown in the formula booklet.

Then for $\left(1-\frac{x}{4}\right)^{\frac{1}{2}}$, the expansion is valid for $\left|\frac{x}{4}\right| < 1$ or $|x| < 4$, i.e. $-4 < x < 4$

When $x = 1$, $\left(1-\frac{x}{4}\right)^{\frac{1}{2}} = \left(1-\frac{1}{4}\right)^{\frac{1}{2}} = \left(\frac{3}{4}\right)^{\frac{1}{2}} = \frac{\sqrt{3}}{2}$

Hence $\frac{\sqrt{3}}{2} \approx 1 - \frac{1}{8} - \frac{1}{128} \approx \frac{111}{128}$

$\frac{\sqrt{3}}{2} \approx \frac{111}{128}$

$\sqrt{3} \approx \frac{111}{64}$

The approximately equals sign is used now because the series is only approximate to the expansion as only the first three terms are used.

③ (a) Expand $\frac{(1+3x)^{\frac{1}{3}}}{(1+2x)^2}$ in ascending powers of x up to and including the term in x^2. State the range of values of x for which your expansion is valid.

(b) Use your expansion to find an approximate non-zero value of x satisfying the equation

$\frac{(1+3x)^{\frac{1}{3}}}{(1+2x)^2} = 1 - 4x - 2x^2.$

Answer

③ (a) $\frac{(1+3x)^{\frac{1}{3}}}{(1+2x)^2} = (1+3x)^{\frac{1}{3}}(1+2x)^{-2}$

$$= \left[1 + \left(\frac{1}{3}\right)(3x) + \frac{\left(\frac{1}{3}\right)\left(-\frac{2}{3}\right)(3x)^2}{1.2} + \ldots\right] \times \left[1 + (-2)(2x) + \frac{(-2)(-3)(2x)^2}{1.2} + \ldots\right]$$

$= [1 + x - x^2 + \ldots][1 - 4x + 12x^2 + \ldots]$

$= 1 - 4x + 12x^2 + x - 4x^2 - x^2 + \ldots$

$= 1 - 3x + 7x^2 + \ldots$

The expansion is valid for $|3x| < 1$ and $|2x| < 1$, i.e. valid for $|x| < \frac{1}{3}$.

(b) Then replacing $\frac{(1+3x)^{\frac{1}{3}}}{(1+2x)^2}$ by $1 - 3x + 7x^2$

we have $1 - 3x + 7x^2 \approx 1 - 4x - 2x^2$

so that $9x^2 = -x$

$x(9x + 1) = 0$

Hence $x = 0$ or $x = -\frac{1}{9}$.

The required approximate non-zero value is $x = -\frac{1}{9}$ or -0.111 correct to 3 decimal places.

Partial fractions

Suppose we want to combine two algebraic fractions to form a single fraction. The following method can be used:

$$\frac{3}{x+3}+\frac{2}{x-1}\equiv\frac{3(x-1)+2(x+3)}{(x+3)(x-1)}\equiv\frac{3x-3+2x+6}{(x+3)(x-1)}\equiv\frac{5x+3}{(x+3)(x-1)}$$

The additional line in the equality indicates an identity, i.e. a result true for all values of x.

If, however, we want to do the reverse and write $\frac{5x+3}{(x+3)(x-1)}$ as two separate fractions then we are said to be expressing the single fraction in terms of partial fractions.

It is obvious what the denominators of the partial fractions will be, but we will need to call the numerators A and B until their values can be determined.

Hence $\frac{5x+3}{(x+3)(x-1)}\equiv\frac{A}{x+3}+\frac{B}{x-1}$

Values of x are chosen so that the contents of one of the brackets become zero.

By letting $x = 1$ means that the first bracket becomes zero and means that the letter A is eliminated. When $x = -3$, the second bracket becomes zero eliminating B in the process.

Multiplying both sides by $(x + 3)(x - 1)$ gives

$5x + 3 \equiv A(x - 1) + B(x + 3)$

Let $x = 1$, so $8 = 4B$ giving $B = 2$

Let $x = -3$, so $-12 = -4A$ giving $A = 3$

Hence the given fraction expressed in partial fractions is $\frac{3}{x+3}+\frac{2}{x-1}$

Partial fractions where there is a repeated factor in the denominator

Suppose you have to write the fraction $\frac{4x+1}{(x+1)^2(x-2)}$ in terms of partial fractions.

There is a repeated linear factor in the denominator (i.e. $(x + 1)^2$). The repeated linear factor means one of the denominators will be $(x + 1)^2$ and another will be $(x + 1)$. There will also be a third partial fraction with denominator $(x - 2)$.

Hence the original expression can be expressed in terms of its partial fractions like this:

$$\frac{4x+1}{(x+1)^2(x-2)}\equiv\frac{A}{(x+1)^2}+\frac{B}{x+1}+\frac{C}{x-2}$$

If the denominator is multiplied out, the highest power of x is 3. This is the same as the required number of constants.

Now multiply through by the denominator of the left-hand side. This will remove the fractions.

$4x + 1 \equiv A(x - 2) + B(x + 1)(x - 2) + C(x + 1)^2$

Let $x = 2$, so $4(2) + 1 = A(2 - 2) + B(2 + 1)(2 - 2) + C(2 + 1)^2$

$9 = 9C$

$C = 1$

Let $x = -1$, so $-3 = -3A$, giving $A = 1$.

Let $x = 0$, so $1 = -2A - 2B + C$

Now as $A = 1$ and $C = 1$, substituting these values into the above equation gives

$1 = -2 - 2B + 1$

Hence, $B = -1$

Alternatively, equate coefficients of x^2.

$0 = B + C$

so $B = -C = -1$

It is a good idea to check the partial fractions by putting a number in for x on both sides of the equation and checking to see if the right-hand side of the equation equals the left-hand side of the equation.

$$\frac{4x+1}{(x+1)^2(x-2)} = \frac{1}{(x+1)^2} - \frac{1}{x+1} + \frac{1}{x-2}$$

Do not let x equal a value that would make one of the denominators zero.

Let $x = 1$, so LHS $= -\frac{5}{4}$ and RHS $= \frac{1}{4} - \frac{1}{2} - 1 = -\frac{5}{4}$

LHS = RHS

Hence the partial fractions are $\frac{1}{(x+1)^2} - \frac{1}{x+1} + \frac{1}{x-2}$

Grade boost

Always perform checks like this as it is easy to make a mistake and often the mistake would lead to further problems later on in the question.

Examples

① Express $\frac{7x^2 - 2x - 3}{x^2(x-1)}$ in terms of partial fractions.

Answer

① $\frac{7x^2 - 2x - 3}{x^2(x-1)} \equiv \frac{A}{x^2} + \frac{B}{x} + \frac{C}{(x-1)}$

$7x^2 - 2x - 3 \equiv A(x-1) + Bx(x-1) + Cx^2$

Notice that x^2 in the denominator of the original fraction is a repeated linear factor.

Let $x = 1$, so $C = 2$

Let $x = 0$, so $A = 3$

Let $x = 2$, so $B = 5$

Alternatively, equate coefficients of x^2.

$7 = B + C$

So $B = 7 - C = 5$

$$\frac{7x^2 - 2x - 3}{x^2(x-1)} = \frac{3}{x^2} + \frac{5}{x} + \frac{2}{(x-1)}$$

Check using $x = 3$: LHS $= \frac{7(3)^2 - 2(3) - 3}{(3)^2(3-1)} = 3$

RHS $= \frac{3}{3^2} + \frac{5}{3} + \frac{2}{(3-1)} = 3$

Hence, partial fractions are $\frac{3}{x^2} + \frac{5}{x} + \frac{2}{(x-1)}$

Partial fractions are often only one part of a question so it is important to spend the time checking them. Any value of x, other than those used already can be used for the check.

② The function f is defined by

$$f(x) = \frac{8 - x - x^2}{x(x-2)^2}$$

(a) Express $f(x)$ in terms of partial fractions. [4]

(b) Use your results to part (a) to find the value of $f'(1)$. [3]

(WJEC C4 June 2010 Q1)

Answer

② (a) $\dfrac{8 - x - x^2}{x(x-2)^2} \equiv \dfrac{A}{x} + \dfrac{B}{(x-2)^2} + \dfrac{C}{x-2}$

The $(x - 2)^2$ is a repeated linear factor.

$8 - x - x^2 \equiv A(x - 2)^2 + Bx + Cx(x - 2)$

Multiply both sides by $x(x - 2)^2$

Let $x = 2$, $2 = 2B$ so $B = 1$

$x = 2$ means two of the brackets will equal zero.

Let $x = 0$, $8 = 4A$ so $A = 2$

Let $x = 3$, $-4 = A + 3B + 3C$ so $C = -3$

Substitute the values already obtained for A and B to find C or equate coefficients of x^2.

Hence $\dfrac{8 - x - x^2}{x(x-2)^2} = \dfrac{2}{x} + \dfrac{1}{(x-2)^2} - \dfrac{3}{x-2}$

Check using $x = 1$: LHS = 6 RHS = 6

Substituting a value such as $x = 1$ into both sides of the equation acts as a check on the values of A, B and C. If the left-hand side equals the right-hand side, then there is a good chance the values are correct.

(b) $f(x) = \dfrac{2}{x} + \dfrac{1}{(x-2)^2} - \dfrac{3}{x-2}$

Express the fractions in index form to enable differentiation.

$f(x) = 2x^{-1} + (x - 2)^{-2} - 3(x - 2)^{-1}$

$f'(x) = -2x^{-2} - 2(x - 2)^{-3} + 3(x - 2)^{-2}$

The Chain rule is used to differentiate the last two terms.

$f'(x) = -\dfrac{2}{x^2} - \dfrac{2}{(x-2)^3} + \dfrac{3}{(x-2)^2}$

Change back to algebraic fractions from index form to make it easy for numbers to be substituted in for x.

$f'(1) = -\dfrac{2}{1^2} - \dfrac{2}{(1-2)^3} + \dfrac{3}{(1-2)^2} = -2 + 2 + 3 = 3$

Examination style questions

① Express $\frac{5x^2-8x-1}{(x-1)^2(x-2)}$ in terms of partial fractions. [3]

Answer

① Let $\frac{5x^2-8x-1}{(x-1)^2(x-2)} \equiv \frac{A}{(x-1)^2} + \frac{B}{(x-1)} + \frac{C}{x-2}$

$5x^2 - 8x - 1 \equiv A(x-2) + B(x-1)(x-2) + C(x-1)^2$

Let $x = 2$, so $C = 3$

Let $x = 1$, so $A = 4$

Let $x = 0$, so $-1 = -2A + 2B + C$ giving $B = 2$

> Alternatively, equate coefficients of x^2.
> $5 = B + C$
> So $B = 5 - C = 2$

Hence $\frac{5x^2-8x-1}{(x-1)^2(x-2)} = \frac{4}{(x-1)^2} + \frac{2}{(x-1)} + \frac{3}{x-2}$

Checking by letting $x = 3$

$$\text{LHS} = \frac{5(3)^2-8(3)-1}{(3-1)^2(3-2)} = 5$$

$$\text{RHS} = \frac{4}{(3-1)^2} + \frac{2}{(3-1)} + \frac{3}{3-2} = 1+1+3 = 5$$

Hence LHS = RHS

Partial fractions are $\frac{4}{(x-1)^2} + \frac{2}{(x-1)} + \frac{3}{x-2}$

② (a) Expand $(4-x)^{\frac{3}{2}}$ as far as the term in x^2. [2]

(b) Use your result in part (a) to expand $\frac{(4-x)^{\frac{3}{2}}}{(1+2x)}$ as far as the term in x^2.

State the range of values of x for which the expansion is valid. [4]

Answer

② (a)

$$(4-x)^{\frac{3}{2}} = \left[4\left(1-\frac{x}{4}\right)\right]^{\frac{3}{2}} = 4^{\frac{3}{2}} \times \left(1-\frac{x}{4}\right)^{\frac{3}{2}} = 8\left(1-\frac{x}{4}\right)^{\frac{3}{2}}$$

> Note that $4^{\frac{3}{2}} = \sqrt{4^3} = 8$

Using the formula for the binomial expansion:

$$(1+x)^n = 1 + nx + \frac{n(n-1)x^2}{2!} + \frac{n(n-1)(n-2)x^3}{3!} + \ldots$$

> This is obtained from the formula booklet.

$$8\left(1-\frac{x}{4}\right)^{\frac{3}{2}}=8\left[1+\left(\frac{3}{2}\right)\left(-\frac{x}{4}\right)+\frac{\left(\frac{3}{2}\right)\left(\frac{1}{2}\right)\left(-\frac{x}{4}\right)^{2}}{2!}+\ldots\right]$$

$$=8\left[1-\frac{3x}{8}+\frac{3x^{2}}{128}+\ldots\right]$$

$$=8-3x+\frac{3x^{2}}{16}+\cdots$$

(b) $(1+2x)^{-1}=1+(-1)(2x)+\frac{(-1)(-2)(2x)^{2}}{2!}+\ldots$

$$=1-2x+4x^{2}+\ldots$$

Note when multiplying out the bracket only terms up to and including x^2 are included.

Hence $\frac{(4-x)^{\frac{3}{2}}}{(1+2x)}=\left(1-2x+4x^{2}+\ldots\right)\left(8-3x+\frac{3x^{2}}{16}+\ldots\right)$

$$=8-3x+\frac{3x^{2}}{16}-16x+6x^{2}+32x^{2}+\ldots$$

$$=8-19x+\frac{611}{4}x^{2}+\ldots$$

$\left(1-\frac{x}{4}\right)^{\frac{3}{2}}$ is valid for $\left|\frac{x}{4}\right|<1$ so $|x|<4$ or $-4<x<4$

$(1+2x)^{-1}$ is valid for $|2x|<1$ so $|x|<\frac{1}{2}$ or $-\frac{1}{2}<x<\frac{1}{2}$

Hence $\frac{(4-x)^{\frac{3}{2}}}{(1+2x)}$ is valid for $|x|<\frac{1}{2}$ or $-\frac{1}{2}<x<\frac{1}{2}$

Notice that the second range is inside the first range and as x has to be valid for both the expansions, the expansions are valid for $|x|<\frac{1}{2}$ or $-\frac{1}{2}<x<\frac{1}{2}$

Test yourself

Answer the following questions and check your answers before moving on to the next topic.

① Express $\dfrac{6x^2+11x+14}{x(x+1)^2}$ in terms of partial fractions.

② Expand $\dfrac{1+x}{\sqrt{1-4x}}$ in ascending powers of x up to and including the term in x^2. State the range of x for which the expansion is valid.

③ (a) Express $\dfrac{5x^2+6x+7}{(x-1)(x+2)^2}$ in partial fractions.

(b) Find $\displaystyle\int\frac{5x^2+6x+7}{(x-1)(x+2)^2}\,dx$

(Note: answers to Test yourself are found at the back of the book.)

1 Expand $(1+4x)^{\frac{1}{2}}$ in ascending powers of x as far as the term in x^2.

State the range of values of x for which your expansion is valid.

Expand $\left(1+4k+16k^2\right)^{\frac{1}{2}}$ in ascending powers of k as far as the term in k^2.

[6]

(WJEC C4 June 2009 Q9)

Answer

1 $$(1+x)^n = 1+nx+\frac{n(n-1)x^2}{2!}+\ldots$$

Here $n=\frac{1}{2}$ and x is replaced by $4x$.

$$(1+4x)^{\frac{1}{2}} = 1+\left(\frac{1}{2}\right)(4x)+\frac{\left(\frac{1}{2}\right)\left(-\frac{1}{2}\right)16x^2}{1\times 2}+\ldots$$

$$= 1+2x-2x^2+\ldots$$

Expansion is valid when $|4x|<1$, $|x|<\frac{1}{4}$ or $-\frac{1}{4}<x<\frac{1}{4}$

$$\left(1+4k+16k^2\right)^{\frac{1}{2}} = \left(1+4\left(k+4k^2\right)\right)^{\frac{1}{2}}$$

$$(1+4x)^{\frac{1}{2}} = 1+2x-2x^2+\ldots$$

Let $x=(k+4k^2)$

Grade boost

Look back at the previous result to see how it can be altered to fit the next part of the question.

So $$\left(1+4\left(k+4k^2\right)\right)^{\frac{1}{2}} = 1+2\left(k+4k^2\right)-2\left(k+4k^2\right)^2+\ldots$$

$$= 1+2k+8k^2-2k^2+\ldots$$

$$= 1+2k+6k^2+\ldots$$

Note here that this last bracket only needs expanding as far as the term in k^2.

2 Expand $(1+2x)^{\frac{1}{2}}$ in ascending powers of x up to and including the term in x^3.

State the range of values of x for which the expansion is valid.

Hence, calculate $\sqrt{1.02}$ correct to six decimal places. [5]

Answer

2 $$(1+2x)^{\frac{1}{2}} = 1+\left(\frac{1}{2}\right)(2x)+\frac{\left(\frac{1}{2}\right)\left(-\frac{1}{2}\right)(2x)^2}{2!}+\frac{\left(\frac{1}{2}\right)\left(-\frac{1}{2}\right)\left(-\frac{3}{2}\right)(2x)^3}{3!}+\ldots$$

$$= 1+x-\frac{x^2}{2}+\frac{x^3}{2}+\ldots$$

so this expansion is convergent for $|x| < \frac{1}{2}$ or $-\frac{1}{2} < x < \frac{1}{2}$

If $x = 0.01$, $\left(1+2(0.01)\right)^{\frac{1}{2}} = (1.02)^{\frac{1}{2}} = \sqrt{1.02} \approx 1+0.01-\frac{(0.01)^2}{2}+\frac{(0.01)^3}{2}$

≈ 1.0099505

≈ 1.009951 (correct to six decimal places)

3 Given that

$$f(x) = \frac{3x}{(1+x)^2(2+x)}$$

(a) express $f(x)$ in terms of partial fractions. [4]

(b) evaluate

$$\int_0^1 f(x)\,\mathrm{d}x,$$

Giving your answer correct to three decimal places. [4]

(WJEC C4 June 2009 Q1)

Answer

3 (a) $$\frac{3x}{(1+x)^2(2+x)} \equiv \frac{A}{(1+x)^2}+\frac{B}{1+x}+\frac{C}{2+x}$$

$$3x \equiv A(2+x)+B(1+x)(2+x)+C(1+x)^2$$

Let $x = -2$ so $C = -6$

Let $x = -1$ so $A = -3$

Equating coefficients of x^2, $\quad 0 = B + C, \quad 0 = B - 6, \quad B = 6$

Hence $f(x) = -\dfrac{3}{(1+x)^2} + \dfrac{6}{1+x} - \dfrac{6}{2+x}$

(b) $\displaystyle\int_0^1 f(x)\,\mathrm{d}x = \int_0^1 \left(-\frac{3}{(1+x)^2} + \frac{6}{1+x} - \frac{6}{2+x}\right)\mathrm{d}x$

$$= \int_0^1 \left(-3(1+x)^{-2} + \frac{6}{1+x} - \frac{6}{2+x}\right)\mathrm{d}x$$

$$= \left[3(1+x)^{-1} + 6\ln(1+x) - 6\ln(2+x)\right]_1^0$$

$$= \left[\frac{3}{1+x} + 6\ln(1+x) - 6\ln(2+x)\right]_0^1$$

$$= \left[\left(\frac{3}{2} + 6\ln 2 - 6\ln 3\right) - (3 + 6\ln 1 - 6\ln 2)\right]$$

$= 0.226$ (correct to three decimal places)

Topic 2 Trigonometry

This topic covers the following:

- Knowledge and use of $\sin(A \pm B)$, $\cos(A \pm B)$ and $\tan(A \pm B)$
- Expressions for $a \cos \theta + b \sin \theta$ in the equivalent forms $R \cos(\theta \pm \alpha)$ or $R \sin(\theta \pm \alpha)$

Knowledge and use of sin(*A* ± *B*), cos(*A* ± *B*) and tan(*A* ± *B*)

There are a number of trigonometric identities which are used when solving trigonometric equations or integrating a trigonometric function.

Trigonometric identities

$\sin(A \pm B) = \sin A \cos B \pm \cos A \sin B$

$\cos(A \pm B) = \cos A \cos B \mp \sin A \sin B$

$\tan(A \pm B) = \dfrac{\tan A \pm \tan B}{1 \mp \tan A \tan B}$

These are all given in the formula booklet and can be looked up.

Double angle formulae

$\sin 2A = 2 \sin A \cos A$

$\cos 2A = \cos^2 A - \sin^2 A$

$= 1 - 2 \sin^2 A$

$= 2 \cos^2 A - 1$

$\tan 2A = \dfrac{2 \tan A}{1 - \tan^2 A}$

Although it is useful to remember these results, they can be obtained from the trigonometric identities above given in the formula booklet. For example, $\sin 2A = 2 \sin A \cos A$ can be obtained by expanding $\sin(A + A)$.

Important rearrangements

Here are some important rearrangements of the above formulae. These are useful for proving some identities and also when integrating expressions.

$\sin^2 A = \dfrac{1}{2}(1 - \cos 2A)$

$\cos^2 A = \dfrac{1}{2}(1 + \cos 2A)$

These rearrangements are obtained by combining the double angle formulae with the identity

$\sin^2 A + \cos^2 A = 1.$

Here is an example of how one of these rearrangements can be used:

Suppose you have to find $\int (2 + \cos^2 \theta)\, d\theta$

Change from $\cos^2 \theta$ to $\frac{1 + \cos 2\theta}{2}$ because it is easier to integrate $\cos 2\theta$ compared to $\cos^2 \theta$.

$$\int (2+\cos^2\theta)\, d\theta = \int \left(2 + \frac{1}{2}(1+\cos 2\theta)\right) d\theta$$

$$= \frac{1}{2}\int (5+\cos 2\theta)\, d\theta$$

$$= \frac{1}{2}\left(5\theta + \frac{1}{2}\sin 2\theta\right) + c$$

Examples

① Showing all your working, find the values of θ in the range $0° \le \theta \le 360°$ satisfying the equation

$\cos 2\theta = \sin \theta$

Change $\cos 2\theta$ to $1 - 2\sin^2\theta$ so that the equation becomes an equation just involving sin.

Answer

$1 - 2\sin^2\theta = \sin\theta$

$2\sin^2\theta + \sin\theta - 1 = 0$

Notice that this is a quadratic equation in $\sin\theta$ that can be factorised and hence solved.

$(2\sin\theta - 1)(\sin\theta + 1) = 0$

Hence $\sin\theta = \frac{1}{2}, -1$

Grade boost

Always check that you only include the solutions in the range specified in the question.

When $\sin\theta = \frac{1}{2}$, $\theta = 30°, 150°$

Use the graphical or CAST method to find the angles in the required range.

When $\sin\theta = -1$, $\theta = 270°$

② Given that $2\cos 2\theta + 3\sin\theta = 3$, show that

$4\sin^2\theta - 3\sin\theta + 1 = 0$

Answer

② $2\cos 2\theta + 3\sin\theta = 3$

Notice the double angle here. Use $\cos 2\theta = 1 - 2\sin^2\theta$. The reason this identity is used rather than one of the others for $\cos 2\theta$ is that we can create a quadratic equation in $\sin\theta$.

$2(1 - 2\sin^2\theta) + 3\sin\theta = 3$

$2 - 4\sin^2\theta + 3\sin\theta = 3$

$4\sin^2\theta - 3\sin\theta + 1 = 0$

③ (a) Prove the identity $\cos 3\theta = 4\cos^3\theta - 3\cos\theta$.

(b) Solve the equation

$\cos 3\theta + \cos^2\theta = 0,$

finding the values of θ in the range $0° \le \theta \le 360°$.

Answer

③ (a) $\cos 3\theta = \cos(2\theta + \theta)$

$= \cos 2\theta \cos \theta - \sin 2\theta \sin \theta$

$= (2\cos^2\theta - 1)\cos \theta - 2\sin \theta \cos \theta \sin \theta$

$= (2\cos^2\theta - 1)\cos \theta - 2\sin^2\theta \cos \theta$

$= (2\cos^2\theta - 1)\cos \theta - 2(1 - \cos^2\theta)\cos \theta$

$= 4\cos^3\theta - 3\cos \theta$

Here the identity $\cos(A + B) = \cos A \cos B - \sin A \sin B$ is used.

(b) $\cos 3\theta + \cos^2\theta = 0$

$4\cos^3\theta - 3\cos \theta + \cos^2\theta = 0$

$\cos \theta\,(4\cos^2\theta + \cos \theta - 3) = 0$

$\cos \theta = 0$ or $4\cos^2\theta + \cos \theta - 3 = 0$

$\cos \theta = 0$ or $(4\cos \theta - 3)(\cos \theta + 1) = 0$

$\cos \theta = 0$ or $\cos \theta = \frac{3}{4}$, $\cos \theta = -1$

$\theta = 90°, 270°, 41.4°, 318.6°, 180°$

④ Prove the identity $\frac{1-\cos 2\theta}{\sin 2\theta} = \tan\theta$

Answer

④ $\frac{1-\cos 2\theta}{\sin 2\theta} = \frac{1-\cos 2\theta}{2\sin\theta\cos\theta}$

Use the double angle formula to remove the double angles.

$= \frac{1-(1-2\sin^2\theta)}{2\sin\theta\cos\theta}$

$= \frac{2\sin^2\theta}{2\sin\theta\cos\theta}$

Divide the numerator and denominator by $2\sin\theta$.

$= \frac{\sin\theta}{\cos\theta}$

$= \tan\theta$

⑤ Find $\int \cos^2 x\,dx$

Answer

⑤ $\int \cos^2 x\,dx = \int \frac{\cos 2x + 1}{2}dx$

Express $\cos^2 x$ in terms of the double angle $\cos 2x$ using a double angle formula.

$= \frac{1}{2}\int(\cos 2x + 1)dx$

It is usually best to take any constant terms outside the integral sign before integrating as it makes the integration easier.

$= \frac{1}{2}\left(\frac{1}{2}\sin 2x + x\right) + c$

$= \frac{1}{4}\sin 2x + \frac{x}{2} + c$

⑥ Show that $\int_0^{\frac{\pi}{2}} \sin^2 \theta \, d\theta = \frac{\pi}{4}$

Answer

⑥ $\int_0^{\frac{\pi}{2}} \sin^2 \theta \, d\theta = \int_0^{\frac{\pi}{2}} \frac{1 - \cos 2\theta}{2} d\theta$

$= \frac{1}{2}\int_0^{\frac{\pi}{2}} 1 - \cos 2\theta \, d\theta$

$= \frac{1}{2}\left[\theta - \frac{\sin 2\theta}{2}\right]_0^{\frac{\pi}{2}}$

$= \frac{1}{2}\left[\left(\frac{\pi}{2} - \frac{1}{2}\sin \pi\right) - \left(0 - \frac{1}{2}\sin 0\right)\right]_0^{\frac{\pi}{2}}$

$= \frac{1}{2}\left[\left(\frac{\pi}{2} - 0\right) - (0 - 0)\right]$

$= \frac{\pi}{4}$

Expressions for $a \cos \theta + b \sin \theta$ in the equivalent forms $R \cos(\theta \pm \alpha)$ or $R \sin(\theta \pm \alpha)$

Expressions in the form $a \cos \theta + b \sin \theta$ can be expressed in the alternative forms $R \cos(\theta \pm \alpha)$ or $R \sin(\theta \pm \alpha)$.

To express $4 \cos \theta + 2 \sin \theta$ in the form $R \cos(\theta - \alpha)$ take the following steps.

$4 \cos \theta + 2 \sin \theta \equiv R \cos(\theta - \alpha)$

Use the trig identity $\cos(A - B) = \cos A \cos B + \sin A \sin B$

$4 \cos \theta + 2 \sin \theta \equiv R \cos \theta \cos \alpha + R \sin \theta \sin \alpha$

The relationship is an identity, i.e. true for all values of θ. Hence we use $\equiv$ instead of $=$.

As the coefficients of $\cos \theta$ must be the same on both sides, so

$R \cos \alpha = 4$

Similarly the coefficients of $\sin \theta$ is the same on both sides, so

$R \sin \alpha = 2$

Dividing these two equations gives $\frac{R \sin \alpha}{R \cos \alpha} = \tan \alpha = \frac{1}{2}$

$\alpha = \tan^{-1}\frac{1}{2} = 26.6°$

$R^2 \sin^2 \alpha + R^2 \cos^2 \alpha = 2^2 + 4^2$

$R^2(\sin^2 \alpha + \cos^2 \alpha) = 2^2 + 4^2$

Remember that $\sin^2 \alpha + \cos^2 \alpha = 1$

$R^2 = 2^2 + 4^2$

$R = \sqrt{2^2 + 4^2} = \sqrt{20}$

The two values R and α have been found so

$4 \cos\theta + 2 \sin\theta = \sqrt{20}\cos(\theta - 26.6°)$

Finding the greatest and least values of a trigonometric function

The greatest or least value of $\sin\theta$ or $\cos\theta$ is 1 or −1 respectively.

For the expression $5\cos\theta$ the greatest and least values would be 5 and −5 respectively.

For the expression $5\cos(\theta - 30°)$ the greatest and least values would be 5 and −5 respectively.

Examples

① Find the greatest and least values of $\frac{1}{6+5\sin(x+30°)}$.

Answer

① $5\sin(x + 30°)$ has greatest and least values of 5 and −5.

Least value of $\frac{1}{6+5\sin(x+30°)}$ would be $\frac{1}{6+5} = \frac{1}{11}$

Notice the least value occurs when the denominator is largest and the greatest value occurs when the denominator is least.

Greatest value of $\frac{1}{6+5\sin(x+30°)}$ would be $\frac{1}{6-5} = 1$

② Given that $5\cos x + 12\sin x = 13\cos(x - 67.4°)$, find the greatest and least values of $5\cos x + 12\sin x$ and write down a value for x for which the least value occurs.

Answer

② $5\cos x - 12\sin x = 13\cos(x - 67.4°)$,

The greatest and least values of $\cos(x - 67.4°)$ are 1 and −1.

Hence greatest value of $5\cos x + 12\sin x = 13 \times 1 = 13$

Least value of $5\cos x + 12\sin x = 13 \times -1 = -13$

Least value occurs when $\cos(x - 67.4°) = -1$

Now $\cos 180° = -1$

Other possible values are 540°, 900°, etc.

Hence $x - 67.4° = 180°$

So $x = 247.4°$

③ If $\sqrt{3}\cos\theta+\sin\theta=2\cos(\theta-30^\circ)$, find the greatest and least values of

$$\frac{1}{\sqrt{3}\cos\theta+\sin\theta-3}$$

Write down a value of θ for which the greatest value occurs.

Answer

③ $$\frac{1}{\sqrt{3}\cos\theta+\sin\theta-3}=\frac{1}{2\cos(\theta-30^\circ)-3}$$

The maximum and minimum values of $\cos(\theta-30^\circ)$ are 1 and -1 respectively.

Hence minimum value of $\frac{1}{\sqrt{3}\cos\theta+\sin\theta-3}$ is $\frac{1}{2-3}=-1$

Maximum value of $\frac{1}{\sqrt{3}\cos\theta+\sin\theta-3}$ is $\frac{1}{-2-3}=-\frac{1}{5}$

For the maximum value of $\frac{1}{\sqrt{3}\cos\theta+\sin\theta-3}$,

where $\cos(\theta-30^\circ)=-1$

so $\theta-30^\circ=180^\circ$

and $\theta=210^\circ$

④ If $\sin\theta+\sqrt{3}\cos\theta=2\sin(\theta+60^\circ)$, find the greatest and least values of

$$\frac{1}{\sin\theta+\sqrt{3}\cos\theta+5}$$

Answer

④ $$\frac{1}{\sin\theta+\sqrt{3}\cos\theta+5}=\frac{1}{2\sin(\theta+60^\circ)+5}$$

The maximum and minimum values of $\sin(\theta+60^\circ)$ are 1 and -1 respectively.

Hence minimum value of $\frac{1}{\sin\theta+\sqrt{3}\cos\theta+5}$ is $\frac{1}{2+5}=\frac{1}{7}$

And maximum value of $\frac{1}{\sin\theta+\sqrt{3}\cos\theta+5}$ is $\frac{1}{-2+5}=\frac{1}{3}$

⑤ (a) Express $3\cos\theta+4\sin\theta$ in the form $R\cos(\theta-\alpha)$, where R and α are constants with $R>0$ and $0^\circ<\alpha<90^\circ$. [3]

(b) Use your results to part (a) to find the least value of

$$\frac{1}{3\cos\theta+4\sin\theta+10}.$$

Write down a value for θ for which this least value occurs. [4]

Answer

⑤ (a) $3\cos\theta+4\sin\theta=R\cos(\theta-\alpha)$

$=R\cos\theta\cos\alpha+R\sin\theta\sin\alpha$

$R\cos\alpha=3$ and $R\sin\alpha=4$

$$\frac{R\sin\alpha}{R\cos\alpha} = \tan\alpha = \frac{4}{3}$$

$\tan\alpha = \frac{4}{3}$ so $\alpha = 53.1°$

Only the positive value for R is used here because $R > 0$ is stated in the question.

$R = \sqrt{3^2 + 4^2} = \sqrt{25} = 5$

Hence $3\cos\theta + 4\sin\theta = 5\cos(\theta - 53.1°)$

(b) $\dfrac{1}{3\cos\theta + 4\sin\theta + 10} = \dfrac{1}{5\cos(\theta - 53.1°) + 10}$

The least value occurs when the denominator is greatest. The greatest value of the cos function is +1.

Hence least value is $\dfrac{1}{5+10} = \dfrac{1}{15}$

This value occurs when $\cos(\theta - 53.1°) = 1$

$\cos^{-1} 1 = 0°$

Hence $\theta - 53.1° = 0$

So $\theta = 53.1°$

⑥ (a) Express $\cos\theta + \sqrt{3}\sin\theta$ in the form $R\sin(\theta + \alpha)$, where $R > 0$, where $R > 0$ and $0° < \alpha < 90°$.

(b) Find all the values of θ in the range $0° \leq \theta \leq 360°$ satisfying the equation

$\cos\theta + \sqrt{3}\sin\theta = 1$

Answer

⑥ (a) $\cos\theta + \sqrt{3}\sin\theta \equiv R\sin(\theta + \alpha)$

$\cos\theta + \sqrt{3}\sin\theta \equiv R\sin\theta\cos\alpha + R\cos\theta\sin\alpha$

$R\sin\alpha = 1$, $R\cos\alpha = \sqrt{3}$

$\therefore \tan\alpha = \dfrac{1}{\sqrt{3}}$ so $\alpha = 30°$

$R = \sqrt{1+3} = 2$

Hence, $\cos\theta + \sqrt{3}\sin\theta \equiv 2\sin(\theta + 30°)$

(b) $\cos\theta + \sqrt{3}\sin\theta = 1$

$2\sin(\theta + 30°) = 1$

$\sin(\theta + 30°) = \dfrac{1}{2}$

$\theta + 30° = 30°, 150°, 390°$

$\theta = 0°, 120°, 360°$

Examination style questions

① Showing all your working, find the values of θ in the range $0° \leq \theta \leq 360°$ satisfying the equation

$\sin 2\theta = \sin \theta$ [4]

Answer

① $\sin 2\theta = \sin \theta$

> Use the double angle formula
> $\sin 2A = 2 \sin A \cos A$

$2 \sin \theta \cos \theta = \sin \theta$

$2 \sin \theta \cos \theta - \sin \theta = 0$

> Do not divide through by $\sin \theta$ or you will lose one of the solutions. Instead take $\sin \theta$ out of the brackets as a factor.

$\sin \theta(2 \cos \theta - 1) = 0$

Hence either $\sin \theta = 0$ or $\cos \theta = \frac{1}{2}$

When $\sin \theta = 0$, $\theta = 0°, 180°, 360°$

When $\cos \theta = \frac{1}{2}$, $\theta = 60°, 300°$

Hence $\theta = 0°, 60°, 180°, 300°, 360°$

② (a) Show that $3 \sin \theta - \cos 2\theta \equiv 2 \sin^2 \theta + 3 \sin \theta - 1$ for all values of θ. [2]

(b) Find the values of θ in the range $0° \leq \theta \leq 360°$ satisfying the equation

$3 \sin \theta - \cos 2\theta + 2 = 0$

Answer

> Use the double angle formula.
> $\cos 2A = \cos^2 A - \sin^2 A$. Note that this is not given directly in the formula booklet.

② (a) $3 \sin \theta - \cos 2\theta = 3 \sin \theta - (\cos^2 \theta - \sin^2 \theta)$

$= 3 \sin \theta - \cos^2 \theta + \sin^2 \theta$

$= 3 \sin \theta - (1 - \sin^2 \theta) + \sin^2 \theta$

> Use $\cos^2 \theta = 1 - \sin^2 \theta$

$= 2 \sin^2 \theta + 3 \sin \theta - 1$

(b) $3 \sin \theta - \cos 2\theta \equiv 2 \sin^2 \theta + 3 \sin \theta - 1$

$3 \sin \theta - \cos 2\theta + 2 = 2 \sin^2 \theta + 3 \sin \theta - 1 + 2$

$0 = 2 \sin^2 \theta + 3 \sin \theta + 1$

$(2 \sin \theta + 1)(\sin \theta + 1) = 0$

$\sin \theta = -\frac{1}{2}, -1$

$\theta = 210°, 330°, 270°$

③ (a) Express $3 \cos \theta + 4 \sin \theta$ in the form $R \cos(\theta - \alpha)$, where $R > 0$ and $0° < \alpha < 90°$ [3]

(b) Use your results to part (a) to find the least value of

$$\frac{1}{3 \cos \theta + 4 \sin \theta + 7}.$$

Write down a value for θ for which this least value occurs. [2]

Answer

③ (a) $3 \cos \theta + 4 \sin \theta \equiv R \cos(\theta - \alpha)$

$3 \cos \theta + 4 \sin \theta \equiv R \cos \theta \cos \alpha + R \sin \theta \sin \alpha$

Hence $R \cos \alpha = 3$ and $R \sin \alpha = 4$

$\frac{R \sin \alpha}{R \cos \alpha} = \tan \alpha = \frac{4}{3}$

$\tan \alpha = \frac{4}{3}$ so $\alpha = 53.1°$

$R = \sqrt{3^2 + 4^2} = \sqrt{25} = 5$

Only the positive value of $\sqrt{25}$ is used because $R > 0$.

Hence $3 \cos \theta + 4 \sin \theta = 5 \cos(\theta - 53.1°)$

(b) $\frac{1}{3 \cos \theta + 4 \sin \theta + 7} = \frac{1}{5 \cos(\theta - 53.1°) + 7}$

The greatest value of $\cos(\theta - 53.1°)$ is 1.

So least value of $\frac{1}{3 \cos \theta + 4 \sin \theta + 7}$ is $\frac{1}{5+7} = \frac{1}{12}$

This occurs when

$\cos(\theta - 53.1°) = 1$

So $\theta - 53.1° = 0$

or $\theta = 53.1°$

Other values of θ are possible.

Test yourself

Answer the following questions and check your answers before moving on to the next topic.

① (a) Express $3 \cos \theta + 2 \sin \theta$ in the form $R \cos(\theta - \alpha)$, where $R > 0$ and $0° < \alpha < 90°$.

(b) Find all the values of θ in the range $0° < \theta < 360°$ satisfying

$$3 \cos \theta + 2 \sin \theta = 1$$

② Showing all your working, find the values of θ in the range $0° \leq \theta \leq 360°$ satisfying the equation

$$3 \cos 2\theta = 1 - \sin \theta$$

③ Showing all your working, find the values of θ between $0°$ and $360°$ satisfying

$$4 \sin \theta + 5 \cos \theta = 2$$

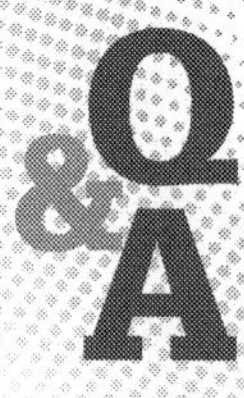

1 Find all the values of θ in the range $0° \leq \theta \leq 360°$ satisfying $3 \sin 2\theta = 2 \sin \theta$. [5]

(WJEC C4 June 2009 Q2)

Answer

1 $3 \sin 2\theta = 2 \sin \theta$

$3(2 \sin \theta \cos \theta) = 2 \sin \theta$

$6 \sin \theta \cos \theta - 2 \sin \theta = 0$

$3 \sin \theta \cos \theta - \sin \theta = 0$

$\sin \theta (3 \cos \theta - 1) = 0$

Hence either $\sin \theta = 0$ or $\cos \theta = \frac{1}{3}$

When $\sin \theta = 0$, $\theta = 0°, 180°, 360°$

When $\cos \theta = \frac{1}{3}$, $\theta = 70.5°, 289.5°$

Hence $\theta = 0°, 70.5°, 180°, 289.5°, 360°$

> Do not be tempted to divide both sides by $\sin \theta$ or $2 \sin \theta$ or you will lose one of your solutions.

> Make sure that you only find the angles in the specified range (i.e. $0° \leq \theta \leq 360°$).

2 (a) Express $\cos \theta + \sqrt{3} \sin \theta$ in the form $R \cos(\theta - \alpha)$, where $R > 0$ and $0° < \alpha < 90°$. [3]

(b) Find all the values of θ in the range $0° \leq \theta \leq 360°$ satisfying

$$\cos \theta + \sqrt{3} \sin \theta = 1$$ [4]

(WJEC C4 June 2009 Q3)

Answer

2 (a) $\cos\theta + \sqrt{3}\sin\theta \equiv R\cos(\theta - \alpha)$,

$\cos\theta + \sqrt{3}\sin\theta \equiv R\cos\theta\cos\alpha + R\sin\theta\sin\alpha$

$R \cos \alpha = 1$ and $R \sin \alpha = \sqrt{3}$

$\tan \alpha = \sqrt{3}$ so $\alpha = 60°$

$R = \sqrt{1+3} = 2$

Hence $\cos \theta + \sqrt{3} \sin \theta = 2 \cos(\theta - 60°)$

(b) $\cos\theta + \sqrt{3}\sin\theta = 1$

$2\cos(\theta - 60°) = 1$

$\cos(\theta - 60°) = \frac{1}{2}$

$\theta - 60 = -60°, 60°, 300°$

Hence $\theta = 0°, 120°, 360°$

> You need to be careful here. Although the $-60°$ is outside the range, the range applies to the final answer and adding the angle of $60°$ will make it $0°$ which will put it in the required range.

Q&A 3

3 (a) Find all the values of θ in the range $0° \leq \theta \leq 360°$ satisfying

$$2\cos 2\theta = 9\cos\theta + 7$$ [5]

(b)(i) Express $5\sin x - 12\cos x$ in the form $R\sin(x - \alpha)$, where R and α are constants with $R > 0$ and $0° < \alpha < 90°$.

(ii) Use your results to part (i) to find the least value of

$$\frac{1}{5\sin x - 12\cos x + 20}.$$

Write down a value for x for which this least value occurs. [6]

(WJEC C4 June 2010 Q3)

Answer

3 (a) $2\cos 2\theta = 9\cos\theta + 7$

$2(2\cos^2\theta - 1) = 9\cos\theta + 7$

$4\cos^2\theta - 2 = 9\cos\theta + 7$

$4\cos^2\theta - 9\cos\theta - 9 = 0$

$(4\cos\theta + 3)(\cos\theta - 3) = 0$

Hence $\cos\theta = -\frac{3}{4}$ or $\cos\theta = 3$ (This value is ignored as max value of a cos function is 1).

When $\cos\theta = -\frac{3}{4}$, $\theta = 138.59°, 221.41°$

> Use $\sin(A \pm B) = \sin A\cos B \pm \cos A\sin B$ obtained from the formula booklet.

(b)(i) $5\sin x - 12\cos x \equiv R\sin(x - \alpha)$

$5\sin x - 12\cos x \equiv R\sin x\cos\alpha - R\cos x\sin\alpha$

$R\cos\alpha = 5$ and $R\sin\alpha = 12$

So $\tan\alpha = \frac{12}{5}$ giving $\alpha = 67.38°$

$R = \sqrt{5^2 + 12^2} = \sqrt{169} = 13$

Hence $5\sin x - 12\cos x = 13\sin(x - 67.38°)$

(ii) $\frac{1}{5\sin x - 12\cos x + 20} = \frac{1}{13\sin(x - 67.38) + 20}$

For this expression to have its least value the denominator must have its largest value.

This would occur when $\sin(x - 67.38°) = 1$ in which case

$$\frac{1}{13\sin(x - 67.38) + 20} = \frac{1}{13 + 20} = \frac{1}{33}$$

Now $\sin(x - 67.38°) = 1$ so $x - 67.38 = 90°$ giving $x = 157.38°$

4	Find the values of A between 0° and 360° satisfying $\tan 2A = 3\tan A$

Answer

4

Use $\tan(A + B)$ formula in the formula booklet to consider $\tan(A + A)$

4 $\tan 2A = \frac{2\tan A}{1 - \tan^2 A}$

$\therefore \tan 2A = 3\tan A$

gives $\frac{2\tan A}{1 - \tan^2 A} = 3\tan A$

$\therefore 2\tan A = 3\tan A(1 - \tan^2 A)$

$\therefore 2\tan A = 3\tan A - 3\tan^3 A$

$\therefore 3\tan^3 A - \tan A = 0$

so $\tan A(3\tan^2 A - 1) = 0$

$\tan A = 0$ or $\tan A = \pm\frac{1}{\sqrt{3}}$

$A = 0°, 180°, 360°, 30°, 150°, 210°, 330°$

5 (a) Express $3\cos\theta - 4\sin\theta$ in the form $R\cos(\theta + \alpha)$ where $R > 0$ and $0° < \alpha\,°\, 90°$.

(b) Solve $3\cos\theta - 4\sin\theta = 2.5$ for values of θ between 0° and 360°.

Answer

5 (a) $3\cos\theta - 4\sin\theta \equiv R\cos(\theta + \alpha)$

$3\cos\theta - 4\sin\theta \equiv R\cos\theta\cos\alpha - R\sin\theta\sin\alpha$

$3 = R\cos\alpha,\ 4 = R\sin\alpha$

$\therefore \tan\alpha = \frac{4}{3},\ \alpha = 53.1°$ and $R = 5$

Hence $3\cos\theta - 4\sin\theta \equiv 5\cos(\theta + 53.1°)$

(b) $3\cos\theta - 4\sin\theta = 2.5$

$5\cos(\theta + 53.1°) = 2.5$

$\cos(\theta + 53.1°) = \frac{1}{2}$

$\therefore \theta + 53.1° = 60°, 300°, 420°$

So $\theta = 6.9°, 246.9°, 366.9°$ (Note the last value is out of range and is discarded)

Hence $\theta = 6.9°, 246.9°$

6 (a) Express $2\cos^2\theta + 6\sin\theta\cos\theta$ in the form $A + B\cos 2\theta + C\sin 2\theta$

(b) Solve the equation $2\cos^2\theta + 6\sin\theta\cos\theta = 2$ for values of θ between 0° and 180°.

Answer

6 (a) $2\cos^2\theta + 6\sin\theta\cos\theta = 2\left(\frac{1+\cos 2\theta}{2}\right) + 3(2\sin\theta\cos\theta)$

$= 1 + \cos 2\theta + 3\sin 2\theta$

(b) $2\cos^2\theta + 6\sin\theta\cos\theta = 2$

becomes $1 + \cos 2\theta + 3\sin 2\theta = 2$

$\therefore \cos 2\theta + 3\sin 2\theta = 1$

Let $\cos 2\theta + 3\sin 2\theta \equiv R\cos(2\theta - \alpha)$

$\cos 2\theta + 3\sin 2\theta = R\cos 2\theta\cos\alpha + R\sin 2\theta\sin\alpha$

$1 = R\cos\alpha,\ 3 = R\sin\alpha$

$\tan\alpha = 3,\ \alpha = 71.57°$ and $R = \sqrt{10}$

Equation becomes $\sqrt{10}\cos(2\theta - 71.57°) = 1$

$\cos(2\theta - 71.57°) = \frac{1}{\sqrt{10}}$

Notice that the negative angle −71.57° needs to be included here.

$2\theta - 71.57 = -71.57°, 71.57°, 288.43°$

$\therefore 2\theta = 0°, 143.14°, 360°$

$\theta = 0°, 71.57°, 180°$

Topic 3 Cartesian and parametric equations of curves

This topic covers the following:

- Cartesian and parametric equations of curves and conversion between the two forms
- Finding the equations of tangents and normals to curves defined parametrically or implicitly

Parametric equations

Suppose we have two equations $x = 2 + t$ and $y = 5 + 3t$ where t can take any value.

Using $t = 0, 1, 2, 3, 4$ the following table is obtained:

t	0	1	2	3	4
x	2	3	4	5	6
y	5	8	11	14	17

You can see from the table that as x increases by 1, y increases by 3 meaning that the line has a gradient of 3. As the point (2, 5) lies on the line, the equation of the line is given by:

$y - y_1 = m(x - x_1)$

So $y - 5 = 3(x - 2)$ giving $y = 3x - 1$

Hence the equation of the straight line is $y = 3x - 1$.

This equation connects x and y and is called the Cartesian equation. The original equations (i.e. $x = 2 + t$ and $y = 5 + 3t$) are called the parametric equations.

If you are given two parametric equations such as $x = 2 + t$ and $y = 5 + 3t$ and want to find the Cartesian equation, you can do this by eliminating the parameter, t.

$x = 2 + t$ so $t = x - 2$

$y = 5 + 3t$ so $y = 5 + 3(x - 2)$

Hence $y = 5 + 3x - 6$

giving the Cartesian equation $y = 3x - 1$.

Parametric equations can also represent curves. For example, the parametric equations $x = 2t^2$, $y = 4t$ represent a parabola.

As with the parametric equations of a straight line, to find the Cartesian equation of a curve, the parameter t must be eliminated leaving the equation in terms of x and y.

Suppose you are given the parametric equations $x = 2t^2$, $y = 4t$ and have to find the Cartesian equation of the curve.

From $y = 4t$, we have $t = \frac{y}{4}$

Substituting this for t into $x = 2t^2$ gives $x = 2\left(\frac{y}{4}\right)^2$

So $x = \frac{y^2}{8}$ or $y^2 = 8x$.

This is now the Cartesian equation as it connects x and y.

Examples

① Find the Cartesian equation of the line given by the parametric equations

$x = 4 + 2t \qquad y = 1 + 2t$

Answer

① $x = 4 + 2t$ so $2t = x - 4$

Substituting $2t = x - 4$ for $2t$ in the equation $y = 1 + 2t$ gives

$y = 1 + x - 4$

$y = x - 3$

> Note that to find the Cartesian equation, the parameter t is eliminated.

② A curve C is given by the parametric equations $x = t^2$, $y = t^3$.

Find the equation of the tangent to the curve at the point given by $t = 2$.

Answer

② $\frac{dx}{dt} = 2t$ and $\frac{dy}{dt} = 3t^2$

> We use the Chain rule to find $\frac{dy}{dx}$.

Hence $\frac{dy}{dx} = \frac{dy}{dt} \times \frac{dt}{dx} = 3t^2 \times \frac{1}{2t} = \frac{3}{2}t$

> Note $\frac{dt}{dx} = \frac{1}{\frac{dx}{dt}}$ so you must remember to invert $\frac{dx}{dt}$.

When $t = 2$, $\frac{dy}{dx} = \frac{3}{2} \times 2 = 3$

When $t = 2$, $x = 2^2 = 4$ and $y = 2^3 = 8$

> $t = 2$ is substituted in for t in the parametric equations $x = t^2$ and $y = t^3$.

Hence point (4, 8) lies on the curve.

Equation of tangent passing through (4, 8) and having gradient 3 is

$y - 8 = 3(x - 4)$

Hence $y - 3x + 4 = 0$

> Use the formula for a straight line $y - y_1 = m(x - x_1)$

③ The curve C has the parametric equations

$x = 3 \cos t$, $y = 4 \sin t$.

The point P lies on C and has parameter p.

(a) Show that the equation of the tangent to C at the point P is

$(3 \sin p)\, y + (4 \cos p)\, x - 12 = 0.$ [5]

(b) The tangent to C at the point P meets the x-axis at the point A and the y-axis at the point B. Given that $p = \frac{\pi}{6}$,

(i) find the coordinates of A and B,

(ii) show that the exact length of AB is $2\sqrt{19}$. [4]

(WJEC C4 June 2011 Q4)

Answer

③ (a) $x = 3\cos t, \quad y = 4\sin t$

Differentiating both with respect to t gives:

$\frac{dx}{dt} = -3\sin t, \quad \frac{dy}{dt} = 4\cos t$

$$\frac{dy}{dx} = \frac{dy}{dt} \times \frac{dt}{dx}$$

$$= 4\cos t \times \frac{1}{-3\sin t}$$

$$= -\frac{4\cos t}{3\sin t}$$

Use $\frac{dt}{dx} = \frac{1}{\frac{dx}{dt}}$

At $P(3\cos p, 4\sin p)$ the gradient $= -\frac{4\cos p}{3\sin p}$

Parameter p indicates that $x = 3\cos p$, $y = 4\sin p$.

Equation of the tangent to C at P is given by

$y - y_1 = m(x - x_1)$

$y - 4\sin p = -\frac{4\cos p}{3\sin p}(x - 3\cos p)$

$3y\sin p - 12\sin^2 p = -4x\cos p + 12\cos^2 p$

$3y\sin p + 4x\cos p = 12(\sin^2 p + \cos^2 p)$

Use $\sin^2 p + \cos^2 p = 1$

Hence $3y\sin p + 4x\cos p = 12$

So $(3\sin p)y + (4\cos p)x - 12 = 0$

(b) (i) Now $p = \frac{\pi}{6}$ and at A, $y = 0$.

$\sin\frac{\pi}{6} = \frac{1}{2}$ and $\cos\frac{\pi}{6} = \frac{\sqrt{3}}{2}$

Hence $\left(3\sin\frac{\pi}{6}\right)(0) + \left(4\cos\frac{\pi}{6}\right)x - 12 = 0$

$$0 + \frac{4\sqrt{3}}{2}x - 12 = 0$$

$$2\sqrt{3}x = 12$$

$$x = \frac{6}{\sqrt{3}}$$

$$x = \frac{6\sqrt{3}}{\sqrt{3}\sqrt{3}} = 2\sqrt{3}$$

Remember to rationalise the denominator by multiplying the top and bottom by $\sqrt{3}$.

Point A has coordinates $(2\sqrt{3}, 0)$

For point B, $x = 0$.

Hence $\left(3 \sin \frac{\pi}{6}\right) y+0-12=0$

$$\left(\sin \frac{\pi}{6}\right) y=4$$

$$\frac{1}{2} y=4$$

$$y=8$$

Point B has coordinates (0, 8)

(ii) The length of a straight line joining the two points (x_1, y_1) and (x_2, y_2) is given by:

$$\sqrt{(x_2-x_1)^2+(y_2-y_1)^2}$$

Hence distance between $A\left(2\sqrt{3}, 0\right)$ and B (0, 8) is

$$\sqrt{(2\sqrt{3}-0)^2+(0-8)^2}$$

$$=\sqrt{12+64}$$

$$=\sqrt{76}$$

$$=\sqrt{4\times 19}$$

$$=2\sqrt{19}$$

Using the Chain rule to find the first and second derivatives

The Chain rule can be used to find the second derivative in terms of a parameter such as t in the following way:

$$\frac{d^2y}{dx^2}=\frac{d}{dx}\left(\frac{dy}{dx}\right)=\frac{d}{dt}\left(\frac{dy}{dx}\right)\frac{dt}{dx}$$

The following example shows this technique.

Example

① The curve C has the parametric equations $x=t^2$, $y=t^2+2t$

(a) Find $\frac{dy}{dx}$ in terms of t, simplifying your result as much as possible.

(b) Find $\frac{d^2y}{dx^2}$ in terms of t, simplifying your result as much as possible.

Answer

① (a) $x=t^2$, $y=t^2+2t$

$$\frac{dx}{dt}=2t, \quad \frac{dy}{dt}=2t+2$$

$$\frac{dy}{dx}=\frac{dy}{dt}\times\frac{dt}{dx}=(2t+2)\times\frac{1}{2t}=\frac{t+1}{t}=1+\frac{1}{t}$$

(b) $\frac{dy}{dx} = 1 + \frac{1}{t} = 1 + t^{-1}$

$$\frac{d^2y}{dx^2} = \frac{d}{dx}\left(\frac{dy}{dx}\right) = \frac{d}{dt}\left(\frac{dy}{dx}\right)\frac{dt}{dx}$$

$$\frac{d^2y}{dx^2} = -t^{-2} \times \frac{dt}{dx} = \frac{-\frac{1}{t^2}}{2t} = -\frac{1}{2t^3}$$

It is necessary to express the first derivative in index form ready to differentiate again.

Here the Chain rule is applied.

Implicit differentiation

Implicit differentiation was covered in Topic 4 of C3.

To recap, finding $\frac{dy}{dx}$ in terms of both x and y is called implicit differentiation. There are a number of rules and these are summarised here.

Here are the rules for differentiating implicitly:

- Terms involving x or constant terms are differentiated as normal.
- For terms just involving y, (e.g. $3y$, $5y^3$, etc.) differentiate with respect to y and then multiply the result by $\frac{dy}{dx}$.
- For terms involving both x and y (e.g. xy, $5x^2y^3$, etc.) the Product rule is used because there are two terms multiplied together. Note the need to include $\frac{dy}{dx}$ when the term involving y is differentiated.

The following examples should be read after briefly looking over Topic 4 of C3.

Examples

① Find the equation of the tangent to the curve

$6x^2 + xy + 3y^2 = 6$

at the point (1, 0).

Answer

① $6x^2 + xy + 3y^2 = 6$

Differentiating with respect to x gives

$$12x + (x)\frac{dy}{dx} + y(1) + 6y\frac{dy}{dx} = 0$$

$$\frac{dy}{dx}(x + 6y) = -12x - y$$

Hence $\frac{dy}{dx} = \frac{-12x - y}{x + 6y}$

At (1, 0), $\frac{dy}{dx} = \frac{-12 - 0}{1 + 0} = -12$

When differentiating $f(y)$ w.r.t. x, we obtain $f'(y)\frac{dy}{dx}$.

The term xy is differentiated using the Product rule.

$\frac{dy}{dx}$ is taken out as a factor.

Equation of the tangent at the point (1, 0) is

$y - 0 = -12(x - 1)$

$y = -12x + 12$

Use $y - y_1 = m(x - x_1)$ to find the equation of the tangent.

② Find the equation of the normal to the curve

$5x^2 + 4xy - y^3 = 5$

at the point (1, –2). [5]

(WJEC C4 June 2010 Q2)

Answer

② $5x^2 + 4xy - y^3 = 5$

Differentiating with respect to x gives

$$10x + (4x)\frac{dy}{dx} + y(4) - 3y^2\frac{dy}{dx} = 0$$

The Product rule is used to differentiate $4xy$.

$$10x + 4y = \frac{dy}{dx}(3y^2 - 4x)$$

$$\frac{dy}{dx} = \frac{10x + 4y}{3y^2 - 4x}$$

At $(1, -2)$, $\dfrac{dy}{dx} = \dfrac{10 - 8}{12 - 4} = \dfrac{1}{4}$

The normal and the tangent at the same point are at right angles to each other so the product of their gradients is –1.

Gradient of the normal = –4

Equation of the normal at the point $(1, -2)$ is

$y + 2 = -4(x - 1)$

$y = -4x + 2$

Use $y - y_1 = m(x - x_1)$ to find the gradient of the normal.

③ The parametric equations of the curve C are

$x = \dfrac{2}{t}, y = 4t$

(a) Show that the tangent to C at the point P with parameter p has equation

$y = -2p^2x + 8p.$

[4]

(b) The tangent to C at the point P passes through the point (2, 3). Show that P can be one of two points. Find the coordinates of each of these two points. [4]

(WJEC C4 June 2010 Q6)

Answer

③ (a) $x = \dfrac{2}{t}, y = 4t$

$x = 2t^{-1}$ so $\dfrac{dx}{dt} = -2t^{-2} = \dfrac{-2}{t^2}$

$\dfrac{dy}{dt} = 4$

$$\frac{dy}{dx} = \frac{dy}{dt} \times \frac{dt}{dx} = 4 \times \frac{t^2}{-2} = -2t^2$$

At p, $x = \frac{2}{p}$, $y = 4p$

Change the parameter from t to p.

Equation of the tangent at P is $y - 4p = -2p^2\left(x - \frac{2}{p}\right)$

$y - 4p = -2p^2x + 4p$

Use $y - y_1 = m(x - x_1)$

$y = -2p^2x + 8p$

(b) The coordinates (2, 3) must satisfy the equation of the tangent. Hence

$y = -2p^2x + 8p$

$3 = -4p^2 + 8p$

$4p^2 - 8p + 3 = 0$

$(2p - 1)(2p - 3) = 0$

giving $p = \frac{1}{2}, \frac{3}{2}$.

Substitute each value of the parameter p giving $x = \frac{2}{p}$, $y = 4p$ to find both pairs of coordinates.

Hence the coordinates of the two points are (4, 2), $\left(\frac{4}{3}, 6\right)$.

Examination style questions

① The parametric equations of the curve C are $x = t^2$, $y = t^3$. The point P has parameter p.

(a) Show that the gradient of the tangent to C at the point P is $\frac{3}{2}p$. [4]

(b) Find the equation of the tangent at P. [2]

Answer

① (a) $\frac{dx}{dt} = 2t$ and $\frac{dy}{dt} = 3t^2$.

Hence $\frac{dy}{dx} = \frac{dy}{dt} \times \frac{dt}{dx} = 3t^2 \times \frac{1}{2t} = \frac{3}{2}t$

At $P(p^2, p^3)$, $\frac{dy}{dx} = \frac{3}{2}p$.

Change the parameter from t to p.

(b) Equation of the tangent at P is $y - p^3 = \frac{3}{2}p\left(x - p^2\right)$

$2y - 2p^3 = 3px - 3p^3$

$3px - 2y = p^3$.

② The curve C has equation

$$4x^2 - 6xy + y^2 = 20$$

(a) Prove that $\frac{dy}{dx} = \frac{3y - 4x}{y - 3x}$. [4]

(b) Points A and B lie on C. If the x-coordinates of A and B are both equal to 0, prove that the y-coordinates of A and B are $\pm 2\sqrt{5}$. [3]

Answer

② (a) $4x^2 - 6xy + y^2 = 20$

Differentiating with respect to x gives

$$8x - 6x\frac{dy}{dx} - y(6) + 2y\frac{dy}{dx} = 0$$

$$(2y - 6x)\frac{dy}{dx} = 6y - 8x$$

$$\frac{dy}{dx} = \frac{6y - 8x}{2y - 6x}$$

Divide the numerator and denominator by 2.

$$\frac{dy}{dx} = \frac{3y - 4x}{y - 3x}$$

(b) $4x^2 - 6xy + y^2 = 20$

Substituting $x = 0$ into this equation gives

$4(0)^2 - 6(0)y + y^2 = 20$

Hence $y^2 = 20$

$y = \pm\sqrt{20}$

$y = \pm\sqrt{4 \times 5}$

$y = \pm 2\sqrt{5}$

Test yourself

Answer the following questions and check your answers before moving on to the next topic.

① The parametric equation of the curve C are $x = 3t^2$, $y = t^3$. The point P has parameter p.

Show that the equation of the normal to C at the point P is $py + 2x = p^2(6 + p^2)$

② Given that $y^2 - 5xy + 8x^2 = 2$, prove that $\frac{dy}{dx} = \frac{5y - 16x}{2y - 5x}$.

③ The parametric equations of the curve C are $x = 2\sin 4t$, $y = \cos 4t$

(a) Prove that $\frac{dy}{dx} = -\frac{1}{2}\tan 4t$

(b) Show that the equation of the tangent to C at the point P with parameter p is

$2y\cos 4p + x\sin 4p = 2$

1 Find the equation of the normal to the curve

$x^2 + 3xy + 3y^2 = 13$

at the point (2, 1).

Answer

1 $x^2 + 3xy + 3y^2 = 13$

Differentiating with respect to x we obtain

$$2x + (3x)\frac{dy}{dx} + y(3) + 6y\frac{dy}{dx} = 0$$

giving $\frac{dy}{dx} = \frac{-2x - 3y}{3x + 6y}$

At the point (2, 1), $\frac{dy}{dx} = \frac{-2(2) - 3(1)}{3(2) + 6(1)} = -\frac{7}{12}$

Gradient of the normal $= \frac{12}{7}$

Using the fact that the product of the gradients of the tangent and normal is -1.

Equation of the normal at the point (2, 1) is

$$y - 1 = \frac{12}{7}(x - 2)$$

Use $y - y_1 = m(x - x_1)$ to find the equation of the normal.

$$7y - 7 = 12x - 24$$

$$7y - 12x + 17 = 0$$

2 The parametric equations of the curve C are $x = t^2$, $y = t^3$. The point P has parameter p.

(a) Show that the equation of the tangent to C at the point P is $3px - 2y = p^3$. [4]

(b) The tangent to C at the point P intersects C again at the point $Q(q^2, q^3)$. Given that $p = 2$, show that q satisfies the equation $q^3 - 3q^2 + 4q = 0$ and determine the value of q. [5]

(WJEC C4 June 2009 Q5)

Answer

2 (a) $\frac{dx}{dt} = 2t$ and $\frac{dy}{dt} = 3t^2$

Hence $\frac{dy}{dx} = \frac{dy}{dt} \times \frac{dt}{dx} = 3t^2 \times \frac{1}{2t} = \frac{3t}{2}$

At $P(p^2, p^3)$, $\frac{dy}{dx} = \frac{3p}{2}$

Equation of tangent at P is $y - p^3 = \frac{3p}{2}(x - p^2)$

$2y - 2p^3 = 3px - 3p^3$

$3px - 2y = p^3$.

As the parameter has been removed, this is now the Cartesian equation of the tangent.

(b) $3px - 2y = p^3$ so when $p = 2$, $6x - 2y = 8$

As Q lies on the tangent its coordinates will satisfy the equation of the tangent.

So substituting $x = q^2$, $y = q^3$ into the equation gives $6q^2 - 2q^3 = 8$

Hence $3q^2 - q^3 = 4$ so $q^3 - 3q^2 + 4 = 0$

Let $f(q) = q^3 - 3q^2 + 4$

$f(1) = 1^3 - 3(1)^2 + 4 = 2$

$f(-1) = (-1)^3 - 3(-1)^2 + 4 = 0$ hence $(q + 1)$ is a factor.

Let $(q + 1)(aq^2 + bq + c) \equiv q^3 - 3q^2 + 4$

Note this is an identity, i.e. true for all values of q.

Equating coefficients of q^3, we obtain $a = 1$

Equating coefficients independent of q, we obtain $c = 4$

Equating coefficients of q^2 gives $b + a = -3$, so $b = -4$

Hence $q^3 - 3q^2 + 4 = (q + 1)(q^2 - 4q + 4) = (q + 1)(q - 2)(q - 2)$

Now $(q + 1)(q - 2)(q - 2) = 0$

Solving, we obtain $q = -1, 2$

The value $q = 2$ relates to point P so $q = -1$.

Topic 4 Simple differential equations and exponential growth

This topic covers the following:

- Formation of simple differential equations
- Exponential growth and decay

Formation of simple differential equations

Differential equations are equations concerning rate of change. Many problems in the real world involve quantities that change with time and therefore involve rates of change. For example, radioactive decay, the depreciation in value of a car, the growth of bacteria, all involve rates of change. By forming a differential equation, the situation can be accurately modelled and the model can be used to provide answers to questions such as what will be the likely value of my car in four years' time or how much of a radioactive isotope will remain after a certain period of time.

Exponential growth and decay

Many quantities exhibit exponential growth or exponential decay as these examples show.

Examples

① A radioactive substance decays so that at any instant, the rate of decrease in the mass is proportional to the mass of the radioactive substance remaining. If the mass of the radioactive substance is m grams after t days, write down a differential equation relating m and t.

Answer

① $\frac{\mathrm{d}m}{\mathrm{d}t} = -km$

When the proportional sign is changed to an equals sign a constant of proportionality k must be included. The minus sign is included here because the mass is decreasing (i.e. m decreases with time).

② The size N of the population of a small island may be modelled as a continuous variable. At time t, the rate of increase of N is directly proportional to the value of N.

(a) Write down the differential equation that is satisfied by N. [1]

(b) Show that $N = Ae^{kt}$, where A and k are constants. [3]

(c) Given that $N = 100$ when $t = 2$ and that $N = 160$ when $t = 12$,

(i) show that $k = 0.047$, correct to three decimal places,

(ii) find the size of the population when $t = 20$. [7]

(WJEC C4 June 2011 Q9)

Answer

> This represents the phrase 'rate of increase of N is directly proportional to the value of N'.

② (a) $\frac{dN}{dt} \alpha N$

so that $\frac{dN}{dt} = k N$

> When the proportionality sign is removed and replaced with an equals sign, a constant of proportionality k is included. Since N increases, $\frac{dN}{dt} > 0$ and $k > 0$.

(b) Separating the variables and integrating, we obtain

$\int \frac{1}{N} dN = k \int dt$

$\therefore \ln N = kt + C \qquad (1)$

If $N = N_o$ when $t = 0$,

$\ln N_o = k(0) + C = C$

Substitute for C in (1)

$\ln N = kt + \ln N_o$

$\therefore \ln N - \ln N_o = kt$

$\ln \frac{N}{N_o} = kt$

> Use one of the laws of logarithms
> $\ln a - \ln b = \ln \frac{a}{b}$

Taking exponentials of both sides

$\frac{N}{N_o} = e^{kt}$

$\therefore N = N_o e^{kt}$

Writing $A = N_o$, we have $N = Ae^{kt}$

(c) (i) $N = 100$ when $t = 2$ and $N = 160$ when $t = 12$,

Hence $100 = Ae^{2k}$ and $160 = Ae^{12k}$

Dividing these two equations to eliminate A we obtain

$\frac{160}{100} = \frac{e^{12k}}{e^{2k}}$

> Note $\frac{e^{12k}}{e^{2k}} = e^{12k-2k} = e^{10k}$

$1.6 = e^{10k}$

Taking ln of both sides we obtain

$\ln 1.6 = 10k$ so $k = \frac{1}{10} \ln 1.6 = 0.047$ (correct to three decimal places)

(ii) $N = Ae^{0.047t}$

$N = 100$ when $t = 2$

so $100 = Ae^{0.047 \times 2}$

$100 = A \times 1.09856$

giving $A = 91.028$ (correct to three decimal places)

Hence $N = 91.028\, e^{0.047t}$

When $t = 20$, $N = 91.028\, e^{0.047 \times 20} = 233$ (nearest whole number)

Examination style questions

① Floating pond weed in a pond covers an area of A m^2 after time t months. The rate of increase of A is directly proportional to A.

(a) Write down a differential equation that is satisfied by A. [1]

(b) The area of the pond weed is initially 4 m^2 and one month later the area covered is 5 m^2. Find an expression for A in terms of t. [6]

Answer

① (a) $\frac{dA}{dt} = kA$

> $k > 0$ since A increases with time

(b) $\frac{dA}{dt} = kA$

Separating the variables and integrating gives

$\int \frac{1}{A} dA = k \int dt$

and $\ln A = kt + C$ (1)

When $t = 0$, $A = 4$ and when $t = 1$, $A = 5$

Substituting these values in (1), we obtain

$\ln 4 = C$ (2)

$\ln 5 = k + C$ (3)

Then $C = \ln 4$

and $k = \ln 5 - \ln 4 = \ln \frac{5}{4} = 0.2231$

substitute for k and C in (1) gives

$\ln A = 0.2231t + \ln 4$

$\therefore \ln A - \ln 4 = 0.2231t$

$\ln \frac{A}{4} = 0.2231t$

> Use one of the laws of logarithms:
> $\ln a - \ln b = \ln\left(\frac{a}{b}\right)$

Take exponentials of both sides

$\frac{A}{4} = e^{0.2231t}$

and $A = 4e^{0.2231t}$

Test yourself

Answer the following questions and check your answers before moving on to the next topic.

① The value of a car decreases with time. When the car has a value of £V after t months, the value decreases at a rate which is proportional to V.

(a) Write down a differential equation relating V and t.

(b) If the car has an initial value of £10 000, solve the differential equation and show that

$V = 10\,000e^{-kt}$ where k is a positive constant.

(c) The value of the car is expected to be £4 000 after 48 months.

Calculate

(i) the value to the nearest pound of the car when it is 12 months old,

(ii) the age of the car to the nearest month when its value is £3 000.

② A lawn contains some clover. The area covered by the clover at time t years is C m^2. The rate of increase of C is directly proportional to C.

(a) Write down a differential equation that is satisfied by C.

(b) The area of the lawn initially covered by the clover is 0.90 m^2 and two years later the area covered is 8 m^2. Find an expression for C in terms of t.

(Note: answers to Test yourself are found at the back of the book.)

1 The value of an electronic component may be modelled as a continuous variable. The value of the component at time t years is £P. The rate of decrease of P is directly proportional to P^3.

(a) Write down a differential equation that is satisfied by P. [1]

(b) The value of the component when $t = 0$ is £20. Show that

$$\frac{1}{P^2} = \frac{1}{400} + At,$$

where A is a positive constant. [5]

(c) Given that the value of the component when $t = 1$ is £10, find the time when the value is £5. [4]

(WJEC C4 June 2009 Q7)

Answer

1 (a) $\frac{dP}{dt} = -kP^3$

The negative sign is introduced because P decreases with time. The constant k is then positive.

(b) Separating variables and integrating gives

$$\int \frac{1}{P^3} dP = -k \int dt$$

Express $\frac{1}{P^3}$ in index form so it can be integrated easily.

$$\int P^{-3} dP = -k \int dt$$

$$-\frac{1}{2P^2} = -kt + c$$

When $t = 0$, $P = £20$

The two known values are entered into the equation so that the value of the constant C can be found.

$$-\frac{1}{2(20)^2} = 0 + c\text{, so } c = -\frac{1}{800}$$

Hence $-\frac{1}{2P^2} = -kt - \frac{1}{800}$

Multiplying through by -2 we obtain $\frac{1}{p^2} = \frac{1}{400} + 2kt$

Letting $A = 2k$ we obtain

$$\frac{1}{P^2} = \frac{1}{400} + At$$

A is >0 because $k > 0$.

(c) When $t = 1$, $P = 10$

So $\frac{1}{100} = \frac{1}{400} + A$ giving $A = \frac{3}{400}$

Hence $\frac{1}{P^2} = \frac{1}{400} + \frac{3}{400}t$

When $P = 5$, $\frac{1}{25} = \frac{1}{400} + \frac{3}{400}t$ giving $t = 5$

Q&A 2

2	The value, £V, of a car may be modelled as a continuous variable. At time t years, the rates of decrease of V is directly proportional to V^2.	
(a)	Write down a differential equation satisfied by V.	[1]
(b)	Given that $V = 12\,000$ when $t = 0$, show that $V = \dfrac{12\,000}{at+1}$ where a is a constant.	[4]
(c)	The value of the car at the end of two years is £9000. Find the value of the car at the end of four years.	[4]
	(WJEC C4 June 2010 Q8)	

Answer

2 (a) $\dfrac{dV}{dt} = -kV^2$

(b) $\displaystyle\int \frac{1}{V^2} dV = -k\int dt$

Separating the variables and integrating.

$\displaystyle\int V^{-2} dV = -k\int dt$

$-\dfrac{1}{V} = -kt + c$

When $t = 0$, $V = 12\,000$

$-\dfrac{1}{12\,000} = c$

The value for c is substituted back into the original equation.

$-\dfrac{1}{V} = -kt - \dfrac{1}{12\,000}$

Multiplying both sides by $-12\,000V$ gives

$12\,000 = 12\,000Vkt + V$

$12\,000 = V(12\,000kt + 1)$

$V = \dfrac{12\,000}{12\,000kt+1}$

Let $a = 12\,000k$

Hence $V = \dfrac{12\,000}{at+1}$

(c) $V = 9\,000$ when $t = 2$

$9\,000 = \dfrac{12\,000}{2a+1}$ so $2a+1 = \dfrac{12\,000}{9\,000}$ giving $a = \dfrac{1}{6}$

Hence $V = \dfrac{12\,000}{\frac{1}{6}t+1}$

When $t = 4$, $V = \dfrac{12\,000}{\frac{1}{6}(4)+1} = £7\,200$

Topic 5 Integration

This topic covers the following:

- Evaluation of volume of revolution
- Integration by substitution and integration by parts
- Integration using partial fractions
- Analytical solution of first order differential equations with separable variables

Evaluation of volume of revolution

The curve below shows the section of the graph of $y = f(x)$ between the lines $x = a$ and $x = b$. The shaded region is to be rotated by four right angles (i.e. 360°) about the x-axis to form a three-dimensional shape called a volume of revolution.

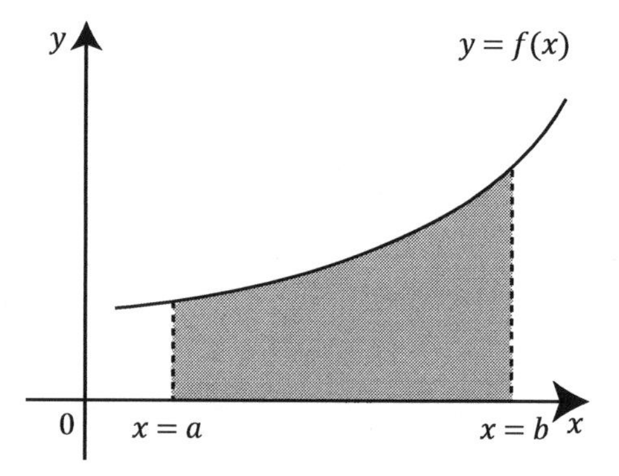

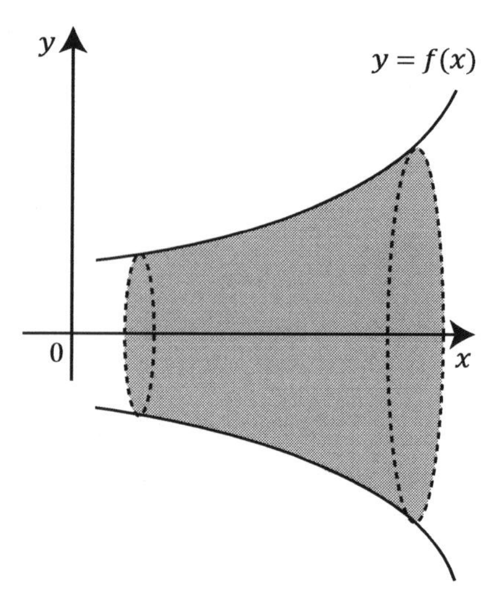

The volume of revolution produced when $y = f(x)$ is rotated by 360° about the x-axis between the lines $x = a$ and $x = b$ is given by the following:

$$\text{Volume of revolution} = \pi \int_a^b y^2 \mathrm{d}x$$

Examples

① The region R is bounded by the curve $= 2x + \frac{1}{\sqrt{x}}$, the x-axis and the lines $x = 1$ and $x = 2$. Find the volume generated when R is rotated through four right angles about the x-axis correct to three decimal places.

Answer

① Volume $= \pi \int_a^b y^2 dx$

$$= \pi \int_1^2 \left(2x + \frac{1}{\sqrt{x}}\right)^2 dx$$

$$= \pi \int_1^2 \left(4x^2 + \frac{4x}{\sqrt{x}} + \frac{1}{x}\right) dx$$

$$= \pi \int_1^2 \left(4x^2 + 4x^{\frac{1}{2}} + \frac{1}{x}\right) dx$$

$$= \pi \left[\frac{4x^3}{3} + \frac{8x^{\frac{3}{2}}}{3} + \ln x\right]_1^2$$

$$= \pi \left[\left(\frac{32}{3} + \frac{8\sqrt{8}}{3} + \ln 2\right) - \left(\frac{4}{3} + \frac{8}{3} + 0\right)\right]$$

$= 46.817$ (correct to three decimal places)

The larger of the limits is usually placed at the top of the integral and the lower limit placed at the bottom.

Note when you expand the bracket you obtain three terms.

$\frac{4x}{\sqrt{x}} = (4x)\left(x^{-\frac{1}{2}}\right) = 4x^{\frac{1}{2}}$

Use a calculator to work this out.

Remember to give the answer correct to the number of decimal places specified in the question.

② The region R bounded by the curve $y = \cos 4x$, the x-axis and the lines $x = 0$, $x = \frac{\pi}{2}$ is rotated about the x-axis through four right angles. Find the volume generated.

Answer

② Volume $= \pi \int_a^b y^2 dx$

$$= \pi \int_0^{\frac{\pi}{2}} \cos^2 4x \, dx$$

$$= \pi \int_0^{\frac{\pi}{2}} \frac{1 + \cos 8x}{2} dx$$

$$= \pi \left[\frac{x}{2} + \frac{\sin 8x}{16}\right]_0^{\frac{\pi}{2}}$$

$$= \pi \left[\left(\frac{\pi}{4} + \frac{\sin 4\pi}{16}\right) - \left(0 + \frac{\sin 0}{16}\right)\right]$$

$= \frac{\pi^2}{4} = 2.467$ (correct to 3 decimal places)

You will recall that $\cos^2 x = \frac{1 + \cos 2x}{2}$.

Similarly, $\cos^2 4x = \frac{1 + \cos 8x}{2}$ can be obtained from $\cos(A + B) = \cos A \cos B - \sin A \sin B$ with $A = 4x$, $B = 4x$. This allows $\cos^2 4x$ to be expressed in terms of $\cos 8x$.

Integration by substitution and integration by parts

Two new methods of integration are introduced here: integration by substitution and integration by parts.

Integration by substitution

Suppose you had to find $\int x(3x+5)^5 dx$. One method would be to expand the bracket and then multiply by x and simplify before finally integrating. There is quite a bit of work in this and there is a simpler method called integration by substitution. This method is shown here.

Suppose you are asked to integrate the following indefinite integral:

$$\int x(3x+1)^5 dx$$

Let $u = 3x + 1$ so $\frac{du}{dx} = 3$. Hence $dx = \frac{du}{3}$

Where there is a bracket raised to a power like this, you usually let u be equal to the contents of the bracket.

Notice that we can now replace $(3x+1)^5$ by u^5 and dx by $\frac{du}{3}$.

There is still an x which needs to be replaced by an expression in terms of u and this can be obtained by rearranging $u = 3x + 1$ to give $x = \frac{u-1}{3}$.

The integral $\int x(3x+1)^5 dx$ now becomes $\int \left(\frac{u-1}{3}\right)u^5 \frac{du}{3}$.

Note that the variable is now u rather than x.

Hence $\int \left(\frac{u-1}{3}\right)u^5 \frac{du}{3} = \frac{1}{9}\int \left(u^6 - u^5\right)du$

$$= \frac{1}{9}\left(\frac{u^7}{7} - \frac{u^6}{6}\right) + c$$

Here the expression in u is integrated. As this is an indefinite integral, it is necessary to include the constant of integration.

u can now be substituted back as $3x + 1$ to give

$$\int x(3x+1)^5 dx = \frac{1}{9}\left[\frac{(3x+1)^7}{7} - \frac{(3x+1)^6}{6}\right] + c$$

Always remember to give the indefinite integral back in terms of x.

Suppose you have the same integral but this time it is a definite integral (i.e. an integral with limits), such as

$$\int_{-\frac{1}{3}}^{0} x(3x+1)^5 dx$$

You would use the substitution to change the variable to u as before and change the limits so that they now apply to u and not x. This is done by substituting each limit for x into the following equation.

$u = 3x + 1$ so when $x = 0$, $u = 1$ and when $x = -\frac{1}{3}$, $u = 0$.

The integral now becomes

$$\frac{1}{9}\int_0^1 \left(u^6 - u^5\right)du = \frac{1}{9}\left[\frac{u^7}{7} - \frac{u^6}{6}\right]_0^1 = -\frac{1}{378}$$

There is no need to give the answer in terms of x: use the u limits.

Integration by parts

Integration by parts is used when there is a product to integrate. The formula for integration by parts is obtained from the formula booklet and is as follows:

$$\int u\frac{dv}{dx}dx = uv - \int v\frac{du}{dx}dx$$

At times, integration by parts can be complicated. However in C4, one of the functions in the integrand is a polynomial, such as $x^2 + 2$, $4x + 3$. Hence in C4 we encounter integrals such as $\int x^2 \sin 2x\,dx$, $\int (3x + 2)\ln x\,dx$ and $\int xe^{3x}\,dx$.

The following rules are useful in C4.

Rule 1

When one of the functions is a polynomial and the other function is easily integrated,

let u = polynomial,

$\frac{dv}{dx}$ = other function.

By easily integrated we mean by the use of C3 techniques.

Rule 2

When one of the functions is a polynomial and the other function is not easily integrated,

Let $\frac{dv}{dx}$ = polynomial in x,

u = other function.

Thus for $\int xe^{3x}\,dx$, we use Rule 1 since e^{3x} is easy to integrate, and we let $u = x$ and $\frac{dv}{dx} = e^{3x}$

In contrast, for $\int x^2 \ln x$ we use Rule 2 since $\ln x$ is difficult to integrate, and we let $u = \ln x$ and $\frac{dv}{dx} = x^2$.

Examples

① Find $\int x \cos 2x\,dx$

The formula for integration by parts can be obtained from the formula booklet.

Answer

①

$$\int u\frac{dv}{dx}dx = uv - \int v\frac{du}{dx}dx$$

Let $u = x$ and $\frac{dv}{dx} = \cos 2x$

Here $\cos 2x$ is easily integrated and we use Rule 1.

So, $\frac{du}{dx} = 1$, $v = \frac{\sin 2x}{2}$

$$\int x \cos 2x \, dx = x\frac{1}{2}\sin 2x - \int \frac{1}{2}\sin 2x \, dx$$

$$= \frac{x}{2}\sin 2x + \frac{1}{4}\cos 2x + c$$

② Find $\int x \ln x \, dx$

Answer

② $\int u\frac{dv}{dx}dx = uv - \int v\frac{du}{dx}dx$

Here $\ln x$ is not easily integrated so we use Rule 2.

Let $u = \ln x$, $\frac{dv}{dx} = x$

so that $\frac{du}{dx} = \frac{1}{x}$, $v = \frac{x^2}{2}$

Remember $\frac{d(\ln x)}{dx} = \frac{1}{x}$

Hence $\int x \ln x \, dx = \ln x\left(\frac{x^2}{2}\right) - \int \frac{x^2}{2}\left(\frac{1}{x}\right)dx$

Note the cancelling of x in the integral.

$$= \frac{x^2}{2}\ln x - \int \frac{x}{2}\,dx$$

$$= \frac{x^2}{2}\ln x - \frac{x^2}{4} + c$$

③ Find $\int \ln x \, dx$

Answer

③ In this case, there is only one function to be integrated and apparently integration by parts cannot be used. The trick is to regard $\ln x$ as $\ln x \times 1$ and use Rule 2.

Then let $u = \ln x$,

$\frac{dv}{dx} = 1$

Thus, $\frac{du}{dx} = \frac{1}{x}$, $v = x$

On substituting in

$$\int u\frac{dv}{dx}\,dx = uv - \int v\frac{du}{dx}dx,$$

we obtain

$$\int \ln x \, dx = (\ln x)x - \int x\left(\frac{1}{x}\right)dx$$

$$= x\ln x - \int 1 \, dx$$

$$= x\ln x - x + c$$

Trigonometric substitution

In some cases we can make integration easier by using a trigonometric substitution.

The following example shows this technique.

Example

① Use the substitution $x = \sin\theta$ to show that

$$\int_0^1 \sqrt{(1-x^2)}\,dx = \frac{\pi}{4}$$

Answer

① Let $x = \sin\theta$ so $\frac{dx}{d\theta} = \cos\theta$ and $dx = \cos\theta\,d\theta$

Use the substitution given in the question.

When $x = 1$, $\sin\theta = 1$ so $\theta = \sin^{-1} 1 = \frac{\pi}{2}$

The limits are changed so that they apply to the new variable θ.

When $x = 0$, $\sin\theta = 0$ so $\theta = \sin^{-1} 0 = 0$

$$\int_0^1 \sqrt{(1-x^2)}\,dx = \int_0^{\frac{\pi}{2}} \sqrt{(1-\sin^2\theta)}\cos\theta\,d\theta$$

Now $1 - \sin^2\theta = \cos^2\theta$

$$\int_0^{\frac{\pi}{2}} \sqrt{(1-\sin^2\theta)}\cos\theta\,d\theta = \int_0^{\frac{\pi}{2}} \sqrt{\cos^2\theta}\cos\theta\,d\theta$$

$$= \int_0^{\frac{\pi}{2}} \cos\theta\cos\theta\,d\theta$$

$$= \int_0^{\frac{\pi}{2}} \cos^2\theta\,d\theta$$

This is a rearrangement of the double angle formula

$\cos 2A = 2\cos^2 A - 1$

This formula is not in the formula booklet but you can derive it from other formulae which are in the formula booklet. Look back at Topic 2 if you are unsure as to how you would do this.

$$= \int_0^{\frac{\pi}{2}} \frac{1}{2}(1+\cos 2\theta)\,d\theta$$

$$= \frac{1}{2}\int_0^{\frac{\pi}{2}} (1+\cos 2\theta)\,d\theta$$

$$= \frac{1}{2}\left[\theta + \frac{1}{2}\sin 2\theta\right]_0^{\frac{\pi}{2}}$$

$$= \frac{1}{2}\left[\left(\frac{\pi}{2} + \frac{1}{2}\sin\pi\right) - \left(0 + \frac{1}{2}\sin 0\right)\right]$$

$$= \frac{1}{2}\left[\left(\frac{\pi}{2} + 0\right) - (0+0)\right]$$

$$= \frac{\pi}{4}$$

Examples

① (a) Find $\int (x+3)e^{2x}\,dx$. [4]

(b) Use the substitution $u = 2\cos x + 1$ to evaluate

$$\int_0^{\frac{\pi}{3}} \frac{\sin x}{\sqrt{(2\cos x + 1)}}\,dx$$ [5]

(WJEC C4 June 2009 Q6)

Answer

This is the formula for integration by parts and is looked up in the formula booklet. Use Rule 1 for the integration by parts.

① (a) $\int u\frac{dv}{dx}dx = uv - \int v\frac{du}{dx}dx$

Let $u = (x+3)$ and $\frac{dv}{dx} = e^{2x}$

As $u = x + 3$, $\frac{du}{dx} = 1$

$$\int (x+3)e^{2x}\,dx = (x+3)\frac{1}{2}e^{2x} - \int \frac{1}{2}e^{2x}(1)dx$$

$$= (x+3)\frac{1}{2}e^{2x} - \frac{1}{4}e^{2x} + c$$

(b) Let $u = 2\cos x + 1$

$\frac{du}{dx} = -2\sin x$ so $dx = \frac{du}{-2\sin x}$

When $x = \frac{\pi}{3}$, $u = 2\cos\frac{\pi}{3} + 1 = 2$

Notice how $\sin x$ appears in both the numerator and the denominator and can therefore be cancelled.

When $x = 0$, $u = 2\cos 0 + 1 = 3$

$$\int_0^{\frac{\pi}{3}} \frac{\sin x}{\sqrt{(2\cos x+1)}}\,dx = \int \frac{\sin x}{\sqrt{u}}\left(\frac{du}{-2\sin x}\right)$$

Note the order of the limits. Do not interchange these limits.

$$= -\frac{1}{2}\int_3^2 u^{-\frac{1}{2}}\,du$$

$$= \left[-u^{\frac{1}{2}}\right]_3^2 = \left[-\sqrt{u}\right]_3^2 = \left[-\sqrt{2} - \left(-\sqrt{3}\right)\right] = -\sqrt{2} + \sqrt{3} = 0.318$$ (correct to three decimal places).

② (a) Find $\int x^3 \ln x\,dx$. [4]

(b) Use the substitution $u = 2x - 3$ to evaluate $\int_1^2 x(2x-3)^4\,dx$. [5]

(WJEC C4 June 2010 Q7)

Answer

You must recognise that there is a product to be integrated so integration by parts is used. Obtain the formula from the formula booklet.

② (a) $\int u\frac{dv}{dx}dx = uv - \int v\frac{du}{dx}dx$

Let $u = \ln x$ and $\frac{dv}{dx} = x^3$

so $\frac{du}{dx} = \frac{1}{x}$, $v = \frac{x^4}{4}$

Then $\int \ln x\,(x^3)dx = \ln x\left(\frac{x^4}{4}\right) - \int\left(\frac{x^4}{4} \times \frac{1}{x}\right)dx$

$$= \frac{x^4}{4}\ln x - \int \frac{x^3}{4}\,dx$$

$$= \frac{x^4}{4}\ln x - \frac{x^4}{16} + c$$

Notice that if you let $\frac{dv}{dx} = \ln x$ it would mean that $\ln x$ would need to be integrated. The integral of $\ln x$ is not known so it is necessary to let $u = \ln x$ to avoid this (i.e. use Rule 2).

(b) $u = 2x - 3$, $\frac{du}{dx} = 2$, so $dx = \frac{du}{2}$ and $x = \frac{u+3}{2}$

$$\int_1^2 x(2x-3)^4\,dx = \int\left(\frac{u+3}{2}\right)u^4\frac{du}{2} = \frac{1}{4}\int\left(u^5 + 3u^4\right)du$$

Remember to change the limits so that they apply to the new variable u.

Change the limits using $u = 2x - 3$. When $x = 2$, $u = 1$ and when $x = 1$, $u = -1$.

Hence $\frac{1}{4}\int_{-1}^{1}\left(u^5 + 3u^4\right)du = \frac{1}{4}\left[\frac{u^6}{6} + \frac{3u^5}{5}\right]_{-1}^{1} = \frac{1}{4}\left[\left(\frac{1}{6} + \frac{3}{5}\right) - \left(\frac{1}{6} - \frac{3}{5}\right)\right] = \frac{3}{10}$

③ (a) Find $\int x \sin 2x\,dx$. [4]

(b) Use the substitution $u = 5 - x^2$ to evaluate

$$\int_0^2 \frac{x}{\left(5 - x^2\right)^3}\,dx$$ [4]

(WJEC C4 June 2011 Q7)

Answer

③ (a) $\int x \sin 2x\,dx$

This is a product and needs to be integrated by parts using the formula obtained from the formula booklet. Use Rule 1.

$$\int u\frac{dv}{dx}dx = uv - \int v\frac{du}{dx}dx$$

Let $u = x$ and $\frac{dv}{dx} = \sin 2x$

and $\frac{du}{dx} = 1$, $v = \frac{-\cos 2x}{2}$

then $\int x \sin 2x\,dx = x\left(-\frac{1}{2}\cos 2x\right) - \int\left(-\frac{1}{2}\cos 2x\right)(1)dx$

$$= -\frac{x}{2}\cos 2x + \frac{1}{4}\sin 2x + c$$

(b) $u = 5 - x^2$ so $\frac{du}{dx} = -2x$ and $dx = \frac{du}{-2x}$

When $x = 2, u = 5 - 2^2 = 1$

$x = 0, u = 5 - 0 = 5$

The limits are changed so that they apply now to u and not x.

Hence $\int_0^2 \frac{x}{(5-x^2)^3} dx = \int_5^1 \frac{x}{u^3}\left(\frac{du}{-2x}\right)$

Notice that the x in the numerator and denominator can be cancelled.

$$= -\frac{1}{2}\int_5^1 \frac{1}{u^3} du$$

$$= -\frac{1}{2}\int_5^1 u^{-3} du$$

$$= -\frac{1}{2}\left[\frac{u^{-2}}{-2}\right]_5^1$$

Notice the order of the limits which must not be changed.

$$= -\frac{1}{2}\left[-\frac{1}{2u^2}\right]_5^1$$

$$= -\frac{1}{2}\left[\left(-\frac{1}{2}\right)-\left(-\frac{1}{50}\right)\right]$$

$$= -\frac{1}{2}\left(-\frac{1}{2}+\frac{1}{50}\right)$$

$$= \frac{6}{25}$$

Integration using partial fractions

Converting a single algebraic fraction into two or more partial fractions was covered in Topic 1 of C4. In this section you will be turning an algebraic fraction into partial fractions and then integrating each of the partial fractions.

The following examples show the technique.

Examples

① (a) If $\frac{6-5x}{(1-x)(2-x)} \equiv \frac{A}{1-x} + \frac{B}{2-x}$,

find the constants A and B.

(b) Hence find $\int_{-1}^{0} \frac{6-5x}{(1-x)(2-x)} dx$

Answer

① (a) $\frac{6-5x}{(1-x)(2-x)} \equiv \frac{A}{1-x} + \frac{B}{2-x}$

$6 - 5x \equiv A(2-x) + B(1-x)$

Let $x = 2$ so $-4 = -B$, $B = 4$

Let $x = 1$ so $A = 1$

Check the values of A and B are correct by substituting another value for x into the equation.

$x = 0$, LHS $= \frac{6-5(0)}{(1)(2)} = 3$.

RHS $= \frac{1}{1} + \frac{4}{2} = 3$. Hence LHS = RHS.

Grade boost

Always check the partial fractions are correct as a mistake may mean the partial fractions are harder to integrate.

(b) $\int_{-1}^{0} \frac{6-5x}{(1-x)(2-x)} \mathrm{d}x \equiv \int_{-1}^{0} \left(\frac{1}{1-x} + \frac{4}{2-x} \right) \mathrm{d}x$

$= \left[-\ln(1-x) - 4\ln(2-x) \right]_{-1}^{0}$

$= [(0 - 4\ln 2) - (-\ln 2 - 4\ln 3)]$

$= 4\ln 3 - 3\ln 2$

When the numerator is the derivative of the denominator, the integral is ln of the denominator because $\int \frac{f'(x)}{f(x)} du$ becomes $\int \frac{1}{u} du$ if we let $u = f'(x)$.

② Given that $f(x) \equiv \frac{3x+4}{(x+3)(3x-1)}$

(a) express $f(x)$ in terms of partial fraction,

(b) show that

$$\int_{1}^{2} f(x)\mathrm{d}x = \frac{1}{2}\ln\frac{25}{8}$$

Answer

② (a) $\frac{3x+4}{(x+3)(3x-1)} \equiv \frac{A}{x+3} + \frac{B}{3x-1}$

$3x + 4 \equiv A(3x-1) + B(x+3)$

Let $x = -3$ so $-5 = -10A$, hence $A = \frac{1}{2}$

Let $x = \frac{1}{3}$, so $5 = \frac{10}{3}B$, hence $B = \frac{3}{2}$

Partial fractions are $\frac{1}{2(x+3)} + \frac{3}{2(3x-1)}$

Remember to check the partial fractions are correct by substituting in a different value of x and check that the left- and right-hand sides of the equation are equal.

(b) $\frac{1}{2}\int_1^2\left(\frac{1}{(x+3)}+\frac{3}{3x-1}\right)dx$

$=\frac{1}{2}\left[\ln(x+3)+\ln(3x-1)\right]_1^2$

$=\frac{1}{2}\left[(\ln 5+\ln 5)-(\ln 4+\ln 2)\right]$

$=\frac{1}{2}\ln\frac{25}{8}$

$\ln 5+\ln 5=\ln(5\times 5)=\ln 25$ and
$\ln 4+\ln 2=\ln(4\times 2)=\ln 8$
$\ln 25-\ln 8=\ln\frac{25}{8}$

Analytical solution of first order differential equations with separable variables

First order differential equations are equations connecting x and y with $\frac{dy}{dx}$. Here these equations can be solved to find an equation just connecting x and y by separating the variables and integrating. The following example shows this technique.

Example

① Solve the differential equation

$$\frac{dy}{dx}=3xy^2$$

Given that $x = 2$ when $y = 1$ give the answer in the form $y = f(x)$.

Answer

① $\frac{dy}{dx}=3xy^2$

Separating the variables and integrating, we obtain

$\int\frac{dy}{y^2}=\int 3x\ dx$

$\int y^{-2}\ dy=\int 3x\ dx$

$-y^{-1}=\frac{3x^2}{2}+c$

$-\frac{1}{y}=\frac{3x^2}{2}+c$

You need to swap the equation around so that all the terms involving x are on one side of the equation and all the terms involving y are on the other side.

When $x = 2, y = 1$

Hence $-1 = 6 + c$ giving $c = -7$

Multiplying both sides by $-2y$ to remove the fractions.

then $-\frac{1}{y} = \frac{3x^2}{2} - 7$

$2 = -3x^2y + 14y$

$2 = y(14 - 3x^2)$

$y = \frac{2}{14 - 3x^2}$

Note that the question asks for the equation to be given in the form $y = f(x)$.

Examination style questions

① (a) Express $\frac{5x^2 + 6x + 7}{(x-1)(x+2)^2}$ as partial fractions. [4]

(b) Using your answer from part (a), find

$\int_2^3 \frac{5x^2 + 6x + 7}{(x-1)(x+2)^2} dx$, giving your answer correct to two decimal places. [4]

Answer

① (a) $\frac{5x^2 + 6x + 7}{(x-1)(x+2)^2} \equiv \frac{A}{(x-1)} + \frac{B}{(x+2)} + \frac{C}{(x+2)^2}$

Note that there is a repeated linear factor of $(x + 2)^2$ here.

$5x^2 + 6x + 7 \equiv A(x + 2)^2 + B(x - 1)(x + 2) + C(x - 1)$

Let $x = 1$ so $18 = 9A$, $A = 2$

Let $x = -2$ so $15 = -3C$, giving $C = -5$

Let $x = 0$ so $7 = 8 - 2B + 5$, giving $B = 3$

$\frac{5x^2 + 6x + 7}{(x-1)(x+2)^2} \equiv \frac{2}{(x-1)} + \frac{3}{(x+2)} - \frac{5}{(x+2)^2}$

Check by letting $x = -1$

LHS $= \frac{5x^2 + 6x + 7}{(x-1)(x+2)^2} = \frac{5(-1)^2 + 6(-1) + 7}{(-1-1)(-1+2)^2} = \frac{6}{-2} = -3$

This provides a useful check that the values of A, B and C are correct.

$$\text{RHS} = \frac{2}{(x-1)} + \frac{3}{(x+2)} - \frac{5}{(x+2)^2} = \frac{2}{(-1-1)} + \frac{3}{(-1+2)} - \frac{5}{(-1+2)^2} = -1+3-5 = -3$$

LHS = RHS

Hence partial fractions are:

$$\frac{2}{(x-1)} + \frac{3}{(x+2)} - \frac{5}{(x+2)^2}$$

(b) $$\int_2^3 \frac{5x^2+6x+7}{(x-1)(x+2)^2}\,dx \equiv \int_2^3 \left(\frac{2}{(x-1)} + \frac{3}{(x+2)} - \frac{5}{(x+2)^2}\right) dx$$

$$= \int_2^3 \left(\frac{2}{(x-1)} + \frac{3}{(x+2)} - 5(x+2)^{-2}\right) dx$$

To integrate $-5(x+2)^{-2}$ increase the index by 1 divide by the derivative of the contents of the bracket and divide by the new index.

$$= \left[2\ln(x-1) + 3\ln(x+2) + 5(x+2)^{-1}\right]_2^3$$

$$= \left[2\ln(x-1) + 3\ln(x+2) + \frac{5}{x+2}\right]_2^3$$

$$= \left[(2\ln 2 + 3\ln 5 + 1) - \left(2\ln 1 + 3\ln 4 + \frac{5}{4}\right)\right]$$

= 1.81 (correct to two decimal places)

② (a) Find $\int x^2 e^{-2x}\,dx$ [4]

(b) Use the substitution $u = 1 + 2x$ to evaluate the integral

$$\int_0^{\frac{1}{2}} \frac{4x}{(1+2x)^4}\,dx$$ [5]

Answer

② (a) $\int x^2 e^{-2x}\,dx$

This is the integral of a product, so integration by parts is used.

$$\int u\frac{dv}{dx}dx = uv - \int v\frac{du}{dx}dx$$

Rule 1 is used since e^{-2x} is easily integrated. Hence we will let $u = x^2$ and $\frac{dv}{dx} = e^{-2x}$. We then obtain $\frac{du}{dx} = 2x$, $v = -\frac{e^{-2x}}{2}$.

$$\int x^2e^{-2x}dx = x^2\left(-\frac{1}{2}e^{-2x}\right) - \int\left(-\frac{1}{2}e^{-2x}\right)2x\,dx$$

$$= \frac{-x^2e^{-2x}}{2} + \int xe^{-2x}\,dx$$

Notice that the integral is a product and will need to be integrated by parts again.

Integrating the second integral by parts again we obtain

$$\int xe^{-2x}\,dx = x\left(-\frac{1}{2}e^{-2x}\right) - \int -\frac{1}{2}e^{-2x}(1)\,dx$$

$$= -\frac{xe^{-2x}}{2} - \frac{e^{-2x}}{4}$$

Let $u = x, \frac{dv}{dx} = e^{-2x}$

So $\frac{du}{dx} = 1, v = \frac{-e^{-2x}}{2}$

Hence $\int x^2e^{-2x}dx = \frac{-x^2e^{-2x}}{2} - \frac{xe^{-2x}}{2} - \frac{e^{-2x}}{4} + c$

Remember that a constant of integration, c will need to be included.

(b) $u = 1 + 2x$ so $\frac{du}{dx} = 2$ giving $dx = \frac{du}{2}$

When $x = \frac{1}{2}, u = 2$

When $x = 0, u = 1$

Note that there is a $4x$ in the integral which needs to be written in terms of the new variable, u.

As $u = 1 + 2x$, on rearranging we obtain $2x = u - 1$

Hence $4x = 2(u - 1)$

Now $\int_0^{\frac{1}{2}} \frac{4x}{(1+2x)^4}\,dx = \int_1^2 \frac{2(u-1)}{u^4}\frac{du}{2}$

$$= \int_1^2 \frac{(u-1)}{u^4}\,du$$

$$= \int_1^2 u^{-4}(u-1)\,du$$

$$= \int_1^2 \left(u^{-3} - u^{-4}\right)du$$

$$= \left[\frac{u^{-2}}{-2} - \frac{u^{-3}}{-3}\right]_1^2$$

$$= \left[-\frac{1}{2u^2} + \frac{1}{3u^3}\right]_1^2$$

$$= \left[\left(-\frac{1}{8} + \frac{1}{24}\right) - \left(-\frac{1}{2} + \frac{1}{3}\right)\right]$$

Use a calculator to work this out, if you prefer.

$$= \frac{1}{12}$$

Test yourself

Answer the following questions and check your answers before moving on to the next topic.

① The region bounded by the curve $y = \sqrt{e^{2x} + 3}$, the x-axis and the lines $x = 0$ and $x = 1$ is rotated through four right angles about the x-axis. Find the volume of the solid generated, giving your answer correct to three decimal places.

② Find $\int (2x + 1)e^{2x}\, dx$

③ By using the substitution $x = 2 \sin \theta$, evaluate

$\int_0^1 \sqrt{(4 - x^2)}\, dx$ giving your answer correct to three decimal places.

④ The region R is bounded by the curve $y = 2x + \frac{2}{\sqrt{x}}$, the x-axis and the lines $x = 1$, $x = 2$.

Find the volume generated when R is rotated through four right angles about the x-axis. Give your answer correct to three decimal places.

⑤ The region enclosed by the curve $y = x^2 - 4$, the x-axis and the lines $x = 2$, $x = 3$ is rotated around the x-axis through four right angles. Find the volume generated, giving your answer correct to three decimal places.

⑥ Solve the equation

$$\frac{dy}{dx} = \frac{y}{x+2},$$

given that $y = 2$ when $x = 0$

(Note: answers to Test yourself are found at the back of the book.)

1 The region R is bounded by the curve $y = \sin x$, the x-axis and the lines $x = \frac{\pi}{6}$, $x = \frac{\pi}{3}$.

Find the volume generated when R is rotated through four right angles about the x-axis. Give your answer correct to three decimal places. [5]

(WJEC C4 June 2010 Q4)

1

Answer

1 Volume of revolution $= \pi\int_{\frac{\pi}{6}}^{\frac{\pi}{3}} y^2 \mathrm{d}x$

This formula is not in the formula booklet so it needs to be remembered.

$$= \pi\int_{\frac{\pi}{6}}^{\frac{\pi}{3}} \sin^2 x \, \mathrm{d}x$$

Here the double angle formula $\sin^2 x = \frac{1-\cos 2x}{2}$ is used.

$$= \frac{\pi}{2}\int_{\frac{\pi}{6}}^{\frac{\pi}{3}} (1-\cos 2x)\ \mathrm{d}x$$

$$= \frac{\pi}{2}\left[x - \frac{\sin 2x}{2}\right]_{\frac{\pi}{6}}^{\frac{\pi}{3}}$$

$$= \frac{\pi}{2}\left[\left(\frac{\pi}{3} - \frac{\sin\frac{2\pi}{3}}{2}\right) - \left(\frac{\pi}{6} - \frac{\sin\frac{\pi}{3}}{2}\right)\right]$$

$$= \frac{\pi}{2}\left[\left(\frac{\pi}{6} - \frac{\sin\frac{2\pi}{3}}{2}\right) + \left(\frac{\sin\frac{\pi}{3}}{2}\right)\right]$$

$$= \frac{\pi^2}{12}$$

$= 0.822$ (correct to three decimal places)

Q&A 2

2 The region bounded by the curve $y = \cos 2x$, the x-axis and the lines $x = 0$, $x = \frac{\pi}{8}$, is rotated about the x-axis through four right angles. Find the volume of the solid generated.

[6]

(WJEC C4 June 2009 Q4)

Answer

2 Volume of revolution $= \pi\int_0^{\frac{\pi}{8}} y^2 \mathrm{d}x$

$$= \pi\int_0^{\frac{\pi}{8}} \cos^2 2x \, \mathrm{d}x$$

$$= \pi\int_0^{\frac{\pi}{8}} \frac{1+\cos 4x}{2} \mathrm{d}x$$

$$= \pi\left[\frac{x}{2} + \frac{\sin 4x}{8}\right]_0^{\frac{\pi}{8}}$$

$$= \pi\left[\left(\frac{\pi}{16} + \frac{1}{8}\right) - (0+0)\right]$$

$= 1.010$ (correct to three decimal places)

Topic 6 Vectors

This topic covers the following:

- Scalars and vectors
- Vectors in two and three dimensions
- Magnitude of a vector
- Algebraic operations of vector addition and multiplication by scalars, and their geometrical interpretations
- Position vectors
- The distance between two points
- Vector equation of a line
- The scalar product and its use for calculating the angle between two lines

Scalars and vectors

A scalar is a quantity that has size only. It is simply represented by a number and has no direction. Distance, speed and time are scalar quantities.

A vector is a quantity such as force, velocity and displacement (i.e. distance in a specific direction) which has both a size (i.e. magnitude) and a direction. A vector can be represented by a line whose length represents the size and a direction in which the line is pointing.

Note that we have defined a vector in terms of magnitude and direction, but have not been specific about the position of the vector in space. Such vectors are called free vectors.

All the lines below which are parallel and of equal magnitude represent the vector **a**.

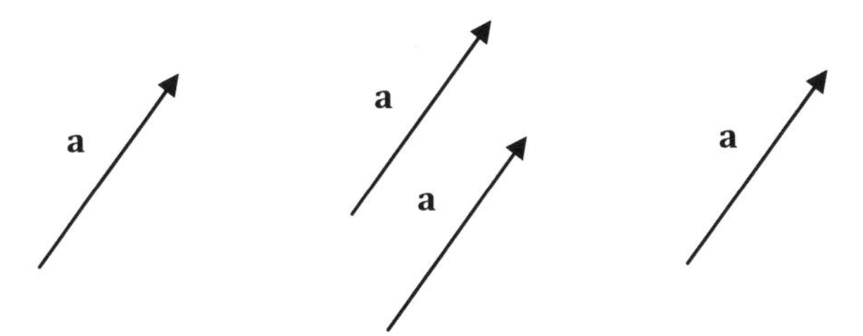

The notation used for vectors

The vector $\overrightarrow{AB}$ can be represented as a single letter in bold (e.g. **r**) but when handwritten it is can be written with the letter underlined like $\underline{r}$. You may also see the vector $\overrightarrow{AB}$ written without the arrow but in bold like **AB**. The length of a vector is written as $|\mathbf{r}|$.

Vectors in two and three dimensions

Vectors can be represented in two or three dimensions. Vectors in two dimensions can be drawn in the plane of the paper. Vectors in three dimensions have an additional axis at right angles to the plane of the paper.

Vectors in two dimensions

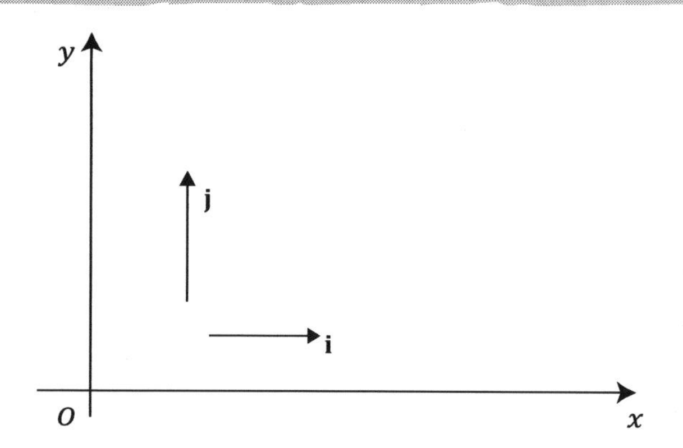

i and **j** are called unit vectors in the directions of Ox and Oy respectively.

Any vector in two dimensions can be written in terms of the unit vectors **i** and **j** in the following way:

$\mathbf{r} = a\mathbf{i} + b\mathbf{j}$ where a and b are scalars.

For example, here are some vectors expressed in terms of the unit vectors.

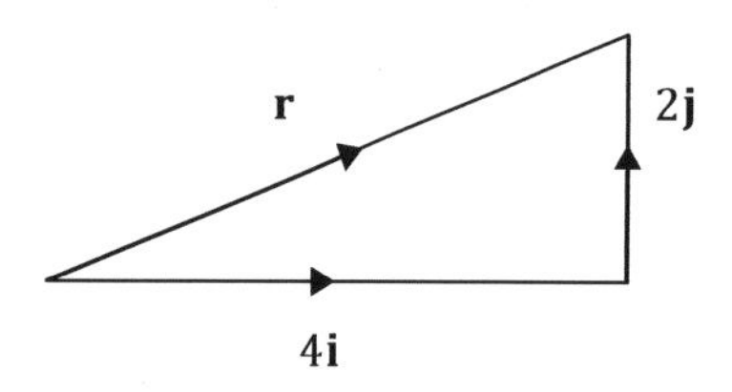

$\mathbf{r} = 4\mathbf{i} + 2\mathbf{j}$

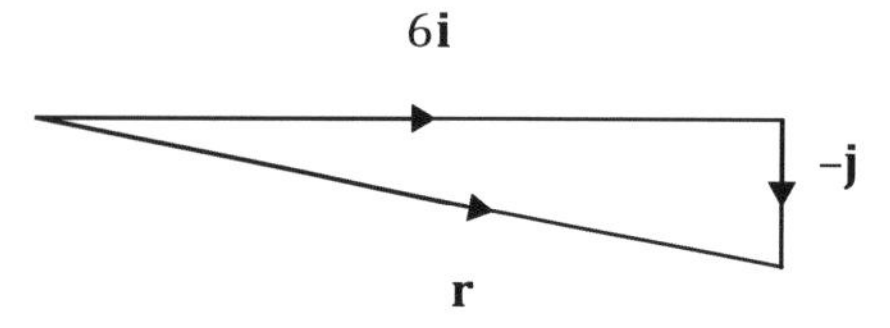

$\mathbf{r} = 6\mathbf{i} - \mathbf{j}$

Vectors in three dimensions

To represent vectors in three dimensions a third axis Oz is needed. The unit vectors are now **i**, **j** and **k** in the directions Ox, Oy and Oz respectively.

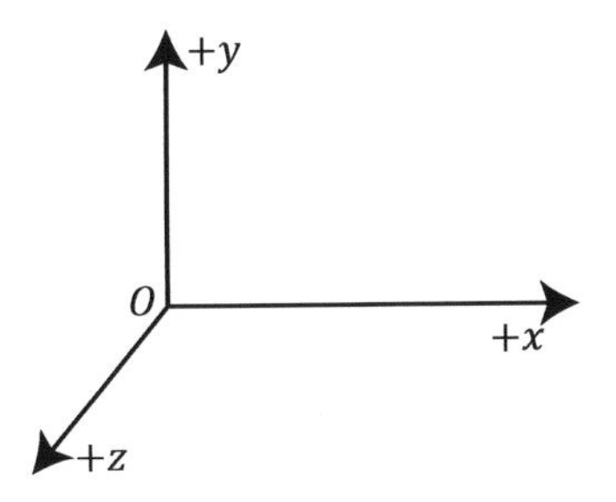

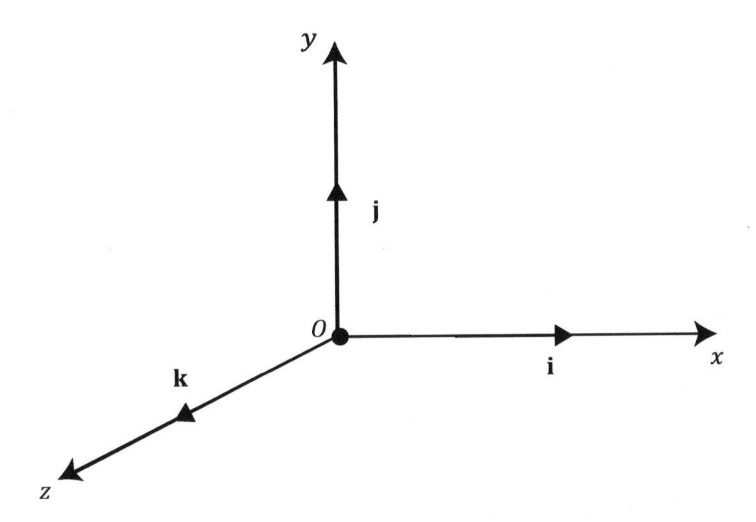

Vectors in three dimensions can be written in terms of the unit vectors **i**, **j** and **k** in the following way:

$a\mathbf{i} + b\mathbf{j} + c\mathbf{k}$ where a, b and c are scalars.

The magnitude of a vector

The magnitude of a vector is the length of the vector.

The vector $\mathbf{r} = a\mathbf{i} + b\mathbf{j} + c\mathbf{k}$ has magnitude given by $|\mathbf{r}| = \sqrt{a^2 + b^2 + c^2}$

Example

Find the magnitude of the vector $\mathbf{a} = 2\mathbf{i} - 2\mathbf{j} + \mathbf{k}$.

Answer

$|\mathbf{a}| = \sqrt{2^2 + (-2)^2 + (1)^2} = \sqrt{9} = 3$

Algebraic operations of vector addition, subtraction and multiplication by scalars, and their geometrical interpretations

Addition, subtraction and multiplication by a scalar can be performed algebraically as the following example shows.

Example

① If $\mathbf{a} = \mathbf{i} + 3\mathbf{j} + 2\mathbf{k}$ and $\mathbf{b} = 3\mathbf{i} - 2\mathbf{j} - \mathbf{k}$, find each of the following.

(a) $\mathbf{a} + \mathbf{b}$

(b) $\mathbf{a} - \mathbf{b}$

(c) $2\mathbf{a}$

(d) $2\mathbf{a} + 3\mathbf{b}$

Answer

① (a) $\mathbf{a} + \mathbf{b} = \mathbf{i} + 3\mathbf{j} + 2\mathbf{k} + 3\mathbf{i} - 2\mathbf{j} - \mathbf{k} = 4\mathbf{i} + \mathbf{j} + \mathbf{k}$

(b) $\mathbf{a} - \mathbf{b} = \mathbf{i} + 3\mathbf{j} + 2\mathbf{k} - (3\mathbf{i} - 2\mathbf{j} - \mathbf{k}) = -2\mathbf{i} + 5\mathbf{j} + 3\mathbf{k}$

(c) $2\mathbf{a} = 2(\mathbf{i} + 3\mathbf{j} + 2\mathbf{k}) = 2\mathbf{i} + 6\mathbf{j} + 4\mathbf{k}$

(d) $2\mathbf{a} + 3\mathbf{b} = 2(\mathbf{i} + 3\mathbf{j} + 2\mathbf{k}) + 3(3\mathbf{i} - 2\mathbf{j} - \mathbf{k}) = 11\mathbf{i} + \mathbf{k}$

The geometrical interpretation of vectors

The geometrical interpretation of the results in 1 (a) to (d) of the previous example is as follows:

1 (a)

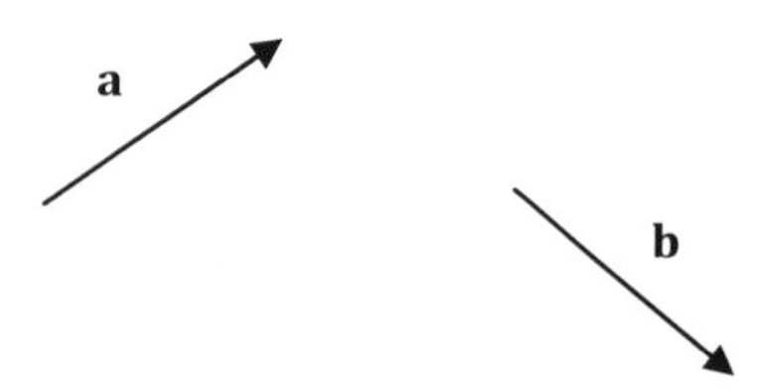

To add two vectors **a** and **b** as shown, place the starting point of **b** at the finishing point of **a** and complete the triangle. The directed third line represents **a** + **b**.

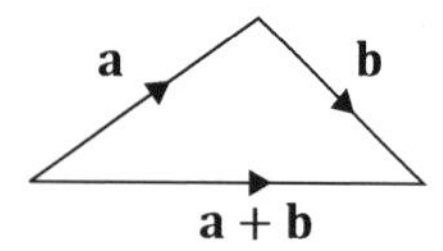

As we are dealing with free vectors, we can move our vector representation.

We could place the starting point of **a** at the finishing point of **b** to form **b** + **a** which equals **a** + **b**. Remember that **a** + **b** and **b** + **a** are free vectors.

1 (b) To draw **a** – **b**, we reverse the direction of **b** to form –**b** and place the starting point of –**b** at the finishing point of **a**.

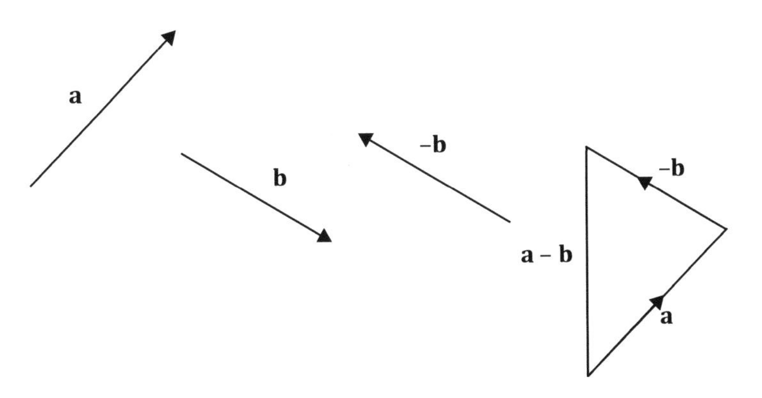

1 (c)

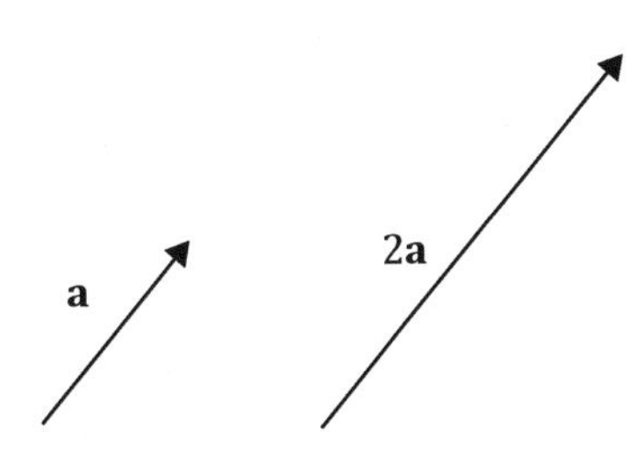

2**a** is a vector parallel to **a** with magnitude equal to twice the magnitude of **a**.

1 (d)

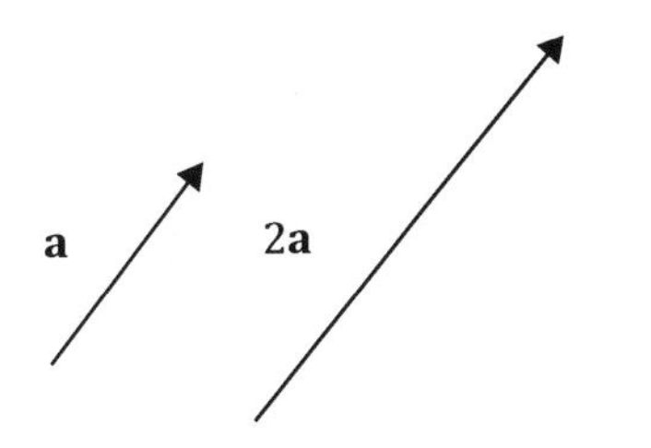

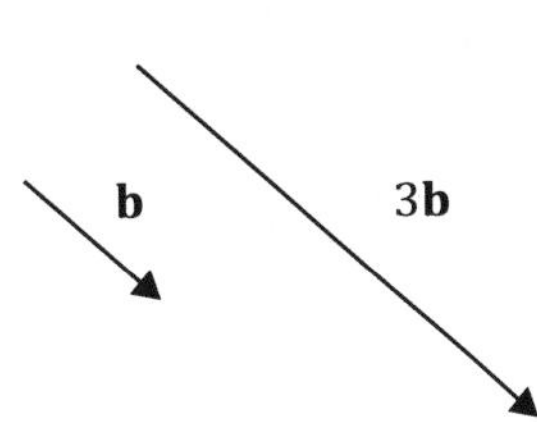

We form 2**a** and 3**b** as shown and use the procedure given in 1(a) to obtain the vector 2**a** + 3**b**.

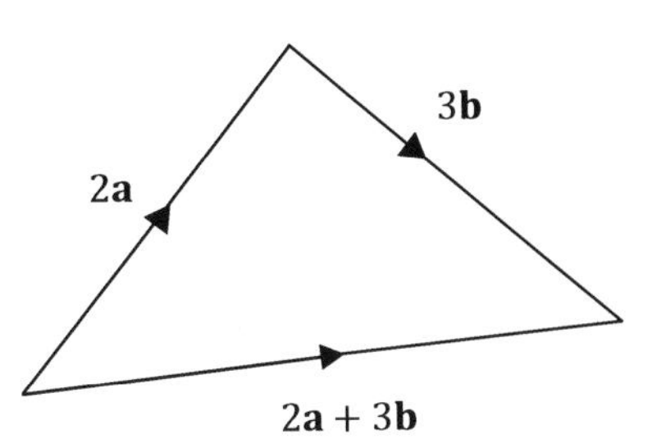

The condition for two vectors to be parallel

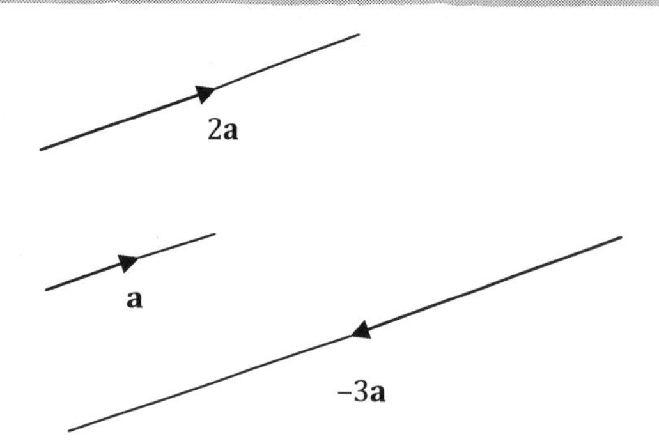

For two vectors **a** and **b** to be parallel one of the vectors must be a multiple of the other, so

$\mathbf{a} = k\mathbf{b}$ where k is a scalar

For example, if $\mathbf{a} = 3\mathbf{i} - \mathbf{j} + 2\mathbf{k}$ and $\mathbf{b} = 6\mathbf{i} - 2\mathbf{j} + 4\mathbf{k}$, $\mathbf{a} = 2\mathbf{b}$ so vectors **a** and **b** are parallel and vector **a** has a magnitude of twice that of **b**.

Position vectors

Position vectors are vectors giving the position of a point, relative to a fixed point (usually the origin). The position vector of a point P relative to the origin O is defined by the vector $\overrightarrow{OP}$. In contrast to a free vector, a position vector is represented by a particular line in space.

If the position vector of A is **a** and the position vector of B is **b** then the following diagram can be drawn showing the two vectors.

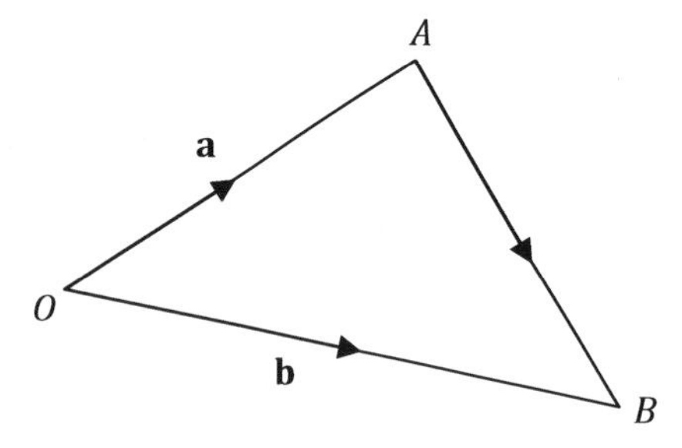

Note that $\overrightarrow{AB}$ can also be written using the alternative notation for vectors as **AB**.

$\overrightarrow{AB} = \overrightarrow{AO} + \overrightarrow{OB} = -\overrightarrow{OA} + \overrightarrow{OB} = -\mathbf{a} + \mathbf{b}$

Hence $\overrightarrow{AB} = \mathbf{b} - \mathbf{a}$

This is an important result and should be remembered.

The distance between two points

The distance between two points $A(x_1, y_1, z_1)$ and $B(x_2, y_2, z_2)$ is given by

$d = \sqrt{(x_2 - x_1)^2 + (y_2 - y_1)^2 + (z_2 - z_1)^2}$

Note that if the points are given in two dimensions (i.e. $A(x_1, y_1)$ and $B(x_2, y_2)$ the formula for the distance between these two points now becomes

$d = \sqrt{(x_2 - x_1)^2 + (y_2 - y_1)^2}$

Example

Find the distance between the points $A(3, 5, 1)$ and $B(4, 7, 3)$.

Answer

$d = \sqrt{(x_2 - x_1)^2 + (y_2 - y_1)^2 + (z_2 - z_1)^2}$

$d = \sqrt{(4-3)^2 + (7-5)^2 + (3-1)^2}$

$d = \sqrt{1+4+4}$

$d = \sqrt{9}$

$d = 3$

Vector equation of a line

The vector equation of a line passing through point A with position vector **a**, where the line is parallel to a vector **b**, is given by:

$\mathbf{r} = \mathbf{a} + \lambda\mathbf{b}$ where λ is a scalar.

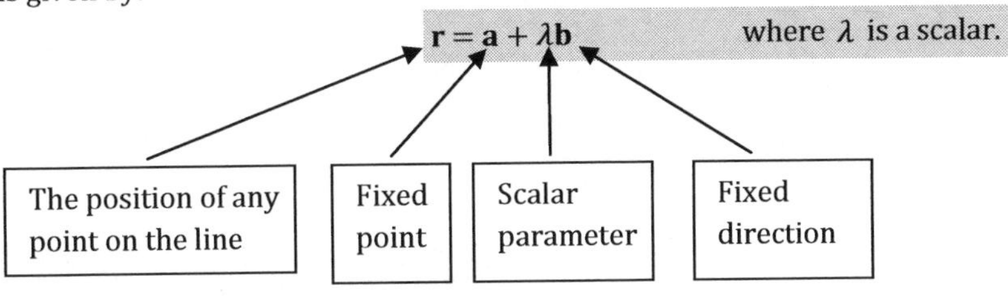

For example, suppose a line joins two points A and B like this:

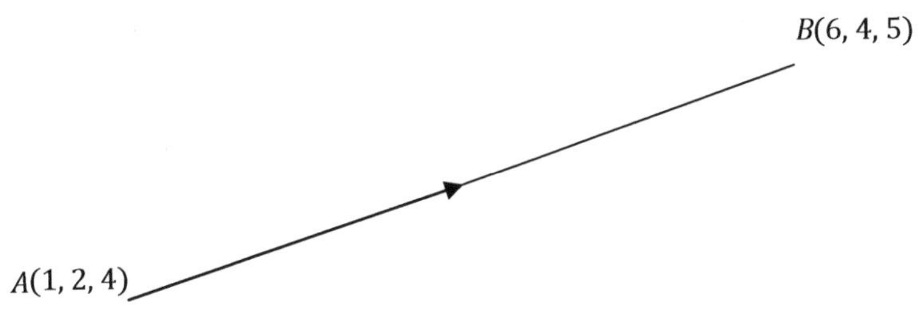

If you look at the diagram you can see that to go from A to B you would move 5 units in the x-direction, 2 units in the y-direction and finally 1 unit in the z-direction. This specifies the direction and is called the direction vector of the line and can be written in terms of the unit vectors in the following way:

Direction vector of $AB = 5\mathbf{i} + 2\mathbf{j} + \mathbf{k}$

It is important to note that if one line has a position vector that is a multiple of a different line, then the two lines are parallel.

For example, if the position vectors of two lines are $5\mathbf{i} + 2\mathbf{j} + \mathbf{k}$ and $15\mathbf{i} + 6\mathbf{j} + 3\mathbf{k}$, then $15\mathbf{i} + 6\mathbf{j} + 3\mathbf{k} = 3(5\mathbf{i} + 2\mathbf{j} + \mathbf{k})$, so the direction vectors (and lines) are parallel.

In order to obtain the vector equation of the line AB it is not sufficient to know the direction vector on its own. You need to know where the line starts. The line AB starts from A and point A has coordinates (1, 2, 4).

The vector equation of the line AB can be written as follows:

$\mathbf{r} = \mathbf{i} + 2\mathbf{j} + 4\mathbf{k} + \lambda(5\mathbf{i} + 2\mathbf{j} + \mathbf{k})$

Example

Find a vector equation for the line AB where A is the point (2, 6, 2) and B is the point (4, 8, 10).

Answer

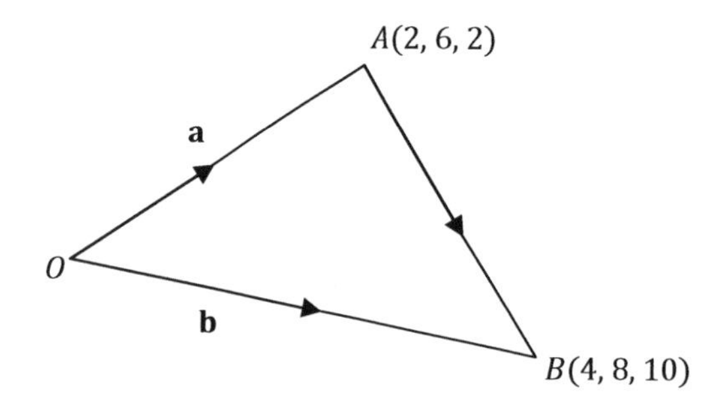

The points A and B have position vectors $2\mathbf{i} + 6\mathbf{j} + 2\mathbf{k}$ and $4\mathbf{i} + 8\mathbf{j} + 10\mathbf{k}$.

Then $\mathbf{a} = 2\mathbf{i} + 6\mathbf{j} + 2\mathbf{k}$

$\mathbf{b} = 4\mathbf{i} + 8\mathbf{j} + 10\mathbf{k}$

$\mathbf{AB} = \mathbf{b} - \mathbf{a}$

$= (4\mathbf{i} + 8\mathbf{j} + 10\mathbf{k}) - (2\mathbf{i} + 6\mathbf{j} + 2\mathbf{k})$
$= (2\mathbf{i} + 2\mathbf{j} + 8\mathbf{k})$

The vector equation of line AB is

λ is a scalar quantity.

$\mathbf{r} = (2\mathbf{i} + 6\mathbf{j} + 2\mathbf{k}) + \lambda(2\mathbf{i} + 2\mathbf{j} + 8\mathbf{k})$

The condition for a pair of lines to intersect

For the two lines with equations $\mathbf{r} = \mathbf{a} + \lambda\mathbf{b}$ and $\mathbf{r} = \mathbf{c} + \mu\mathbf{d}$ to intersect, there must be values of λ and μ so that the following equation is true:

$\mathbf{a} + \lambda\mathbf{b} = \mathbf{c} + \mu\mathbf{d}$

This expresses the fact that two intersecting lines have a point in common.

The method for finding the numerical value of λ and μ usually involves the use of simultaneous equations as the following example shows.

Example

① The line L_1 has vector equation $\mathbf{r} = 6\mathbf{i} - 3\mathbf{j} - 2\mathbf{k} + \lambda(-\mathbf{i} + 2\mathbf{j} + 3\mathbf{k})$. Line L_2 has vector equation $\mathbf{r} = -5\mathbf{i} + 15\mathbf{j} + 3\mathbf{k} + \mu(2\mathbf{i} - 3\mathbf{j} + \mathbf{k})$. Prove that lines L_1 and L_2 intersect and find the coordinates of their point of intersection.

Answer

① At the point of intersection, the position vectors given by the two equations are equal.

Equating coefficients of **i**, we have

$6 - \lambda = -5 + 2\mu$ ....(1)

> The numbers in front of the **i**'s (i.e the coefficients) in lines L_1 and L_2 are equated.

Equating coefficients of **j**, we have

$-3 + 2\lambda = 15 - 3\mu$ ....(2)

> The coefficients of **j** in the equations for lines L_1 and L_2 are now equated.

Multiplying equation (1) by 2 and then adding to equation (2) we obtain

> The two resulting equations are now solved simultaneously so that the values of μ and λ can be found.

$9 = 5 + \mu$ giving $\mu = 4$

Substituting $\mu = 4$ into equation (1) we obtain $6 - \lambda = -5 + 8$ giving $\lambda = 3$

Equating coefficients of **k** gives

$-2 + 3\lambda = 3 + \mu$

LHS $= -2 + 3(3) = 7$

RHS $= 3 + 4 = 7$

> The coefficients of **k** are equated and the values of μ and λ are put into both sides of the equation. If both sides are equal then the values of μ and λ satisfy all three equations thus proving that the two lines L_1 and L_2 intersect.

As the LHS = RHS the two lines intersect.

Putting $\lambda = 3$ into the vector equation for line L_1 gives

$$\begin{aligned}\mathbf{r} &= 6\mathbf{i} - 3\mathbf{j} - 2\mathbf{k} + 3(-\mathbf{i} + 2\mathbf{j} + 3\mathbf{k})\\ &= 6\mathbf{i} - 3\mathbf{j} - 2\mathbf{k} - 3\mathbf{i} + 6\mathbf{j} + 9\mathbf{k}\\ &= 3\mathbf{i} + 3\mathbf{j} + 7\mathbf{k}\end{aligned}$$

> The values of λ or μ are substituted into either of the equations of the lines. The result is the position vector of the point of intersection. The coefficients of **i**, **j** and **k** give the coordinates of the point of intersection.

Hence the coordinates of the point of intersection are (3, 3, 7)

Scalar product

The scalar product of two vectors **a** and **b** is written as **a.b** (pronounced A dot B).

The scalar product of two vectors is given by the following:

$$\mathbf{a.b} = (x_1\mathbf{i} + y_1\mathbf{j} + z_1\mathbf{k}).(x_2\mathbf{i} + y_2\mathbf{j} + z_2\mathbf{k})$$
$$= x_1x_2 + y_1y_2 + z_1z_2$$

Example

If **a** = 2**i** – 2**j** + **k** and **b** = **i** – 4**j** + 8**k**, find the scalar product of the vectors.

Answer

$\mathbf{a.b} = (2\mathbf{i} - 2\mathbf{j} + \mathbf{k}).(\mathbf{i} - 4\mathbf{j} + 8\mathbf{k}) = (2)(1) + (-2)(-4) + (1)(8) = 2 + 8 + 8 = 18$

The angle between two vectors

The angle θ between two vectors **a** and **b** can be found by using the scalar (or dot) product given by

$\mathbf{a.b} = |\mathbf{a}||\mathbf{b}| \cos \theta$

a.b is the scalar product.

|**a**| and |**b**| are the magnitudes of the vectors **a** and **b** respectively.

Example

① Find the angle between the following two vectors:

a = 2**i** + 4**j** + **k**

b = 8**i** +**j** + 5**k**

Answer

① $\mathbf{a.b} = (2\mathbf{i} + 4\mathbf{j} + \mathbf{k}).(8\mathbf{i} + \mathbf{j} + 5\mathbf{k})$
$= (2)(8) + (4)(1) + (1)(5)$
$= 16 + 4 + 5$
$= 25$

$|\mathbf{a}| = \sqrt{2^2 + 4^2 + 1^2} = \sqrt{21}$

$|\mathbf{b}| = \sqrt{8^2 + 1^2 + 5^2} = \sqrt{90}$

$\mathbf{a.b} = |\mathbf{a}||\mathbf{b}| \cos \theta$

$$\cos \theta = \frac{\mathbf{a.b}}{|\mathbf{a}||\mathbf{b}|}$$
$$= \frac{25}{\sqrt{21}\sqrt{90}}$$
$$= 0.5751$$
$$\theta = \cos^{-1}(0.5751)$$
$$= 54.9°$$

Condition for vectors to be perpendicular to each other

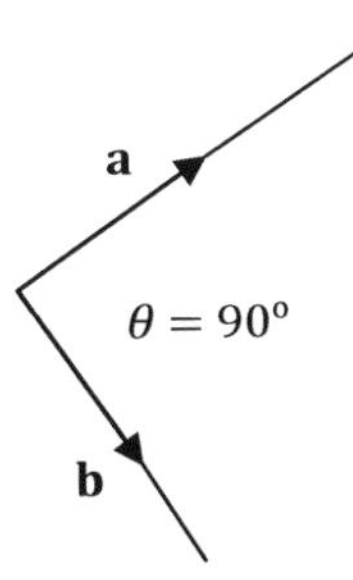

$\mathbf{a}.\mathbf{b} = |\mathbf{a}||\mathbf{b}| \cos \theta$ and when $\theta = 90°$, $\cos 90° = 0$.

So $\mathbf{a}.\mathbf{b} = 0$

Provided that neither or both of the vectors are zero, if the scalar product of the vectors is zero, then the two vectors are perpendicular to each other.

Hence for perpendicular vectors **a** and **b**, $\mathbf{a}.\mathbf{b} = 0$

Example

If $\mathbf{a} = 3\mathbf{i} + 4\mathbf{j} - 2\mathbf{k}$ and $\mathbf{b} = -2\mathbf{i} + \mathbf{j} - \mathbf{k}$, show that these two vectors are perpendicular to each other.

Answer

$\mathbf{a}.\mathbf{b} = (3\mathbf{i} + 4\mathbf{j} - 2\mathbf{k}).(-2\mathbf{i} + \mathbf{j} - \mathbf{k}) = (3)(-2) + (4)(1) + (-2)(-1) = -6 + 4 + 2 = 0$

Since $\mathbf{a}.\mathbf{b} = 0$, vectors **a** and **b** are perpendicular.

Example

① The position vectors of the points A and B are given by

$\mathbf{a} = 2\mathbf{i} - 2\mathbf{j} + \mathbf{k}$,

$\mathbf{b} = \mathbf{i} - 4\mathbf{j} + 8\mathbf{k}$,

respectively.

(a) Find the angle between the vectors **a** and **b**. [4]

(b) (i) Write down the vector **AB**.

(ii) Find the vector equation of the line AB. [3]

(c) The vector equation of the line L is given by

$$\mathbf{r} = -\mathbf{i} - 4\mathbf{j} - 2\mathbf{k} + \mu(\mathbf{i} + \mathbf{j} - \mathbf{k}).$$

Show that the lines AB and L intersect and find the position vector of the point of intersection. [6]

(WJEC C4 June 2010 Q9)

Answer

① (a) $\mathbf{a.b} = (2\mathbf{i} - 2\mathbf{j} + \mathbf{k}).(\mathbf{i} - 4\mathbf{j} + 8\mathbf{k})$
$= (2)(1) + (-2)(-4) + (1)(8)$
$= 18$

Use the scalar product formula
$\mathbf{a.b} = (x_1\mathbf{i} + y_1\mathbf{j} + z_1\mathbf{k}).(x_2\mathbf{i} + y_2\mathbf{j} + z_2\mathbf{k})$
$= x_1x_2 + y_1y_2 + z_1z_2$

$|\mathbf{a}| = \sqrt{2^2 + (-2)^2 + 1^2} = \sqrt{9} = 3$

$|\mathbf{b}| = \sqrt{1^2 + (-4)^2 + 8^2} = \sqrt{81} = 9$

The magnitude of each vector is now found using
$|\mathbf{a}| = \sqrt{x_1^2 + y_1^2 + z_1^2}$ and
$|\mathbf{b}| = \sqrt{x_2^2 + y_2^2 + z_2^2}$

$\mathbf{a.b} = |\mathbf{a}||\mathbf{b}| \cos\theta$

$\cos\theta = \frac{\mathbf{a.b}}{|\mathbf{a}||\mathbf{b}|} = \frac{18}{3 \times 9} = \frac{2}{3}$

Note that you are not given this formula in the formula booklet so it must be remembered.

$\theta = \cos^{-1}\left(\frac{2}{3}\right) = 48.2°$

(b) (i)

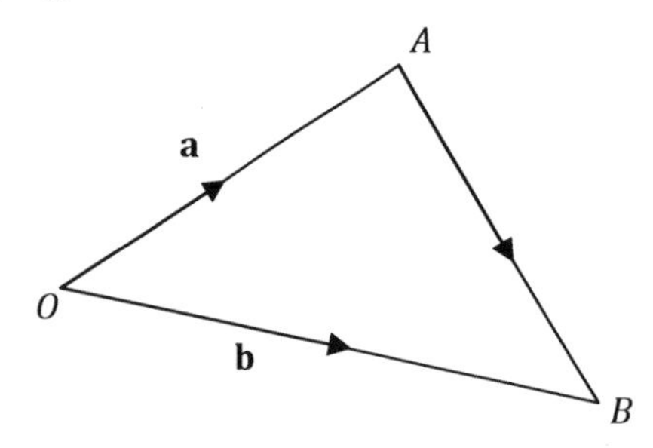

$\mathbf{AB} = \mathbf{AO} + \mathbf{OB}$
$= -\mathbf{a} + \mathbf{b}$
$= -(2\mathbf{i} - 2\mathbf{j} + \mathbf{k}) + (\mathbf{i} - 4\mathbf{j} + 8\mathbf{k})$
$= -\mathbf{i} - 2\mathbf{j} + 7\mathbf{k}$

(ii) The vector equation of line AB is

$\mathbf{r} = \mathbf{a} + \lambda(\mathbf{b} - \mathbf{a})$
$= (2\mathbf{i} - 2\mathbf{j} + \mathbf{k}) + \lambda(-\mathbf{i} - 2\mathbf{j} + 7\mathbf{k})$

(c) $\mathbf{r} = (2\mathbf{i} - 2\mathbf{j} + \mathbf{k}) + \lambda(-\mathbf{i} - 2\mathbf{j} + 7\mathbf{k})$
$\mathbf{r} = (-\mathbf{i} - 4\mathbf{j} - 2\mathbf{k}) + \mu(\mathbf{i} + \mathbf{j} - \mathbf{k})$

This is the equation of line AB.

This is the equation of line L.

Equate the position vectors

$2 - \lambda = -1 + \mu$ ....(1)
$-2 - 2\lambda = -4 + \mu$ ....(2)
$1 + 7\lambda = -2 - \mu$ ....(3)

Each of these three equations is found by comparing the coefficients for **i**, **j** and **k** respectively for each of the two lines.

Solve these equations simultaneously.

Adding (2) and (3), we obtain
$-1 + 5\lambda = -6$
Hence $\lambda = -1$

Substituting $\lambda = -1$ into equation (3) we have
$1 - 7 = -2 - \mu$
Hence $\mu = 4$
Checking in (1) we have $2 - (-1) = -1 + 4$
Hence $\lambda = -1, \mu = 4$

Grade boost

Not checking the answers of simultaneous equations may lose you marks.

Substituting $\lambda = -1$ into the equation of AB we have

$\mathbf{r} = (2\mathbf{i} - 2\mathbf{j} + \mathbf{k}) + -1(-\mathbf{i} - 2\mathbf{j} + 7\mathbf{k})$
$\mathbf{r} = (2\mathbf{i} + \mathbf{i}) + (-2\mathbf{j} + 2\mathbf{j}) + (\mathbf{k} - 7\mathbf{k})$
$\mathbf{r} = (3\mathbf{i} - 6\mathbf{k})$

The point of intersection can be found by substituting the value of either λ or μ into either equation of the intersecting lines.

The position vector of a point dividing a line in a given ratio

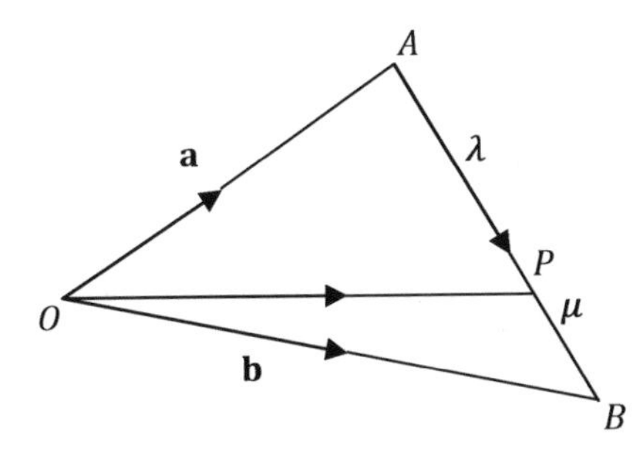

The point P dividing AB in the ratio $\lambda : \mu$ has position vector $\overrightarrow{OP}$

where $\overrightarrow{OP} = \dfrac{\mu\mathbf{a} + \lambda\mathbf{b}}{\lambda + \mu}$

You are required to be able to derive the above formula. It can be derived as follows:

$$\begin{aligned}
\overrightarrow{OP} &= \overrightarrow{OA} + \overrightarrow{AP} \\
&= \mathbf{a} + \frac{\lambda}{\lambda + \mu}\overrightarrow{AB} \\
&= \mathbf{a} + \frac{\lambda}{\lambda + \mu}(\mathbf{b} - \mathbf{a}) \\
&= \frac{(\lambda + \mu)\mathbf{a} + \lambda(\mathbf{b} - \mathbf{a})}{\lambda + \mu} \\
&= \frac{\mu\mathbf{a} + \lambda\mathbf{b}}{\lambda + \mu}
\end{aligned}$$

Example

①

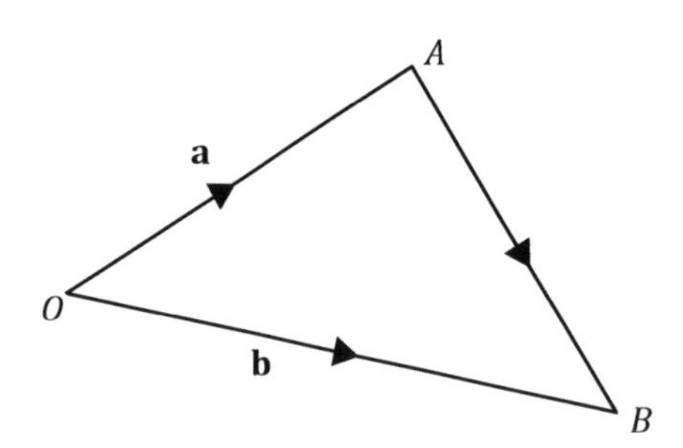

The vectors $\mathbf{a} = 3\mathbf{i} + 2\mathbf{j} + \mathbf{k}$ and $\mathbf{b} = 6\mathbf{i} - 3\mathbf{j} + 5\mathbf{k}$ are the position vectors of A and B respectively.

(a) Find $\overrightarrow{AB}$

(b) Point P divides line AB in the ratio 3 : 1.

Find the position vector $\overrightarrow{OP}$.

Answer

① (a) $\overrightarrow{AB} = \overrightarrow{AO} + \overrightarrow{OB} = -\overrightarrow{OA} + \overrightarrow{OB} = -\mathbf{a} + \mathbf{b}$

Hence $\overrightarrow{AB} = \mathbf{b} - \mathbf{a} = 6\mathbf{i} - 3\mathbf{j} + 5\mathbf{k} - (3\mathbf{i} + 2\mathbf{j} + \mathbf{k}) = 3\mathbf{i} - 5\mathbf{j} + 4\mathbf{k}$

(b)

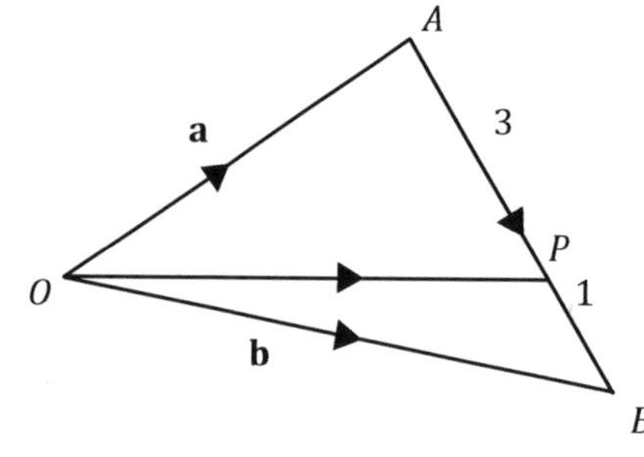

Draw a diagram showing point P splitting line AB in the ratio 3 : 1. Notice that the line is divided into 4 equal parts so AP is three-quarters of the line AB.

$$\overrightarrow{OP} = \overrightarrow{OA} + \overrightarrow{AP}$$

$$= \mathbf{a} + \frac{3}{3+1}\overrightarrow{AB}$$

$$= \mathbf{a} + \frac{3}{4}(3\mathbf{i} - 5\mathbf{j} + 4\mathbf{k})$$

$$= 3\mathbf{i} + 2\mathbf{j} + \mathbf{k} + \frac{3}{4}(3\mathbf{i} - 5\mathbf{j} + 4\mathbf{k})$$

$$= 3\mathbf{i} + 2\mathbf{j} + \mathbf{k} + \frac{9}{4}\mathbf{i} - \frac{15}{4}\mathbf{j} + 3\mathbf{k}$$

$$= \frac{21}{4}\mathbf{i} - \frac{7}{4}\mathbf{j} + 4\mathbf{k}$$

An alternative method to the method shown would be to use the formula $\overrightarrow{OP} = \frac{\mu\mathbf{a} + \lambda\mathbf{b}}{\lambda + \mu}$ which can be obtained from the formula booklet.

Examination style questions

① The position vectors of the points A and B, relative to a fixed origin O, are $3\mathbf{i} - 2\mathbf{j} + 2\mathbf{k}$ and $\mathbf{i} + 3\mathbf{j} - \mathbf{k}$ respectively.

(a) Find **AB**. (2)

(b) Find the vector equation of the line AB. (2)

Answer

① (a)

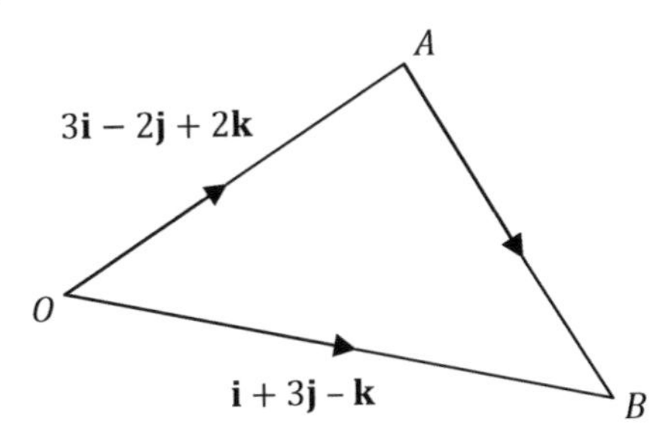

$\mathbf{AB} = -\mathbf{OA} + \mathbf{OB} = -(3\mathbf{i} - 2\mathbf{j} + 2\mathbf{k}) + \mathbf{i} + 3\mathbf{j} - \mathbf{k}$

$\mathbf{AB} = -2\mathbf{i} + 5\mathbf{j} - 3\mathbf{k}$

(b) The vector equation of line AB is

$\mathbf{r} = 3\mathbf{i} - 2\mathbf{j} + 2\mathbf{k} + \lambda(-2\mathbf{i} + 5\mathbf{j} - 3\mathbf{k})$

The alternative notation for vectors could be used here so instead of **r** you could use **AB** or $\overrightarrow{AB}$. It is important to note that you should not give it like this: equation = ( ) **i** + ( ) **j** + ( ) **k**, i.e. you must have **r**, **AB**, $\overrightarrow{AB}$ or left-hand side.

② The line L_1 has equation $\mathbf{r} = 6\mathbf{i} - \mathbf{j} + 5\mathbf{k} + \mu(2\mathbf{i} - \mathbf{j} + 4\mathbf{k})$ and line L_2 has equation $\mathbf{r} = 3\mathbf{i} - 2\mathbf{j} + 5\mathbf{k} + \lambda(-\mathbf{i} + 3\mathbf{j} - 8\mathbf{k})$. Prove that these two lines intersect. [5]

Answer

② Assume that L_1 and L_2 intersect. Equating coefficients of **i** we obtain

$6 + 2\mu = 3 - \lambda$ (1)

Equating coefficients of **j** we obtain

$-1 - \mu = -2 + 3\lambda$ (2)

Multiplying equation (2) by 2 we obtain

$-2 - 2\mu = -4 + 6\lambda$

Adding this equation to (1) we obtain

$4 = -1 + 5\lambda$

$\lambda = 1$

When $\lambda = 1$, in (1), $6 + 2\mu = 3 - 1$

Hence $\mu = -2$

Equating coefficients of **k** we obtain

$5 + 4\mu = 5 - 8\lambda$

When $\mu = -2$, $5 + 4\mu = -3$

When $\lambda = 1$, $5 - 8\lambda = -3$

Hence LHS = RHS so L_1 and L_2 intersect.

③ (a) Find the angle between the vectors $\mathbf{a} = 4\mathbf{i} - \mathbf{j} - 3\mathbf{k}$ and $\mathbf{b} = \mathbf{i} - 2\mathbf{j} - \mathbf{k}$. [3]

(b) Show that the vectors $2\mathbf{i} + 4\mathbf{j} - 2\mathbf{k}$ and $3\mathbf{i} + \mathbf{j} + 5\mathbf{k}$ are perpendicular. [2]

Answer

③ (a) $\mathbf{a.b} = (4\mathbf{i} - \mathbf{j} - 3\mathbf{k}).(\mathbf{i} - 2\mathbf{j} - \mathbf{k}) = 4 + 2 + 3 = 9$

$|\mathbf{a}| = \sqrt{4^2 + (-1)^2 + (-3)^2} = \sqrt{26}$

$|\mathbf{b}| = \sqrt{1^2 + (-2)^2 + (-1)^2} = \sqrt{6}$

$\mathbf{a.b} = |\mathbf{a}||\mathbf{b}| \cos\theta$

So $\cos\theta = \dfrac{\mathbf{a.b}}{|\mathbf{a}||\mathbf{b}|} = \dfrac{9}{\sqrt{26}\sqrt{6}}$

giving $\theta = 43.9°$

(b) $(2\mathbf{i} + 4\mathbf{j} - 2\mathbf{k}).(3\mathbf{i} + \mathbf{j} + 5\mathbf{k}) = (2)(3) + (4)(1) + (-2)(5) = 0$

The scalar product is zero so the vectors are perpendicular.

Test yourself

Answer the following questions and check your answers before moving onto the next topic.

① Find the angle between the vectors $5\mathbf{i} + \mathbf{j} + 2\mathbf{k}$ and $\mathbf{i} - \mathbf{j} + 3\mathbf{k}$.

② The position vectors of the points A and B are given by $\mathbf{a} = 3\mathbf{i} + 2\mathbf{j} + \mathbf{k}$ and $\mathbf{b} = 2\mathbf{i} - \mathbf{j} + \mathbf{k}$.

(a) Write down the vector **AB**.

(b) Find the vector equation of the line AB.

③ Two vectors are given by

$\mathbf{a} = 3\mathbf{i} + 4\mathbf{j} + 5\mathbf{k}$ and $\mathbf{b} = \mathbf{i} + 2\mathbf{j} + 3\mathbf{k}$.

(a) Calculate **a.b**

(b) Find the angle between **a** and **b** giving your answer in degrees to one decimal place.

(Note: answers to Test yourself are found at the back of the book.)

Q&A 1

1 (a) The position vectors of the points A and B are given by

$\mathbf{a} = 3\mathbf{i} + 4\mathbf{j} + 7\mathbf{k}$, $\mathbf{b} = 4\mathbf{i} + 2\mathbf{j} + 10\mathbf{k}$.

(i) Find the vector equation of the line AB.

(ii) The vector equation of the line L is

$\mathbf{r} = 5\mathbf{i} + 6\mathbf{j} + \mathbf{k} + \mu(3\mathbf{i} - 2\mathbf{j} + \mathbf{k})$.

Show that AB and L intersect and find the position vector of the point of intersection. [9]

(b) Show that the vectors $3\mathbf{i} - 2\mathbf{j} + 2\mathbf{k}$ and $2\mathbf{i} + \mathbf{j} - 2\mathbf{k}$ are perpendicular. [2]

(WJEC C4 June 2009 Q8)

Answer

1 (a)(i)

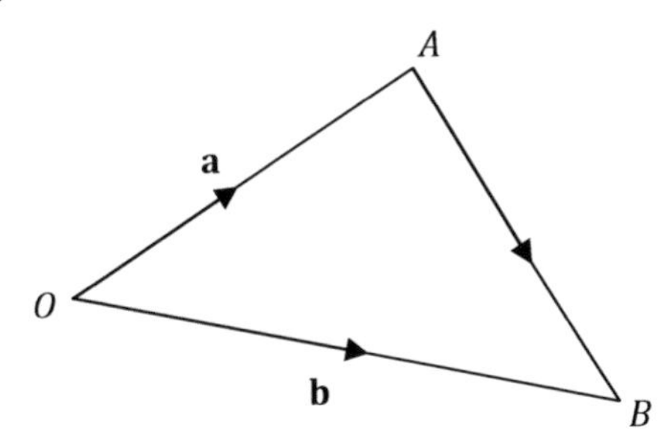

$$\mathbf{AB} = \mathbf{AO} + \mathbf{OB}$$
$$= -\mathbf{a} + \mathbf{b}$$
$$= -(3\mathbf{i} + 4\mathbf{j} + 7\mathbf{k}) + (4\mathbf{i} + 2\mathbf{j} + 10\mathbf{k})$$
$$= \mathbf{i} - 2\mathbf{j} + 3\mathbf{k}$$

Equation of AB is

$\mathbf{r} = \mathbf{a} + \lambda\mathbf{AB}$

giving $\mathbf{r} = 3\mathbf{i} + 4\mathbf{j} + 7\mathbf{k} + \lambda(\mathbf{i} - 2\mathbf{j} + 3\mathbf{k})$

(ii) The given equation of L is

$\mathbf{r} = 5\mathbf{i} + 6\mathbf{j} + \mathbf{k} + \mu(3\mathbf{i} - 2\mathbf{j} + \mathbf{k})$.

Assume that AB and L intersect. Equating coefficients of **i**, **j** we obtain

$3 + \lambda = 5 + 3\mu$

$4 - 2\lambda = 6 - 2\mu$

Solving these two equations simultaneously we obtain

$\mu = -\frac{3}{2}, \lambda = -\frac{5}{2}$

Grade boost

Many students solve the simultaneous equations correctly but do not go on to check that these fit the third equation to prove that the two lines intersect.

Check that the coefficients of **k** for both equations are equal.

LHS $7+\left(-\frac{5}{2}\right)(3)=-\frac{1}{2}$

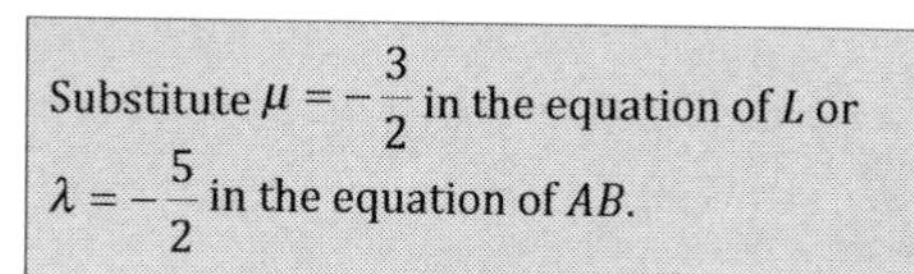
Substitute $\mu=-\frac{3}{2}$ in the equation of L or $\lambda=-\frac{5}{2}$ in the equation of AB.

RHS $1+\left(-\frac{3}{2}\right)=\left(-\frac{1}{2}\right)$

Hence lines AB and L intersect.

Using $\mathbf{r}=5\mathbf{i}+6\mathbf{j}+\mathbf{k}+\left(\frac{-3}{2}\right)(3\mathbf{i}-2\mathbf{j}+\mathbf{k})$.

we have $\mathbf{r}=5\mathbf{i}+6\mathbf{j}+\mathbf{k}-\frac{9}{2}\mathbf{i}+3\mathbf{j}-\frac{3}{2}\mathbf{k}$.

and $\mathbf{r}=\frac{1}{2}\mathbf{i}+9\mathbf{j}-\frac{1}{2}\mathbf{k}$.

(b) $(3\mathbf{i}-2\mathbf{j}+2\mathbf{k}).(2\mathbf{i}+\mathbf{j}-2\mathbf{k})=6-2-4=0$

This proves that the vectors are perpendicular.

Q&A 2

2 (a) Given that the vectors $5\mathbf{i}-8\mathbf{j}+4\mathbf{k}$ and $4\mathbf{i}+6\mathbf{j}+a\mathbf{k}$ are perpendicular, find the value of the constant a.

(b) The line L_1 passes through the point with position vector $8\mathbf{i}+3\mathbf{j}-7\mathbf{k}$ and is parallel to the vector $2\mathbf{i}+\mathbf{j}+2\mathbf{k}$

(i) Write down the vector equation of the line L_1. [3]

(ii) The line L_2 has vector equation

$\mathbf{r}=4\mathbf{i}+7\mathbf{j}+5\mathbf{k}+\mu(-2\mathbf{i}+\mathbf{j}+3\mathbf{k})$

Show that L_1 and L_2 do not intersect. [6]

(WJEC C4 June 2011 Q9)

Answer

2 (a) As the two vectors are perpendicular their scalar product must be zero.

Then $(5\mathbf{i}-8\mathbf{j}+4\mathbf{k}).(4\mathbf{i}+6\mathbf{j}+a\mathbf{k})=0$

so $20-48+4a=0$

Hence $a=7$

Use $(x_1\mathbf{i}+y_1\mathbf{j}+z_1\mathbf{k}).(x_2\mathbf{i}+y_2\mathbf{j}+z_2\mathbf{k})=x_1x_2+y_1y_2+z_1z_2$

(b)(i) The vector equation of the line L_1 is

$\mathbf{r}=8\mathbf{i}+3\mathbf{j}-7\mathbf{k}+\lambda(2\mathbf{i}+\mathbf{j}+2\mathbf{k})$.

As L_1 is parallel to vector $2\mathbf{i}+\mathbf{j}+2\mathbf{k}$ the direction vector of L_1 is $(2\mathbf{i}+\mathbf{j}+2\mathbf{k})$.

(ii) Assume that L_1 and L_2 intersect. Equating coefficients of **i**, **j** we obtain

$8+2\lambda=4-2\mu$ (1)

$3+\lambda=7+\mu$ (2)

Multiplying equation (2) by 2 and then adding the resulting equation to (1) we obtain

$14 + 4\lambda = 18$,

giving $\lambda = 1$

Substituting $\lambda = 1$ into equation (1) gives

$8 + 2 = 4 - 2\mu$

giving $\mu = -3$

Checking that the coefficients of **k** for both equations are equal, we consider

$-7 + 2\lambda = 5 + 3\mu$

As $\lambda = 1$, LHS $= -5$ and as $\mu = -3$, RHS $= -4$

Since LHS $\neq$ RHS, the lines L_1 and L_2 do not intersect.

Summary C4

1 Binomial expansions, simplification of expressions and partial fractions

The binomial expansion of $(a+b)^n$ where n is a positive integer is

$$(a+b)^n = a^n + \binom{n}{1}a^{n-1}b + \binom{n}{2}a^{n-2}b^2 + \cdots + \binom{n}{r}a^{n-r}b^r + \cdots + b^n$$

$$\binom{n}{r} = {}^nC_r = \frac{n!}{r!(n-r)!}$$

The binomial expansion of $(1+x)^n$ for negative or fractional n is

$$(1+x)^n = 1 + nx + \frac{n(n-1)}{2!}x^2 + \frac{n(n-1)(n-2)}{3!}x^3 + \ldots \qquad |x| < 1$$

Partial fractions

$$\frac{\alpha x+\beta}{(cx+d)(ex+f)} \equiv \frac{A}{cx+d} + \frac{B}{ex+f} \qquad \text{(i)}$$

$$\frac{\alpha x^2+\beta x+\gamma}{(cx+d)(ex+f)^2} \equiv \frac{A}{cx+d} + \frac{B}{ex+f} + \frac{C}{(ex+f)^2} \qquad \text{(ii)}$$

In both cases, clear the fractions and choose appropriate values of x.
In (ii), an equation involving coefficients of x^2 may be used.

2 Trigonometry

Trigonometric identities

$\sin(A \pm B) = \sin A \cos B \pm \cos A \sin B$

$\cos(A \pm B) = \cos A \cos B \mp \sin A \sin B$

$$\tan(A \pm B) = \frac{\tan A \pm \tan B}{1 \mp \tan A \tan B}$$

Double angle formulae

$\sin 2A = 2 \sin A \cos A$

$\cos 2A = \cos^2 A - \sin^2 A$

$= 1 - 2 \sin^2 A$

$= 2 \cos^2 A - 1$

$$\tan 2A = \frac{2 \tan A}{1 - \tan^2 A}$$

Important rearrangements of the double angle formulae

$$\sin^2 A = \frac{1}{2}(1 - \cos 2A)$$

$$\cos^2 A = \frac{1}{2}(1 + \cos 2A)$$

3 Cartesian and parametric equations of curves

Cartesian and parametric equations

Cartesian equations connect x and y in some way. For example, $y = 4x^3$ is a Cartesian equation.

Parametric equations express x and y in terms of a parameter such as t, for example

$x = 4 + 2t \qquad y = 1 + 2t.$

To obtain the Cartesian equation from the parametric equation it is necessary to eliminate the parameter.

Note that $\frac{dy}{dx} = \frac{dy}{dt} \times \frac{dt}{dx}$

Using the Chain rule to find the second derivative

The Chain rule can be used to find the second derivative in terms of a parameter such as t in the following way:

$$\frac{d^2y}{dx^2} = \frac{d}{dx}\left(\frac{dy}{dx}\right) = \frac{d}{dt}\left(\frac{dy}{dx}\right)\frac{dt}{dx}$$

Implicit differentiation

Here are the basic rules

$$\frac{d(3x^2)}{dx} = 6x$$

Terms involving x or constant terms are differentiated as normal.

$$\frac{d(6y^3)}{dx} = 18y^2 \times \frac{dy}{dx}$$

Differentiate with respect to y and then multiply the result by $\frac{dy}{dx}$.

$$\frac{d(y)}{dx} = 1 \times \frac{dy}{dx}$$

When you are differentiating a term just involving y, you differentiate with respect to y and then multiply the result by $\frac{dy}{dx}$. This is an application of the Chain rule.

$$\frac{d(x^2y^3)}{dx} = (x^2)\left(3y^2 \times \frac{dy}{dx}\right) + (y^3)(2x)$$

$$= 3x^2y^2\frac{dy}{dx} + 2xy^3$$

Because there are two terms here, the Product rule is used. Notice the need to include $\frac{dy}{dx}$ when the term involving y is differentiated.

4 Simple differential equations and exponential growth

Formation of simple differential equations

If a quantity x has a rate of **increase** in x that is proportional to x, then this can be written as a differential equation by including a constant of proportionality k as $\frac{dx}{dt} = kx$. $k > 0$

If a quantity x has a rate of **decrease** in x that is proportional to x, then this can be written as a differential equation by including a constant of proportionality k as $\frac{dx}{dt} = -kx$. $k > 0$

Separating variables and integrating

If $\frac{dm}{dt} = -km$ and at $t = 0$, then variables can be separated and integrated as follows:

$$\int \frac{1}{m} dm = -k \int dt$$

$\therefore \ln m = -kt + c$ (1)

When $t = 0$, $m = m_o$

Substituting these values in (1), we obtain

$c = \ln m_o$

Hence we obtain

$\ln m = -kt + \ln m_o$

$\ln m - \ln m_o = -kt$

$$\ln\left(\frac{m}{m_o}\right) = -kt$$

Taking exponentials of both sides

This is done to remove the ln from the left-hand side.

$$\frac{m}{m_o} = e^{-kt}$$

Hence $m = m_o e^{-kt}$

Similarly, if

$$\frac{dP}{dt} \alpha f(P)$$

Usually, $f(P) = V^n$ where n is a constant.

$$\frac{dP}{dt} = kf(P)$$

$k > 0$ if P increases with time and
$k < 0$ if P decreases with time.

Then $\int \frac{1}{f(P)} = \int k dt$

5 Integration

Volume of revolution

If the graph of $y = f(x)$ is rotated by 360° (4 right angles) about the x-axis between the lines $x = a$ and $x = b$, then the volume of revolution is given by

$V = \pi\int_a^b y^2 \mathrm{d}x.$

Integration by parts

Integration by parts is used when there is a product to integrate.

$$\int u\frac{\mathrm{d}v}{\mathrm{d}x}\mathrm{d}x = uv - \int v\frac{\mathrm{d}u}{\mathrm{d}x}\mathrm{d}x$$

Integration by substitution

An integral of the type $\int f(x)dx$ is converted into the integral $\int f(x)\frac{\mathrm{d}x}{\mathrm{d}u}\mathrm{d}u$, where x and v are replaced by a given substitution. In the case of definite integrals, the x limits are converted into u limits by means of the given substitution.

First order differential equations with separable variables

Equations of the type

$$\frac{\mathrm{d}y}{\mathrm{d}x} = f(x)g(y)$$

can be solved by separating the variables and integrating both sides of the resulting equation, i.e.

$$\int \frac{1}{g(y)}\mathrm{d}y = \int f(x)\,\mathrm{d}x$$

6 Vectors

Condition for two vectors to be parallel

For two vectors **a** and **b** to be parallel

$\mathbf{a} = k\mathbf{b}$, where k is a scalar

The magnitude of a vector

The vector $\mathbf{r} = a\mathbf{i} + b\mathbf{j} + c\mathbf{k}$ has magnitude given by $|\mathbf{r}| = \sqrt{a^2 + b^2 + c^2}$

The distance between two points

The distance between two points $A(x_1, y_1, z_1)$ and $B(x_2, y_2, z_2)$ is given by

$$d = \sqrt{(x_2 - x_1)^2 + (y_2 - y_1)^2 + (z_2 - z_1)^2}$$

Scalar product

The scalar product of two vectors **a** and **b** is written as **a.b** where

$$\mathbf{a}.\mathbf{b} = (x_1\mathbf{i} + y_1\mathbf{j} + z_1\mathbf{k}).(x_2\mathbf{i} + y_2\mathbf{j} + z_2\mathbf{k}) = x_1x_2 + y_1y_2 + z_1z_2$$

The angle between two vectors

The angle θ between two vectors **a** and **b** can be found by using the scalar (or dot) product given by

$$\mathbf{a}.\mathbf{b} = |\mathbf{a}||\mathbf{b}|\cos\theta$$

a.b is the scalar product.

$|\mathbf{a}|$ and $|\mathbf{b}|$ are the magnitudes of the vectors **a** and **b** respectively.

The vector equation of a line

The vector equation of a line passing through points A and B with position vectors **a** and **b** respectively, is $\mathbf{r} = \mathbf{a} + \lambda(\mathbf{b} - \mathbf{a})$, where λ is a scalar.

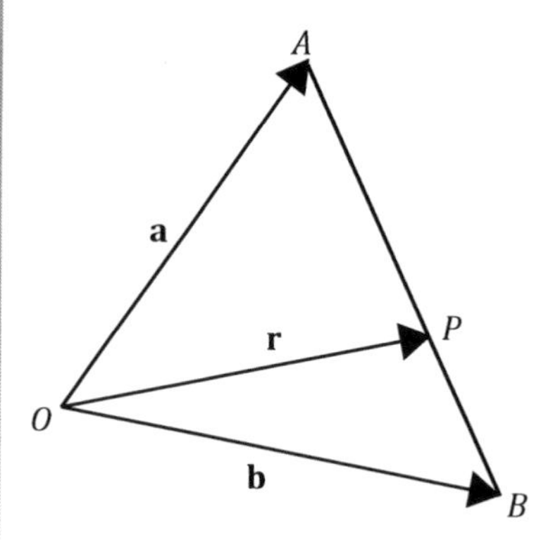

The vector equation of a line passing through a point with position vector **a** and which is parallel to the vector **c** is $\mathbf{r} = \mathbf{a} + \lambda\mathbf{c}$.

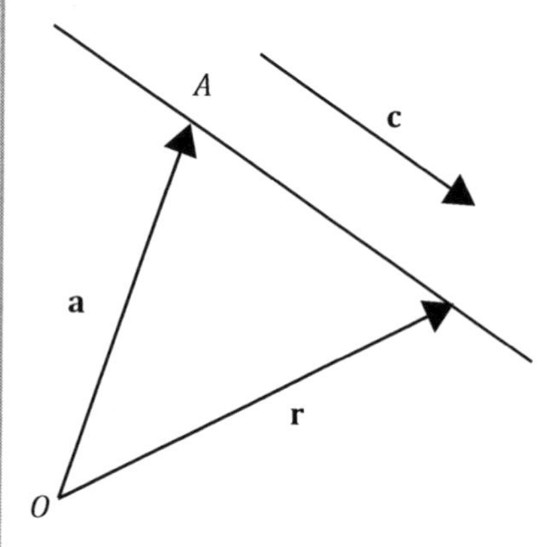

To find the point of intersection of two lines, we equate the terms in **i**, **j**, **k** and solve any two of the resulting equations for λ and μ.

The position vector of a point dividing a line in a given ratio

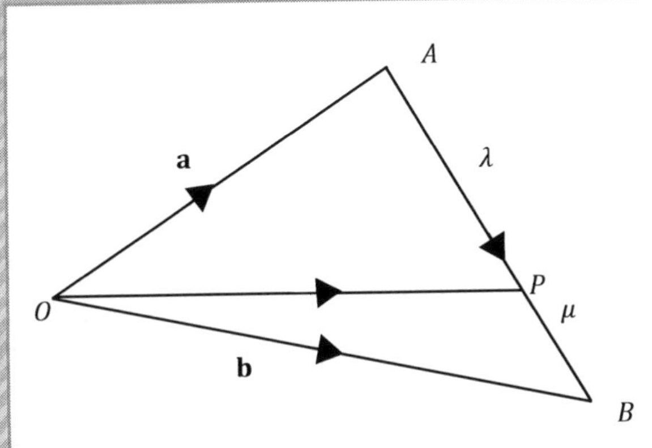

Point P dividing AB in the ratio $\lambda : \mu$ has position vector $\overrightarrow{OP}$

where $\overrightarrow{OP} = \dfrac{\mu\mathbf{a} + \lambda\mathbf{b}}{\lambda + \mu}$

Test yourself answers

C3 Pure Mathematics

1 Functions

① (a) The range of f is $[-1, \infty)$

(b) Let $y = (x + 2)^2 - 1$

$y + 1 = (x + 2)^2$

$\pm\sqrt{y+1} = x + 2$

$-\sqrt{y+1} - 2 = x$

$f^{-1}(x) = -\sqrt{x+1} - 2$

The domain of f^{-1} is the range of f so the domain of f^{-1} is $[-1, \infty)$

The range of f^{-1} is the domain of f so the range of f^{-1} is $(-\infty, -2]$

Imagine the graph of $y = (x + 2)^2 - 1$. The curve would be U-shaped with a minimum point at $(-2, -1)$. Hence the smallest value of f is -1 at $x = -2$. According to the domain $x \leq -2$, all x values including and to the left of -2 are allowable. This will mean that the range of f will be $[-1, \infty)$.

Only the negative square root is used because according to the domain $x \leq -2$.

② $y = f(x)$ to $y = 2f(x - 1)$ represents a translation of 1 unit to the right and a stretch of scale factor 2 parallel to the y-axis.

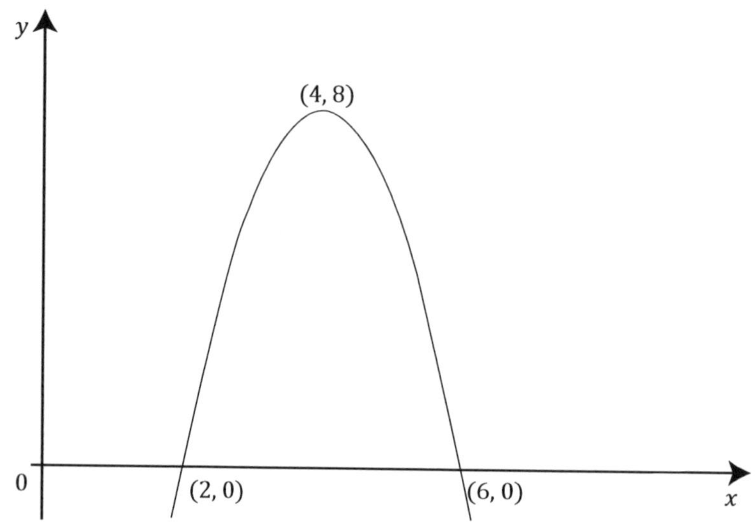

③ (a) $3|x - 1| + 7 = 19$

$3|x - 1| = 12$

$|x - 1| = 4$

$x - 1 = \pm 4$

$x = 5$ or -3

(b) $6|x|-3=2|x|+5$

$4|x|=8$

$|x|=2$

$x=\pm 2$

2 Trigonometry

① Let $\theta=\frac{\pi}{2}$

Note that $\cos\frac{\pi}{2}=0$ and $\cos 2\pi=1$

LHS $=\cos 4\theta=\cos 4\left(\frac{\pi}{2}\right)=\cos 2\pi=1$

RHS $=4\cos^3\theta-3\cos\theta=4\cos^3\frac{\pi}{2}-3\cos\frac{\pi}{2}=0$

$1\neq 0$ so the statement $\cos 4\theta\equiv 4\cos^3\theta-3\cos\theta$ is false.

② $2\sec^2\theta+\tan\theta=8$

You need to use the trigonometric identity $\sec^2\theta=1+\tan^2\theta$. This identity must be remembered.

$2(1+\tan^2\theta)+\tan\theta-8=0$

$2\tan^2\theta+\tan\theta-6=0$

$(2\tan\theta-3)(\tan\theta+2)=0$

tan θ is positive in the first and third quadrants and negative in the second and fourth quadrants.

$\tan\theta=\frac{3}{2}$ or $\tan\theta=-2$

When $\tan\theta=\frac{3}{2}$, $\theta=56.3°$ or $236.3°$

When $\tan\theta=-2$, $\theta=180-63.4=116.6°$ or $\theta=360-63.4=296.6°$.

Hence solutions are $\theta=56.3°, 116.6°, 236.3°$ or $296.6°$

③ (a) Let $\theta=\frac{\pi}{4}$

LHS $=\tan 2\theta=\tan\frac{\pi}{2}=\infty$

Note $\tan\frac{\pi}{4}=1$

RHS $=\frac{2\tan\theta}{1+\tan^2\theta}=\frac{2\tan\frac{\pi}{4}}{1+\tan^2\frac{\pi}{4}}=\frac{2}{1+1}=1$

$\infty\neq 1$ so the statement $\tan 2\theta\equiv\frac{2\tan\theta}{1+\tan^2\theta}$ is false.

(b) $2\sec\theta+\tan^2\theta=7$

$2\sec\theta+\sec^2\theta-1=7$

$\sec^2\theta+2\sec\theta-8=0$

$(\sec\theta-2)(\sec\theta+4)=0$

Hence $\sec\theta=2$ or $\sec\theta=-4$

So $\dfrac{1}{\cos\theta} = 2$ or $\dfrac{1}{\cos\theta} = -4$

Hence $\cos\theta = \dfrac{1}{2}$ or $\cos\theta = -\dfrac{1}{4}$

When $\cos\theta = \dfrac{1}{2}$, $\theta = 60°$ or $300°$

When $\cos\theta = -\dfrac{1}{4}$, $\theta = 104.5°$ or $255.5°$

Hence $\theta = 60°, 104.5°, 255.5°$ or $300°$

$\cos\theta$ is negative in the second and third quadrants, so $\theta = 180 - 75.5 = 104.5°$ or $360 - 75.5 = 255.5°$

3 The functions e^x and $\ln x$

① Note that in the exam this graph would be hand-drawn.

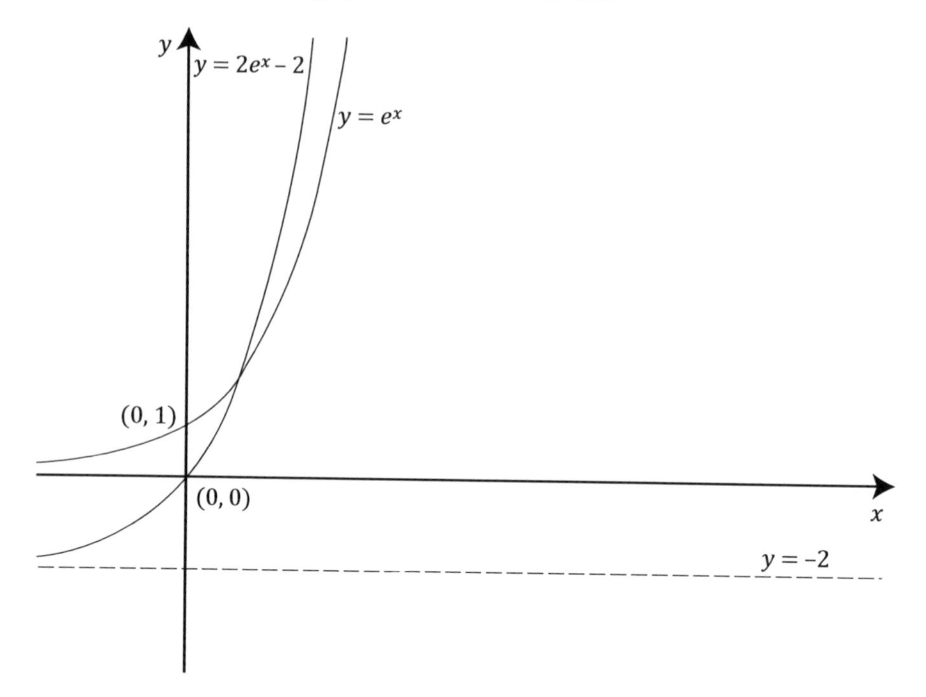

For $y = f(x)$

Curve cuts the y-axis at (0, 1)

② (a) Domain of fg is the domain of $g = (0, \infty)$

Range of fg is $(0, \infty)$

The domain of a composite function fg is the set of all x in the domain of g for which $g(x)$ is in the domain of f.

$R(g) = (-\infty, \infty)$ and $D(f) = (-\infty, \infty)$ hence $D(fg) = D(g) = (0, \infty)$

The range of fg is found by substituting values from the domain into the composite function (i.e. $fg(x) = 16x^3$).

(b) $fg(x) = 2e^{3g(x)}$

$fg(x) = 2e^{3\ln 2x}$

$fg(x) = 2e^{\ln(2x)^3}$

$fg(x) = 2e^{\ln 8x^3}$

$fg(x) = 16x^3$

Since $fg(x) = 128$

$16x^3 = 128$

$x^3 = 8$

$x = 2$

$3\ln 2x = \ln(2x)^3$

$e^{\ln a} = a$

4 Differentiation

① $y = (4x^3 + 3x)^3$

$$\frac{dy}{dx} = 3(4x^3+3x)^2(12x^2+3)$$

$$\frac{dy}{dx} = 9(4x^2+1)(4x^3+3x)^2$$

② $y = (3-2x)^{10}$

$$\frac{dy}{dx} = 10(3-2x)^9(-2)$$

$$\frac{dy}{dx} = -20(3-2x)^9$$

③ $x = 3t^2$

$$\frac{dx}{dt} = 6t$$

$y = t^4$

$$\frac{dy}{dt} = 4t^3$$

$$\frac{dy}{dx} = \frac{dy}{dt} \times \frac{dt}{dx}$$

$$= 4t^3 \times \left(\frac{1}{6t}\right)$$

$$= \frac{2}{3}t^2$$

④ $4x^3 - 6x^2 + 3xy = 5$

Differentiating implicitly with respect to x gives

$$12x^2 - 12x + (3x)(1)\left(\frac{dy}{dx}\right) + (y)(3) = 0$$

$$12x^2 - 12x + 3x\left(\frac{dy}{dx}\right) + 3y = 0$$

$$3x\left(\frac{dy}{dx}\right) = 12x - 12x^2 - 3y$$

Simplify by dividing both sides by 3.

$$x\left(\frac{dy}{dx}\right) = 4x - 4x^2 - y$$

$$\frac{dy}{dx} = \frac{4x - 4x^2 - y}{x}$$

⑤ (a) $y = \ln(x^3)$

$$\frac{dy}{dx} = \frac{3x^2}{x^3}$$

$$= \frac{3}{x}$$

Note also that $\ln x^3 = 3 \ln x$ (laws of logs) so we are in effect differentiating $3 \ln x$.

(b) $y = \sin^{-1} 2x$

Use the Chain rule with $u = 2x$ or note that $\frac{d}{dx}\left(\sin^{-1}(f(x))\right) = \frac{1}{\sqrt{1-(f(x))^2}} \times f'(x)$.

$$\frac{dy}{dx} = \frac{2}{\sqrt{1-(2x)^2}}$$

$$= \frac{2}{\sqrt{1-4x^2}}$$

(c) $y = \ln(\sin x)$

$$\frac{dy}{dx} = \frac{\cos x}{\sin x} = \cot x$$

5 Integration

① (a) $\int \frac{6}{5x+1}\, dx = 6\int \frac{1}{5x+1}\, dx = \frac{6}{5}\ln|5x+1| + c$

(b) $\int \cos 7x\, dx = \frac{1}{7}\sin 7x + c$

(c) $\int \frac{4}{(3x+1)^3}\, dx$

$$= 4\int \frac{1}{(3x+1)^3}\, dx$$

$$= 4\int (3x+1)^{-3}\, dx$$

$$= \frac{4}{3x(-2)}(3x+1)^{-2} + c$$

$$= -\frac{2}{3}(3x+1)^{-2} + c$$

② (a) $\int \sin 4x \; dx = -\frac{1}{4}\cos 4x + c$

(b) $\int \frac{1}{2x+1} \; dx = \frac{1}{2}\ln|2x+1| + c$

(c) $\int \frac{4}{(2x+1)^5} \; dx = 4\int (2x+1)^{-5} dx$

$$= -\frac{1}{2}(2x+1)^{-4} + c$$

③ $\int_0^2 \frac{1}{(2x+1)^3} \; dx = \int_0^2 (2x+1)^{-3} dx$

$$= \left[-\frac{1}{4}(2x+1)^{-2}\right]_0^2$$

$$= -\frac{1}{4}\left[\frac{1}{(2x+1)^2}\right]_0^2$$

$$= -\frac{1}{4}\left[\left(\frac{1}{25}\right) - (1)\right]$$

$$= \left(-\frac{1}{4}\right) \times \left(-\frac{24}{25}\right)$$

$$= \frac{6}{25}$$

④ $\int_0^3 \frac{1}{5x+2} \; dx = \frac{1}{5}\left[\ln|5x+2|\right]_0^3$

$$= \frac{1}{5}[\ln 17 - \ln 2]$$

$$= \frac{1}{5}\ln\left(\frac{17}{2}\right)$$

6 Roots, iterative methods and numerical integrations

① $\int_a^b y \; dx = \int_0^1 \frac{1}{1+x^2} \; dx$

Always work to more decimal places than is requested in the question.

$$h = \frac{b-a}{n} = \frac{1-0}{4} = 0.25$$

When $x = 0, y_0 = \dfrac{1}{1+(0)^2} = 1$

$x = 0.25, y_1 = \dfrac{1}{1+(0.25)^2} = 0.941176$

$x = 0.50, y_2 = \dfrac{1}{1+(0.5)^2} = 0.8$

$x = 0.75, y_3 = \dfrac{1}{1+(0.75)^2} = 0.64$

$x = 1, y_n = \dfrac{1}{1+(1)^2} = 0.50$

$$\int_a^b y \ \mathrm{d}x \approx \frac{1}{3}h\{(y_o + y_n) + 4(y_1 + y_3 + \ldots + y_{n-1}) + 2(y_2 + y_4 + \ldots + y_{n-2})\}$$

$$\int_0^1 \frac{1}{1+x^2} \ \mathrm{d}x \approx \frac{1}{3} \times 0.25\{(1+0.5) + 4(0.941176 + 0.64) + 2(0.8)\}$$

≈ 0.785392

≈ 0.785 (Correct to three decimal places)

② $x_0 = 1.1$

$x_1 = 1 + e^{-2(1.1)} = 1.11080316$

$x_2 = 1 + e^{-2(1.11080316)} = 1.10843479$

$x_3 = 1 + e^{-2(1.10843479)} = 1.10894963$

$x_3 = 1.1089$ (correct to 4 decimal places)

Let $f(x) = (x - 1)e^{2x} - 1$

$f(1.10885) = (1.10885 - 1)e^{2(1.10885)} - 1 = -0.000087$

$f(1.10895) = (1.10895 - 1)e^{2(1.10895)} - 1 = 0.001034$

As there is a sign change, $\alpha = 1.1089$ correct to four decimal places.

C4 Pure Mathematics

1 Binomial series

① $\dfrac{6x^2 + 11x + 14}{x(x+1)^2} \equiv \dfrac{A}{x} + \dfrac{B}{(x+1)^2} + \dfrac{C}{(x+1)}$

$6x^2 + 11x + 14 \equiv A(x + 1)^2 + Bx + Cx(x + 1)$

Let $x = -1$, so $B = -9$

Let $x = 0$, so $A = 14$

Let $x = 1$, so $31 = 4A + B + 2C$, giving $C = -8$

Alternatively, equate coefficients of x^2,

$A + C = 6$

$C = 6 - 14 = -8$

Hence $\dfrac{6x^2+11x+14}{x(x+1)^2} \equiv \dfrac{14}{x} - \dfrac{9}{(x+1)^2} - \dfrac{8}{(x+1)}$

Checking by letting $x = 2$

$\text{LHS} = \dfrac{6(2)^2+11(2)+14}{2(2+1)^2} = \dfrac{10}{3}$

$\text{RHS} = \dfrac{14}{x} - \dfrac{9}{(x+1)^2} - \dfrac{8}{(x+1)} = \dfrac{10}{3}$

LHS = RHS

Hence partial fractions are: $\dfrac{14}{x} - \dfrac{9}{(x+1)^2} - \dfrac{8}{(x+1)}$

② $\dfrac{1+x}{\sqrt{1-4x}} = (1+x)(1-4x)^{-\frac{1}{2}}$

$$= (1+x)\left(1 + \left(-\frac{1}{2}\right)(-4x) + \frac{\left(-\frac{1}{2}\right)\left(-\frac{3}{2}\right)(-4x)^2}{2!} + \ldots\right)$$

Note that $1 + x$ is not involved in the condition for convergence because $1 + x$ is not an expansion.

$= 1 + 2x + 6x^2 + x + 2x^2 + 6x^3 + \ldots$

$= 1 + 3x + 8x^2 + \ldots$

$|4x| < 1$ so this expansion is convergent for $|x| < \dfrac{1}{4}$ or $-\dfrac{1}{4} < x < \dfrac{1}{4}$

③ (a)

$\dfrac{5x^2+6x+7}{(x-1)(x+2)^2} \equiv \dfrac{A}{(x+2)^2} + \dfrac{B}{x+2} + \dfrac{C}{x-1}$

$5x^2 + 6x + 7 \equiv A(x-1) + B(x+2)(x-1) + C(x+2)^2$

Let $x = 1$, so $18 = 9C$, giving $C = 2$

Let $x = -2$, so $15 = -3A$, giving $A = -5$

Let $x = 0$, so $7 = -A - 2B + 4C$, giving $B = 3$

Hence $\dfrac{5x^2+6x+7}{(x-1)(x+2)^2} \equiv \dfrac{-5}{(x+2)^2} + \dfrac{3}{x+2} + \dfrac{2}{x-1}$

Alternatively, equate coefficients of x^2

$5 = B + C$

$B = 5 - C = 3$

Checking by letting $x = 2$

$\text{LHS} = \dfrac{5(2)^2 + 6(2) + 7}{(2-1)(2+2)^2} = \dfrac{39}{16}$

$\text{RHS} = \dfrac{-5}{(2+2)^2} + \dfrac{3}{2+2} + \dfrac{2}{2-1} = \dfrac{-5}{16} + \dfrac{3}{4} + 2 = \dfrac{39}{16}$

Hence LHS = RHS

Partial fractions are: $\dfrac{-5}{(x+2)^2} + \dfrac{3}{x+2} + \dfrac{2}{x-1}$

(b) $\int \frac{5x^2+6x+7}{(x-1)(x+2)^2}\,dx = \int \left[\frac{-5}{(x+2)^2}+\frac{3}{x+2}+\frac{2}{x-1}\right] dx$

$$\int \left[-5(x+2)^{-2}+\frac{3}{x+2}+\frac{2}{x-1}\right] dx$$

$$= \frac{-5(x+2)^{-1}}{-1}+3\ln|x+2|+2\ln|x-1|+c$$

$$= \frac{5}{x+2}+3\ln|x+2|+2\ln|x-1|+c$$

2 Trigonometry

① (a) $3\cos\theta+2\sin\theta = R\cos(\theta-\alpha)$

$3\cos\theta+2\sin\theta = R\cos\theta\cos\alpha + R\sin\theta\sin\alpha$

$R\cos\alpha = 3$ and $R\sin\alpha = 2$

$\tan\alpha = \frac{2}{3}$ so $\alpha = 33.7°$

$R = \sqrt{3^2+2^2} = \sqrt{13}$

Hence $3\cos\theta+2\sin\theta = \sqrt{13}\cos(\theta-33.7°)$

(b) $\sqrt{13}\cos(\theta-33.7°)=1$

$\cos(\theta-33.7°)=\frac{1}{\sqrt{13}}$

$(\theta-33.7°) = 73.9, 286.1°$

$\theta = 107.6°, 319.8°$

Use $\cos 2\theta = 1-2\sin^2\theta$ to obtain a quadratic equation in just $\sin\theta$.

② $3\cos 2\theta = 1-\sin\theta$

$3(1-2\sin^2\theta) = 1-\sin\theta$

$3-6\sin^2\theta = 1-\sin\theta$

$6\sin^2\theta-\sin\theta-2=0$

$(3\sin\theta-2)(2\sin\theta+1)=0$

Hence $\sin\theta = \frac{2}{3}$ or $\sin\theta = -\frac{1}{2}$

When $\sin\theta = \frac{2}{3}$, $\theta = 41.8°, 138.2°$

When $\sin\theta = -\frac{1}{2}$, $\theta = 210°, 330°$

Hence $\theta = 41.8°, 138.2°, 210°, 330°$

③ $4 \sin \theta + 5 \cos \theta \equiv R \cos(\theta - \alpha)$

$4 \sin \theta + 5 \cos \theta \equiv R \cos \theta \cos \alpha + R \sin \theta \sin \alpha$

$R \cos \alpha = 5$ and $R \sin \alpha = 4$

$\tan \alpha = \frac{4}{5}$ so $\alpha = 38.7°$

$R = \sqrt{4^2 + 5^2} = \sqrt{41}$

Hence $4 \sin \theta + 5 \cos \theta = \sqrt{41} \cos(\theta - 38.7°)$

$\sqrt{41} \cos(\theta - 38.7°) = 2$

gives $\cos(\theta - 38.7°) = \frac{2}{\sqrt{41}}$

$(\theta - 38.7°) = 71.8°, 288.2°$

Hence $\theta = 110.5°, 326.9°$

There is also the following alternative method

$4 \sin \theta + 5 \cos \theta \equiv R \sin(\theta + \alpha)$

$4 \sin \theta + 5 \cos \theta \equiv R \sin \theta \cos \alpha + R \cos \theta \sin \alpha$

$\therefore R \cos \alpha = 4$ and $R \sin \alpha = 5$

$\tan \alpha = \frac{5}{4}$, $\alpha = 51.3°$, $R = \sqrt{4^2 + 5^2} = \sqrt{41}$

Hence $4 \sin \theta + 5 \cos \theta \equiv \sqrt{41} \sin(\theta + 51.3°)$

Then $\sqrt{41} \sin(\theta + 51.3°) = 2$

$\sin(\theta + 51.3°) = \frac{2}{\sqrt{41}}$

$\theta + 51.3° = 18.2°, 161.8°, 378.2°$

$\therefore \theta = -33.1°, 110.5°, 326.9°$

$\theta = -33.1°$ is outside the required range and is therefore rejected.

Hence $\theta = 110.5°, 326.9°$

3 Cartesian and parametric equations of curves

① $\frac{dx}{dt} = 6t$ and $\frac{dy}{dt} = 3t^2$

Hence $\frac{dy}{dx} = \frac{dy}{dt} \times \frac{dt}{dx} = 3t^2 \times \frac{1}{6t} = \frac{t}{2}$

Gradient of normal $= -\frac{2}{t}$

At $P(3p^2, p^3)$ gradient of normal $= -\frac{2}{p}$

Equation of the normal is $y - p^3 = -\frac{2}{p}\left(x - 3p^2\right)$

$$py - p^4 = -2x + 6p^2$$

$$py + 2x = 6p^2 + p^4$$

$$py + 2x = p^2(6 + p^2)$$

② $y^2 - 5xy + 8x^2 = 2$

Differentiating with respect to x gives

$$2y\frac{dy}{dx} = (5x)\frac{dy}{dx} + (y)(-5) + 16x = 0$$

$$\frac{dy}{dx}(2y - 5x) = 5y - 16x$$

Hence $\frac{dy}{dx} = \frac{5y - 16x}{2y - 5x}$

③ (a) $\frac{dx}{dt} = 8\cos 4t$, $\quad \frac{dy}{dt} = -4\sin 4t$

The Chain rule is used to find $\frac{dx}{dt}$ and $\frac{dy}{dt}$.

$$\frac{dy}{dx} = \frac{dy}{dt} \times \frac{dt}{dx}$$

$$= -4\sin 4t \times \frac{1}{8\cos 4t}$$

Use $\frac{dt}{dx} = \frac{1}{\frac{dx}{dt}}$

$$= \frac{-\sin 4t}{2\cos 4t}$$

$$= -\frac{1}{2}\tan 4t$$

(b) $y - y_1 = m(x - x_1)$

$$y - \cos 4p = -\frac{\sin 4p}{2\cos 4p}(x - 2\sin 4p)$$

For convenience, we have written $\frac{dy}{dx} = \frac{-\sin 4p}{2\cos 4p}$

$$2y\cos 4p - 2\cos^2 4p = -x\sin 4p + 2\sin^2 4p$$

$$2y\cos 4p + x\sin 4p = 2\sin^2 4p + 2\cos^2 4p$$

$$2y\cos 4p + x\sin 4p = 2(\sin^2 4p + \cos^2 4p)$$

Use the fact that $\sin^2 4p + \cos^2 4p = 1$

$$2y\cos 4p + x\sin 4p = 2$$

4 Simple differential equations and exponential growth

① (a) $\frac{dV}{dt} = -kV$

The negative sign is included here because V decreases with time. The constant k is positive.

(b) Separating variables and integrating

$\int \frac{1}{V} dV = -k \int dt$

$\ln V = -kt + C$ (1)

When $t = 0$, $V = 10\,000$

Substitution of these values in (1) gives

$\ln 10\,000 = -k(0) + C = C$

Substitute for C in (1)

$\ln V = -kt + \ln 10\,000$

$\ln V - \ln 10\,000 = -kt$

$\ln \frac{V}{10\,000} = -kt$

Taking exponentials of both sides

$\frac{V}{10\,000} = e^{-kt}$

$\therefore V = 10\,000e^{-kt}$

(c) (i) When $t = 48$, $V = 4\,000$

Hence $4\,000 = 10\,000e^{-48k}$

So $e^{-48k} = 0.4$

Taking ln of both sides

$-48k = \ln 0.4$

$k = 0.019$

Hence $V = 10\,000e^{-0.019t}$

When $t = 12$, $V = 10\,000e^{-0.019 \times 12} = £7\,961$ (correct to the nearest pound)

If no guidance is given in the question, you should give your answer to three significant figures.

Once k has been found, the equation can be used by entering a value to find the other value.

(ii) $V = 10\,000e^{-kt}$

When $V = 3\,000$, $3\,000 = 10\,000e^{-0.019t}$

So $0.3 = e^{-0.019t}$

Taking ln of both sides

$\ln 0.3 = -0.019t$

Giving $t = 63$ months (to the nearest month)

② (a) $\frac{dC}{dt} = kC$

(b) $\frac{dC}{dt} = kC$

Separating the variables and integrating we obtain

$\int \frac{1}{C} dC = k \int dt$

As the variable is now C, we take the constant of integration to be A.

$\ln C = kt + A \qquad (1)$

When $t = 0$, $C = 0.90$

When $t = 2$, $C = 8$

Substitute these values in (1)

$\ln 0.90 = A$

$\ln 8 = 2k + A$

Subtract these two equations to eliminate A.

Then $\ln 0.90 - \ln 8 = A - 2k - A$

giving $\ln 0.90 - \ln 8 = -2k$

$\ln \frac{0.90}{8} = -2k$

$-2.18 = -2k$

$k = 1.09$ (correct to 3 significant figures)

Substitute for A and k in (1)

$\ln C = 1.09t + \ln 0.90$

$\ln C - \ln 0.90 = 1.09t$

$\therefore \ \ln \frac{C}{0.90} = 1.09t$

Taking exponentials of both sides

$$\frac{C}{0.90} = e^{1.09t}$$

$\therefore \quad C = 0.90e^{1.09t}$

In the previous examples, a feature of the solutions was that they all involved exponentials, hence the names for such problems are exponential growth or exponential decay. The exponential function occurred in the solutions of differential equations such as

$$\frac{dC}{dt} = kC$$

$$\frac{dV}{dt} = -kV$$

because the right-hand sides involved C^1 or V^1 (i.e. to the power one).

Exponentials will not arise when the powers are not unity (i.e. one) such as

$$\frac{dP}{dt} = kP^2 \text{ and } \frac{dV}{dt} = -kP^3$$

5 Integration

① Volume of revolution $= \pi\int_0^1 y^2 \ dx$

$$= \pi\int_0^1 \left(\sqrt{e^{2x}+3}\right)^2 \ dx$$

$$= \pi\int_0^1 \left(e^{2x}+3\right) \ dx$$

$$= \pi\left[\frac{e^{2x}}{2}+3x\right]_0^1$$

$$= \pi\left[\left(\frac{e^2}{2}+3\right)-\left(\frac{e^0}{2}+0\right)\right]$$

$$= \pi\left(\frac{e^2}{2}+2.5\right)$$

= 19.461 (correct to three decimal places)

② $\int u\frac{dv}{dx}dx = uv - \int v\frac{du}{dx}dx$

Let $u = 2x + 1$ and $\frac{dv}{dx} = e^{2x}$

Use Rule 1.

So $\frac{du}{dx} = 2$, $v = \frac{e^{2x}}{2}$

$$\int (2x+1)e^{2x} \ dx = (2x+1)\frac{1}{2}e^{2x} - \int \frac{1}{2}e^{2x}(2) \ dx$$

$$= \frac{1}{2}e^{2x}(2x+1) - \frac{1}{2}e^{2x} + c$$

$$= xe^{2x} + c$$

③ Let $x = 2\sin\theta$ so $\frac{dx}{d\theta} = 2\cos\theta$ giving $dx = 2\cos\theta \, d\theta$

When $x = 1$, $1 = 2\sin\theta$, hence $\theta = \sin^{-1}\left(\frac{1}{2}\right) = \left(\frac{\pi}{6}\right)$

When $x = 0$, $0 = 2\sin\theta$, hence $\theta = \sin^{-1} 0 = 0$

$$\int_0^1 \sqrt{\left(4-x^2\right)}dx = \int_0^{\frac{\pi}{6}} \sqrt{\left(4-4\sin^2\theta\right)} \ 2\cos\theta \ d\theta$$

$1-\sin^2\theta = \cos^2\theta$

$$= \int_0^{\frac{\pi}{6}} \sqrt{4\left(1-\sin^2\theta\right)} \ 2\cos\theta \ d\theta$$

$$= \int_0^{\frac{\pi}{6}} \sqrt{4\cos^2\theta} \ 2\cos\theta \ d\theta$$

$$= \int_0^{\frac{\pi}{6}} 2\cos\theta \ 2\cos\theta \ d\theta$$

$$= \int_0^{\frac{\pi}{6}} 4\cos^2\theta \ \mathrm{d}\theta$$

$$= \int_0^{\frac{\pi}{6}} 4\frac{(1+\cos 2\theta)}{2} \mathrm{d}\theta$$

This is a rearrangement of the double angle formula
$\cos 2A = 2\cos^2 A - 1$

$$= 2\int_0^{\frac{\pi}{6}} (1+\cos 2\theta)\mathrm{d}\theta$$

$$= 2\left[\theta + \frac{1}{2}\sin 2\theta\right]_0^{\frac{\pi}{6}}$$

$$= 2\left[\left(\frac{\pi}{6} + \frac{1}{2}\sin\frac{\pi}{3}\right) - \left(0 + \frac{1}{2}\sin 0\right)\right]$$

$= 1.913$ (correct to three decimal places)

④ Volume of revolution $= \int_1^2 y^2 \ \mathrm{d}x$

$$= \pi\int_1^2 \left(2x + \frac{2}{\sqrt{x}}\right)^2 \ \mathrm{d}x$$

$$= \pi\int_1^2 \left(2x + \frac{2}{\sqrt{x}}\right)\left(2x + \frac{2}{\sqrt{x}}\right)\mathrm{d}x$$

$$= \pi\int_1^2 \left(4x^2 + \frac{4x}{\sqrt{x}} + \frac{4x}{\sqrt{x}} + \frac{4}{x}\right)\mathrm{d}x$$

$$= \pi\int_1^2 \left(4x^2 + \frac{8x}{\sqrt{x}} + \frac{4}{x}\right)\mathrm{d}x$$

$$\frac{8x}{\sqrt{x}} = \frac{8\sqrt{x}\sqrt{x}}{\sqrt{x}} = 8\sqrt{x} = 8x^{\frac{1}{2}}$$

$$= \pi\int_1^2 \left(4x^2 + 8x^{\frac{1}{2}} + \frac{4}{x}\right)\mathrm{d}x$$

$$= \pi\left[\frac{4x^3}{3} + \frac{8x^{\frac{3}{2}}}{\frac{3}{2}} + 4\ln x\right]_1^2$$

$$= \pi\left[\left(\frac{4(2)^3}{3} + \frac{8(2)^{\frac{3}{2}}}{\frac{3}{2}} + 4\ln 2\right) - \left(\frac{4(1)^3}{3} + \frac{8(1)^{\frac{3}{2}}}{\frac{3}{2}} + 4\ln 1\right)\right]$$

$= 68.667$(correct to three decimal places)

⑤ Volume of revolution $= \pi\int_a^b y^2 \ \mathrm{d}x$

$$= \pi\int_2^3 \left(x^2 - 4\right)^2 \ \mathrm{d}x$$

$$= \pi\int_2^3 \left(x^4 - 8x^2 + 16\right) \ \mathrm{d}x$$

$$= \pi\left[\frac{x^5}{5} - \frac{8x^3}{3} + 16x\right]_2^3$$

$$= \pi\left[\left(\frac{243}{5} - \frac{8 \times 3^3}{3} + 48\right) - \left(\frac{32}{5} - \frac{8 \times 2^3}{3} + 32\right)\right]$$

$= 23.667$ (correct to three decimal places)

⑥ $\frac{dy}{dx} = \frac{y}{x+2}$

This equation is of the form $\frac{dy}{dx} = f(x)g(y)$

Separating variables and integrating, we obtain

$$\int \frac{1}{y} dy = \int \frac{1}{x+2} dx$$

So that $\ln y = \ln(x + 2) + c$

Integrals such as $\int \frac{1}{x+2} dx$ are considered in C3.

When $x = 0$, $y = 2$,

$\therefore \ln 2 = \ln 2 + c$

$\therefore c = 0$

and solution is

$\ln y = \ln(x + 2)$

Take exponentials to remove logs

$\therefore y = x + 2$

6 Vectors

①

$\mathbf{a.b} = (5\mathbf{i} + \mathbf{j} + 2\mathbf{k}).(\mathbf{i} - \mathbf{j} + 3\mathbf{k}) = 5 - 1 + 6 = 10$

$|\mathbf{a}| = \sqrt{5^2 + (1)^2 + (2)^2} = \sqrt{30}$

$|\mathbf{b}| = \sqrt{1^2 + (-1)^2 + (3)^2} = \sqrt{11}$

$\mathbf{a.b} = |\mathbf{a}||\mathbf{b}|\cos\theta$

So $\cos\theta = \frac{\mathbf{a.b}}{|\mathbf{a}||\mathbf{b}|} = \frac{10}{\sqrt{30}\sqrt{11}} = 0.5505$

$\theta = \cos^{-1}(0.5505) = 56.6°$

② (a) $\mathbf{AB} = \mathbf{b} - \mathbf{a} = 2\mathbf{i} - \mathbf{j} + \mathbf{k} - (3\mathbf{i} + 2\mathbf{j} + \mathbf{k}) = -\mathbf{i} - 3\mathbf{j}$

(b) Equation of the line AB

$\mathbf{r} = \mathbf{a} + \lambda\,\mathbf{AB}$

So $\mathbf{r} = 3\mathbf{i} + 2\mathbf{j} + \mathbf{k} + \lambda(-\mathbf{i} - 3\mathbf{j})$

③ (a) $\mathbf{a.b} = 3 \times 1 + 4 \times 2 + 5 \times 3 = 26$

(b) $|\mathbf{a}| = \sqrt{(3)^2 + (4)^2 + (5)^2} = \sqrt{50}$

$|\mathbf{b}| = \sqrt{1^2 + (2)^2 + (3)^2} = \sqrt{14}$

$\mathbf{a.b} = |\mathbf{a}||\mathbf{b}| \cos \theta$

So $\cos\theta = \dfrac{\mathbf{a.b}}{|\mathbf{a}||\mathbf{b}|} = \dfrac{26}{\sqrt{50}\sqrt{14}} = 0.9827$

$\theta = 10.7°$ (correct to one decimal place)